1982

The Bradford Book of
Collector's Plates

Charles Winthrope & Sons

The Bradford Book

Detail from the front cover:
1982 "Juin" ("June") **18-D15-5.4**
The Very Rich Hours, D'Arceau-Limoges

Detail from the inside front cover:
1982 "Rapunzel" **22-K46-2.2**
Grimm's Fairy Tales, Königszelt Bavaria

Detail from the inside back cover:
1982 "Little Jack Horner" **84-R60-2.4**
McClelland's Mother Goose, Reco

1982
of Collector's Plates

The official guide to all editions
traded on the world's largest exchange

Charles Winthrope & Sons
New York

The Bradford Exchange, Ltd.
Niles Chicago, Illinois

Detail from the back cover:
1982 "Angelica" **26-R62-11.3**
Portraits of Innocence, Royal Doulton

Cover

The cover of the 1982 Bradford Book of Collector's Plates was printed by Black Box Collotype of Chicago, Illinois, using the continuous-tone process of screenless lithography. This process creates an extremely fine resolution of 400 to 500 lines per inch, making it today's printing process of choice throughout the world for museum-quality, fine-art reproductions.

Editors

Scott Bryant
Gerald Eckert
Clark Flint
Mike Griffin
Sylvia Inglis
Paul Traiber
Anita Varallo
Peggy Williams
Fred Woodley

Design

Gary John Fedota
Herbert Jackson
Sylvia Koenig

Photography

Richard Izui
Thomas Ryan

Acknowledgements:

Dave Armstrong, *Armstrong's*
April C. Bargout, *Schmid*
Stephen S. Barnet, *Hutschenreuther*
Gerard Boyer, *D' Arceau-Limoges*
Jacqueline Breslow, *Anna-Perenna, Inc.*
Elvin M. Bright, Sr., *Incolay Studios Inc.*
Matthew P. Brummer, *Kern Collectibles*
Bernadette Bunning
Jim Carter, *Crown Parian, Ltd.*
Karl Claussner, *Schmid*
Karen Cohen, *Lenox China Co.*
Joan Doyle, *Bing & Grøndahl Copenhagen Porcelain, Inc.*
Trudy H. Fennell, *Porcelana Granada*
Jim Fulks, *Wedgwood, Incorporated*
Richard Gabbe, *Creative World, Ltd.*
Susan Gardiner
Robert H. Gartlan, *Royal Doulton & Co.*
Joanna Gray
Richard Habeeb, *Vague Shadows*
James Hackett, *Hackett American Collectors Co.*
Melanie Hart, *The Hamilton Mint*
Cindy Haskins, *International Silver Co.*
Frederick Haviland, *Haviland & Co., Inc.*
Joyce Hendlewich, *Royal Worcester Spode Inc.*
William Hibel, *Hibel Studio*
Thomas W. Hogan, *Fairmont China*
Ivar Ipsen, *Royal Copenhagen Porcelain Corp.*
Per Jensen, *Svend Jensen*
Patrice Johnson, *Reed & Barton*
Hubert E. W. Kaiser, *Kaiser Porcelain Co.*
James LaFond, *Artists of the World*

Ellen S. Miller, *Rosenthal U.S.A. Limited*
Horst Mueller, *Christian Bell Porcelain Ltd.*
Barbara O'Connor, *Gorham Division of Textron, Inc.*
Dick Oster, *Waterford Glass Inc.*
Tom J. O'Meara, *Viletta China Co.*
Pat Owen, *Viking Import House, Inc.*
Arch Patterson, *River Shore, Ltd.*
Henry Pickard, *Pickard China Co.*
Walter A. Rautenberg, *Wara Intercontinental Co.*
Heio Reich, *Reco International Corp.*
Marcia Richards, *Villeroy & Boch*
Dieter Schneider, *Goebel of North America*
Larry D. Smith, *Pickard China Co.*
Richard Spiegel, *River Shore, Ltd.*
Dennis Vizenor, *Arabia of Finland*
Klaus D. Vogt, *Anna-Perenna, Inc.*
Steven B. Weinreich, *Dave Grossman Designs, Inc.*
Raymond W. Zrike, *Kosta Boda U.S.A. Ltd.*

A Guide to the Bradex Numbering System

Every plate pictured in *The Bradford Book of Collector's Plates* is listed in numerical sequence by its Bradex number, a four-part identification code which categorizes it first by country of origin, then by its maker, its series, and finally by individual plate. To illustrate how the Bradex numbering system works, we have selected Bing & Grøndahl's second plate in its *Christmas* series, entitled, "New Moon over Snow-covered Trees." Its Bradex number is **14-B36-1.2**.

14-B36-1.2

14   **Country of Plate's Origin.** Countries have been assigned numbers in alphabetical order; Denmark's code is **14**.

B36   **Plate Maker.** Plate makers have also been assigned numbers in alphabetical order; Bing & Grøndahl's code is **B36**.

1   **Maker's Series.** Each series by a particular plate maker is assigned a code in chronological order. The *Christmas* series was Bing & Grøndahl's first series; therefore, its code is **1**.

2   **Individual Plate.** Each plate in a particular series is assigned a code in chronological order. Since "New Moon over Snow-covered Trees" is the second plate in the *Christmas* series, its number is **2**.

Please note: When plates are issued in sets, a fifth code is added to the Bradex number. For example, the Bradex number for the 1979 "Madonna and Child" in the *Triptych* series is **22-A3-3.1-2**, the last digit indicating that it is the second plate within the set.

How to Find a Plate Listing in the Bradford Book

All the plate listings on the following pages are categorized in numerical sequence by their Bradex numbers.

To find the Bradex number of an individual plate, plate maker, or sponsor, refer to the cross-referencing indexes in the back of this book. They begin on page 341 and provide alphabetical listings by plate and plate maker (as well as plate artist), all with their respective Bradex numbers. In addition, the alphabetical index by plate title (which begins on page 342), also includes an alphabetical listing by series type.

For your added convenience, Bradex guide numbers (similar to guide words in a dictionary) are at the top of every two facing pages to indicate the first and last plates listed on those pages.

Please note that even though all plate listings are in numerical sequence, they are not necessarily consecutive. You will find, for example, that Germany's code is **22** and the next country listed is Great Britain, which has a code of **26**.

Organization of Each Plate Listing

As the official directory of all major issues regularly traded on the market, *The Bradford Book of Collector's Plates* is organized not only to locate and identify all plates quickly and accurately, but also to provide definitive information on the plates in a convenient format. As illustrated on the preceding page, all plates are categorized by their Bradex number; each "country of origin" category includes three types of listings: the maker listing, the series listing, and the plate listing.

The maker listing includes information on company history and trademarks.

The series listing includes the names of artists who created plates for the series, along with information on the series edition limits, numbering provisions, plate medium, plate diameter, and hanging provisions.

The plate listing below each plate pictured identifies the plate's Bradex number, title, artist, and issue price.

A Word About Edition Limits

As noted earlier, series listings include information on edition limits. The terminology used here bears further explanation:

Edition size limited to 10,000 – 10,000 was the maximum number of plates produced in the edition; each plate was numbered.

Edition size limited by announced quantity of 10,000 – only 10,000 plates were issued in the edition; plates were not numbered.

Edition size undisclosed, limited by period of issue – the edition was limited to the number of plates produced during an announced time period.

Edition size undisclosed, limited by year of issue – the edition was limited to the number of plates produced during the year of issue.

Edition size undisclosed – the maker provided no information regarding edition size.

A Final Note

This edition of *The Bradford Book of Collector's Plates* includes complete 1982 plate listings, except where the maker did not provide information by press time.

Contents

Bing & Grøndahl's 1895 "Behind the Frozen Window" — the first true collector's plate (see page 9).

A History of Collector's Plates

On a cold December morning in 1895, we are told, Mr. Harald Bing, director of the Danish porcelain house of Bing & Grøndahl, ordered his astonished workers to smash the mold for the small blue and white plate the company had produced to commemorate the Christmas holiday.

The plate was "Behind the Frozen Window." With Bing's command, it became the first known limited-edition collector's plate and the cornerstone of what is now the world's most actively traded form of art.

Limited edition plates are bought and sold all over the world today by collectors who are seeking out rare old plates like "Behind the Frozen Window" and recent issues from many makers in many countries as well. These collectors know the pleasure of owning these rare and special objects; their passion for limited-edition plates puts them squarely in the tradition of the connoisseurs who, over the years, have collected art in the medium of plates: the hand-painted terracotta plates of the ancient Egyptians, the lead- and tin-glazed plates and soft-paste porcelains of the Renaissance, the earthenware, china, and porcelain commemorative plates honoring generals, coronations, and battles which were issued in the 1700s by Meissen, Königliche Porzellan-Manufaktur Berlin (KPM), Wedgwood, and the French Royal factory at Sèvres.

By the latter half of the nineteenth century, plate sets (as distinct from series) were popular in Italy. Decorated with thematically related scenes such as the months, signs of the Zodiac, seasons and biblical events, they foreshadowed the concept of the collector's plate series.

Yet as close as many of these predecessors came to being collector's plates, none fit the exact definition used today — they were *not* produced in limited editions. Makers would gladly produce an additional quantity of an issue if demand warranted it. An example was Villeroy & Boch's "Snow White and the Seven Dwarfs" by Heinrich Schlitt, produced from 1890 to 1905 to meet continuing demand.

It remained for one maker, Bing & Grøndahl, to create a limited-edition plate which would be the first in a continuing series of the same theme. When Harald Bing ordered his workers to break the mold for "Behind the Frozen Window" (Bradex number **14-B36-1.1**), he changed the course of collecting history.

The Collector's Plate is Born

Designed by Frans August Hallin, "Behind the Frozen Window" was decorated in the cobalt blue underglaze technique introduced by Arnold Krog at Royal Copenhagen seven years earlier and known as "Copenhagen blue." More importantly, it was the first commemorative plate on which key information — date and occasion of issuance — was permanently fired into

Harald Bing

14-R59-1.1
1908 Royal Copenhagen *Christmas*

22-R55-1.1
1910 Rosenthal *Traditional Christmas*

the porcelain itself.

Issued in a limited edition (knowledgeable estimates put the size of the edition at about 400 plates), "Behind the Frozen Window" was the first known true collector's plate. When it was followed the next year by a new plate dated simply "Jule Aften 1896," the collector's plate tradition was born.

Harald Bing could not have known that his "Behind the Frozen Window" plate — which originally sold for two Kroner (then about 50¢) — would one day trade on the U.S. plate market at $4,004.00. Yet other porcelain manufacturers had some inkling of the potential of Bing's idea, because within a few years, they had begun to produce collector's plate series of their own.

Aluminia, a majolica factory in Copenhagen (previously acquired by Royal Copenhagen), introduced its *Children's Day Christmas* plate series (**OTC**) in 1904 and produced an annual issue until the outbreak of the Second World War in 1939. Rörstrand of Sweden (**76-R54-0**) also began a series in 1904 (**OTC**) which survived until 1926. The Norwegian house of Porsgrund (**54-P62-0**) offered a Christmas plate in 1909 (**OTC**) but failed to follow it up as a series. (Neither maker re-entered the modern collector's plate market until 1968 when the new American enthusiasm was already in full swing.)

In 1908, Royal Copenhagen began its famous *Christmas* series (**14-R59-1**) which has continued every year to this day, despite wars and economic crises — making it the second oldest continuing series.

The German manufacturer Rosenthal joined with a Danish department store, Buck & Nissen, to produce a *Christmas* series (**OTC**) for the Danish market as early as 1905. As the number of German collectors grew, Rosenthal began to promote the series in Germany under its own hallmark. This dual edition of identical artwork continued for three years, from 1907 through 1909. In 1910, Rosenthal severed its relationship with Buck & Nissen and issued its first proprietary plate, "Winter Peace" (**22-R55-1.1**), the first issue in its *Traditional Christmas* series, which continued for 65 years, ending in 1974.

Two other German makers began series of Christmas plates prior to World War I. The Hutschenreuther *Christmas* series (**OTC**) began in 1910 and ended in 1935, and the Königliche Porzellan-Manufaktur Berlin (KPM) series (**OTC**) began in 1914 but managed to survive only until the mid-1920s.

Throughout the 1920s and 1930s, the vast upheavals caused by widespread economic depression left people with little money for — or interest in — collecting what many considered little more than curios and few, if any, manufacturers introduced new collector's plate series. During the Second World War, collector's plates became even scarcer as shortages of natural resources forced the reduction of edition sizes.

Although the early Christmas plates are true collector's plates, they were not collected or traded at their time of issue as new issues are today. Families — especially in Denmark and Germany — bought them, never suspecting that one edition might be more valuable than another, and little thought was given to searching out previous editions to complete collections.

Danish Immigrants Bring Plates to America

Although Danes emigrating to the United States often brought their plate collections with them, until the late 1940s few Americans had ever seen a collector's plate unless they chanced upon one in an antique store in a Scandinavian neighborhood. In fact, if a few enterprising American dealers had not taken a chance, collector's plates might have remained forever in those Scandinavian homes and shops, quaint relics from the old country.

Shortly after World War II, however, the first American dealers entered what we now know as the collector's plate market.

"If you had told me in 1947 that someday there would be millions of plate collectors, I just wouldn't have believed you," says one of those pioneers, Chicago antique dealer William Freudenberg, Jr. Yet that year he became the very first to recognize the potential of Danish plates when he began reselling them to other antique dealers.

William Freudenberg, Jr.

Pat Owen

Elias Rasmussen

Jon Nielsen

Svend Jensen

"I simply found them (the Danish plates) at an auction house and took a few to see what I could do," he says. Freudenberg's asking price for Bing & Grøndahl's "Behind the Frozen Window," the oldest collector's plate of all, was a mere $4.50.

Two years later, in 1949, Pat Owen of Viking Import House in Florida, became the first American dealer to sell collector's plates to gift shops and department stores. She obtained her plates in a roundabout business arrangement. A Danish company wanted to buy American cash registers for resale in Denmark but couldn't pay for them in Kroner because of the government ban on the exportation of Danish currency. To get around this, the firm bought collector's plates from young Danes who had no interest in their families' collections, and then resold them to Mrs. Owen in the U.S. for dollars.

Also in 1949, the Reverend Elias Rasmussen, a Norwegian-born minister from Minneapolis, was traveling in Denmark when he met an elderly lady who was trying — in vain — to sell her plates. As an act of kindness, Reverend Rasmussen brought them back to America to see if he could sell them for her. Within a few years, he was reselling plates by the thousands. A year later, Jon Nielsen of Denmark emigrated to Michigan and began importing plates along with antiques from the old country.

The Modern Market Begins
But the event that really moved collector's plates out of the realm of antiques and giftware took place in 1951. Svend Jensen, a Danish immigrant settled in New York, who had begun importing plates the year before, printed and circulated the first back-issue price list. It was based simply on his estimates of the rarity of each edition and, with its issuance, the modern collector's plate market was born.

Antique dealers and gift shops around the country were soon quoting Jensen's prices. Word spread over the next two years and, as collectors who owned the more recent issues began to become aware of the value of those earlier plates, the scramble to complete their collections

was on: the resulting prices were bid up well beyond those of Svend Jensen's early lists.

Two early winners on the budding plate market were the 1945 Royal Copenhagen *Christmas* issue, "A Peaceful Motif" (**14-R59-1.38**), and the 1951 Royal Copenhagen *Christmas* plate, "Christmas Angel"(**14-R59-1.44**), both by Richard Bocher. Issued at $4.00 and $5.00 respectively, both plates were trading as high as $300.00 by 1959.

By 1960, the supply of older plates was dwindling, and more and more collectors were asking for current editions of the Danish Christmas plates. Antique dealers began to sell current plate editions — even though they could hardly be considered antiques; new issues began to appear in gift shops as well; and new collectors began to look for earlier issues, creating a circular pattern of back-issue trading among dealers.

Some enterprising dealers found they could bypass American distributors and deal directly with sources in Denmark. In 1960, Earl Falack of Edward's 5th Avenue in New York found some Danish dealers still blithely unaware of the growing demand across the Atlantic. He recalls that random Royal Copenhagen back issues could still be purchased in lots of 1,000 or even 2,000 at $2.00 to $5.00 a plate.

In 1962, a combination of factors — demand from Americans who had visited Copenhagen, nostalgic about their homeland, and the growing army of plate collectors and other people who were simply attracted to the plate itself — created a sensational sellout of Royal Copenhagen's "The Little Mermaid at Wintertime," (**14-R59-1.55**). Issued at $11.00, it immediately rose in market price, appreciating even more rapidly when word leaked out that the mold had broken before the entire edition had been completed. By spring of 1963, the plate had shot up to about $30.00 in Denmark and $50.00 in the U.S. Little more than a decade later, it brought $190.00 in Denmark, and $160.00 in the U.S.

The success of "Little Mermaid" spurred an increased demand for back issues in the series, followed by rapid

18-L3-1.1
1965 Lalique *Annual*

14-B36-3.1
1969 Bing & Grøndahl *Mother's Day*

price increases. Excited by the appreciation of this issue, casual collectors turned into avid seekers of plates with similar market promise.

Crystal Shatters Market

In 1965, the French maker Lalique — whose crystalware was selling in shops where Danish plates were unheard of — introduced an etched crystal plate showing two entwined birds. Entitled *"Deux Oiseaux"* (**18-L3-1.1**), the plate shattered the previously accepted boundaries of plate collecting; it was not porcelain, not blue-and-white, not Danish, not even a Christmas plate. It was simply called an "annual" (the series continued for twelve years to 1976) and its market success firmly established limited-edition plates as true "collector's items." By 1968, "Deux Oiseaux" traded at $100.00 — four times its $25.00 issue price. By 1973 it brought $965.00; by the end of 1974 it traded at $1,740.00; and at the close of trading in 1981 the plate was priced on the Bradford Exchange at $1,770.00 — 7,080% of issue price.

News of the success of "Deux Oiseaux" was late in reaching Europe because the plate was distributed only in North America. But eventually European makers and collectors alike learned of its precedent-shattering reception in the U.S., and were alerted to the profit potential in limited-edition plates.

In 1967, Bareuther of Germany introduced a *Christmas* series (**22-B7-1**) to commemorate its one hundredth anniversary; in 1968 its Danish Church *Christmas* series (**22-D5-1**) began, followed by a *Father's Day* series (**22-B7-2**) in 1969.

Rörstrand of Sweden (**76-R54-1**) and Porsgrund of Norway (**54-P62-1**) both re-entered the market in 1968 with *Christmas* series that were successful in their own countries as well as the United States. Königliche Porzellan-Manufaktur (KPM), some 45 years after discontinuing its first collector's plates, re-entered the market in 1969 with a new *Christmas* series (**OTC**).

Despite the growing success of collec-

tor's plates, Bing & Grøndahl issued the first Mother's Day plate, "Dog and Puppies" (**14-B36-3.1**) in 1969 with remarkable caution. The previous success of "Little Mermaid" had sparked the production of expanded edition sizes, which in turn had softened the market throughout the mid-1960s. "Dog and Puppies" was thus given only a modest production run.

American collectors, however, were becoming increasingly aware of the high prices commanded by back-issue Bing & Grøndahl plates. Given the opportunity to acquire a first issue from the world's most prominent collector's plate manufacturer, they scrambled to buy it at the U.S. issue price of $9.75. Their hunches paid off when the U.S. allocation sold out within weeks and the price jumped to $25.00. By Christmas, the figure was already at $65.00. Four years later, in 1974, it was priced at $245.00. At the end of 1981, "Dog and Puppies" had appreciated to $500.00.

The maker's concern about the soft Danish market proved well-founded, however, as Danish collectors had little immediate interest in the first Mother's Day plate. In the spring of 1969, Michigan antique dealer, Jon Nielsen, returning from a Danish buying trip, could still purchase 18 plates at a gift shop in the Copenhagen airport for $3.50 each. The manager said he had 125 more if Nielsen wanted them. Nielsen did. Other American dealers also bought the issue in bulk and resold the plates to U.S. collectors, making "Dog and Puppies" virtually unobtainable in Europe. This scarcity continued over the decade and explains why the plate's 1981 market price in Germany, for example, was still almost 32% greater than its price in the United States.

Danish indifference to "Dog and Puppies" didn't last long, however. The shortage caused by the drain of plates to the U.S. market soon became evident in Denmark, and the price of the plate rose sharply. By late summer of 1969 it brought the equivalent of $30.00 in Denmark, and $50.00 by Christmas. The plate continued to rise throughout the 1970s and late in 1981 brought up to 3036 Kroner (about $416.00).

Wedgwood Plate Sparks British Market

Later that same year, Wedgwood of England issued its first *Christmas* plate, "Windsor Castle" (**26-W90-1.1**), intended mainly for export to the North American market. Response was quick and enthusiastic: the entire allocation sold out immediately, and within a year the plate was priced at twice its $25.00 U.S. issue price.

Wedgwood shifted 40% of their English allocation to the U.S. to meet this sudden demand abroad, only to learn to their surprise that "Windsor Castle" was just as well received by the home market. British dealers who were able to get the plate sold it to customers at 20% above its £4.20 ($10.00) issue price. By Christmas the figure had jumped to £20.00 ($48.00), nearly five times the issue price. Further speculation pushed the price of "Windsor Castle" up to £100.00 ($240.00) by spring and £130.00 by the end of 1970. On the strength of the resounding success of this one plate, the English limited-edition plate market was born.

With rising demand for limited-edition plates on both sides of the Atlantic, more and more manufacturers began to design and produce editions to meet it. In 1970 Kaiser and Berlin Design in Germany, Haviland in France, Belleek in Northern Ireland, Santa Clara in Spain, Orrefors in Sweden, and Lenox, Pickard, and Reed & Barton in the U.S. all started making collector's plates. All were successful.

The Franklin Mint, another U.S. producer, made history in 1970 by issuing the first silver collector's plate, "Bringing Home the Tree" (**84-F64-1.1**) portraying commissioned artwork by Norman Rockwell, and it, too, was a runaway success, doubling in market price from $100.00 to $200.00 in the first year.

The excitement spread north into Canada where thousands of new collectors vied with their U.S. counterparts for the most popular issues. Wedgwood's 1969 "Windsor Castle" was the first big winner in Canada. Spurred by U.S. trading, the 1969 Royal Copenhagen *Christmas* plate (**14-R59-1.62**) also in-

26-W90-1.1
1969 Wedgwood *Christmas*

18-H8-1.1
1971 Haviland & Parlon *Tapestry I*

38-V22-1.1
1971 Veneto Flair *Bellini* plate

22-G54-1.1
1971 Goebel *Hummel Annual*

22-S12-1.1
1971 Schmid *Hummel Christmas*

spired delayed but extraordinary demand and was priced late in 1970 at triple its $14.00 Canadian issue price.

The thousands of new Canadian collectors also added fuel to the growing "boom" on the U.S. side of the border. In 1971, still more makers, Fürstenberg of Germany, Gorham of the U.S., and Lladró of Spain all entered the U.S. market. Haviland & Parlon of France began a unique and successful series based on medieval tapestries (**18-H8-1**). Older makers such as Royal Copenhagen and Wedgwood introduced *Mother's Day* series (**14-R59-2** and **26-W90-2**). Rosenthal began a new *Christmas* series (**22-R55-2**) by Danish artist Bjørn Wiinblad, which was at first overlooked by German collectors but did quite well on the Danish and U.S. markets. Veneto Flair in Italy entered the market with a hand-made single issue (**38-V22-1**).

Also in 1971, two German makers, Goebel (**22-G54-1**) and Schmid (**22-S12-1**), introduced series in which both first issues were the same design by Sister Maria Innocentia Hummel, who had become widely known for her unique portraits of children. Both series were highly successful, but the coincidence sparked lawsuits concerning the rights to Hummel works. The Siessen Convent near Stuttgart, Germany, where Sister Hummel resided, claimed sole ownership of all her creations and contracted with Goebel to reproduce them in figurines and plates. Viktoria Hummel, the Sister's mother, disputed the claim and granted permission for production of certain works in her possession to Schmid.

In 1974, the West German Federal Supreme Court ruled that the convent would have rights to all Hummel creations started after April 22, 1931 — the day Berta Hummel entered the convent and took the name of Sister Maria Innocentia. Her family would maintain rights to all works completed before Berta took her vows. Litigation was still pending in 1981 over advertising methods as Goebel alleged that Schmid's packaging of Hummel works created prior to her entry into the convent under the title of "Sister Berta" knowingly misconstrued their secular origin. Meanwhile, both series continued despite the controversy.

Back in the United States, the new surge in plate supply still could not keep up with collector demand. So as the number of collectors and dealers increased, prices continued to rise. In December, 1971, the *Wall Street Journal* ran an article based on the spectacular price-rise of the first Franklin Mint *Rockwell Christmas* plate with the headline "While You Were Going Under, Granny Got in at $100, Got out at $450." Reporter Scott R. Schmedel also singled out the 1969 Wedgwood *Christmas* plate which was then selling for about $200.00 — 800% of issue price. To show this could be only temporary inflation, Mr. Schmedel quoted a serious Wedgwood collector who predicted its value would fall back and stabilize around $80.00. (Instead, it held its price and was priced at $275.00 at the end of 1981.) The *Wall Street Journal* article and others like it were widely reprinted and set the stage for 1972 as the year of the speculator.

The "Crash of '72"

As prices continued to rise in early 1972, still more makers leapt into the market, some of them less than reputable. Plates of poor design and quality were rushed into production. Thousands of new dealers and collectors began speculating with little or no knowledge of plates or the market. New "mints" sprang up to mass produce silver plates on the heels of the Franklin Mint's success. One, the George Washington Mint, introduced *six* new silver plates in 1972 alone.

Another such new mint, the Lincoln Mint, advertised its silver plate, "Collies," (**OTC**) with pictures of an acid-etched plate, and thousands were sold before the plate was produced. Prices rose dramatically, but the actual plate was *stamped,* not etched, and many collectors were sadly disillusioned as the price of the issue plummeted.

Suddenly dealers all over the country found themselves overstocked as prices for the 1972 silver plates fell below issue. As the year ended, all other plates began to fall on the heels of the silver crash. In 1973 dealers panicked, and the speculator-collectors, many of whom had gone into part-time business as "bedroom dealers," saw their visions of quick riches vanish.

After the "crash of '72" — so-called because unsold 1972 issues still glutted the market in 1973 — the following year became the year of the "shake-out." Several "mints" closed their doors. Some 100,000 fewer silver plates were issued in 1973 than in 1972, and thousands of those in existence were melted down. Established makers cut back production dramatically, and the bedroom dealers disappeared.

The effect of the U.S. "crash of '72" spread to Denmark. Overproduction of traditional lines by Bing & Grøndahl and Royal Copenhagen, coupled with a host of new issues from competitors, glutted the market there as well. With little potential for appreciation on their purchases, many collectors stayed out of the market, and dealers found themselves hopelessly overstocked.

In the midst of the bear market of 1973, American interest was rekindled by two new series from Europe. A series for the American Bicentennial, the *Lafayette Legacy Collection* from D'Arceau-Limoges (**18-D15-1**) in France, was unavailable to U.S. dealers. But the plates were imported directly from France by enough individual American collectors to become the most sought-after of all U.S. Bicentennial issues. The first issue was quoted at $48.00 — 324% of its $14.82 issue price — in late 1981.

"Colette and Child" (**26-R62-2.1**) from Royal Doulton was the first plate by artist Edna Hibel and helped lead the market toward recovery, selling out immediately and climbing to $355.00 — 888% of its $40.00 issue price — within two years of its appearance. And as marginal plates disappeared from trading, established plates gradually regained their market strength.

The Canadian, German, and United Kingdom markets were relatively untouched by the American crash. In 1973 Carl Sorvin for Hutschenreuther introduced a series specifically for Canadian collectors. The Hutschenreuther *Canadian Christmas* (**OTC**) — produced in West Germany exclusively for Canadian distribution — was well received and rose moderately in aftermarket trading.

As the U.S. market recovered in 1974 and 1975, it felt for the first time a "reverse demand" from European collectors and dealers. As news of the American recovery slowly spread in Europe, plates that had originated there but had languished in their home markets — issues such as the Rörstrand *Christmas* series (**76-R54-1**) in Sweden — were bid up even higher in the American market when European dealers and their agents began buying them up for resale back in Europe. The Rosenthal *Wiinblad Christmas* series (**22-R55-2**) had gone relatively unnoticed when it was introduced on the German market in 1971. But, "Maria mit Kind" (**22-R55-2.1**), the first issue, was sought after in the U.S. and Denmark because it was a radical departure from traditional plate art.

As news of the issue's mounting success began to reach the German market via magazine articles in 1973 and 1974, a brisk aftermarket developed in which German dealers and individual collectors bought plates abroad at appreciated

1972 "Collies " (OTC)
The plate that set off the "crash of '72"

18-D15-1.1
1973 D'Arceau-Limoges
Lafayette Legacy

prices and resold them to German collectors — many of whom were willing to pay even higher prices to obtain the scarce first issue. This in turn caused a scarcity on the U.S. market and drove the price up. In December of 1981, "Maria mit Kind" was priced in the U.S. at $1,620.00 — more than 1,600% of its $100.00 issue price; in Germany at DM4,100.00 ($1,828.30) 2,828% of its DM145.00 issue price.

The Market Matures

The U.S. market's recovery proved that even a dramatic crash couldn't permanently stifle collector demand and speculator optimism. In 1974 both Gorham (**84-G58-3**) and the Rockwell Society of America (**84-R70-1**) introduced series for Christmas with the artwork of Norman Rockwell. Within a year, each first issue had doubled in market price.

In 1975, D'Arceau-Limoges came out with *Noël Vitrail Christmas* series (**18-D15-2**) in stained-glass style on translucent Limoges porcelain. It, too, sold out quickly and within a year had doubled in market price.

In contrast, the Danish market continued sluggishly as makers were slow to cut back edition sizes in reaction to the glut of plates issued in 1972-1973.

In the United Kingdom "Victorian Boy and Girl" (**26-R62-7.1**), the 1976 first issue in Royal Doulton's *Valentine's Day* series, proved to be a new market catalyst, reminiscent of Wedgwood's "Windsor Castle" seven years earlier. It sold out within days of its introduction and more than doubled in price during its first year on the market.

In the Canadian market, the first plate to generate exceptional excitement since the 1973 Hutschenreuther *Canada Christmas* was the 1977 first issue in the Wedgwood *Blossoming of Suzanne* series (**26-W90-4.1**), "Innocence," by the English painter, Mary Vickers. The plate sold out in Canada in less than a month. Issued at $60.00, it shot up to $225.00 in some areas as dealers scrambled to meet the sharp demand. And some six months later, dealers were still buying plates on the U.S. market for resale in Canada.

This in turn drove up the price of "Innocence" in the U.S. where it was

84-G58-3.1
1974 Gorham *Rockwell Christmas*

84-R70-1.1
1974 Rockwell Society *Christmas*

26-W90-4.1
1977 Wedgwood
Blossoming of Suzanne

38-V90-1.1
1976 Studio Dante di Volteradici
Grand Opera

priced at triple the issue price by mid-summer of 1978. The Canadian price finally leveled off in the same range.

New materials began to appear in 1976. "Rigoletto" (**38-V90-1.1**) the first *Grand Opera* plate in high relief from Italy's Studio Dante di Volteradici, was the first plate ever produced in a material called ivory alabaster. It almost tripled in price within a year, and ended 1981 at $180.00 — 514% of its $35.00 issue price. "Brown's Lincoln" (**84-R69-1.1**) was also issued in 1976, the first *Famous Americans* plate from River Shore and the first copper collector's plate. Demolishing the crash-inspired myth that metal plates were losers, it soared on the secondary market, ending 1981 at $420.00 — 1,050% of its $40.00 issue price. "She Walks in Beauty" (**84-I31-1.1**) was issued in 1977, the first *Romantic Poets* plate from Incolay Studios of California and the first cameo-style collector's plate. It was priced in December 1981 at $275.00 — 458% of its $60.00 issue price.

The late 1970s also brought a "world market" closer to reality with issues of various national origins traded simultaneously on several markets. Thus, the U.S. made 1978 Rockwell Society *Heritage* issue, "The Cobbler" (**84-R70-3.2**), ended 1981 priced in the U.S. at $167.00 — or 856% of issue price; in Canada at Can.$255.00 — 864%; in Germany at DM274.00 (U.S. $122.20) — 609%; and in England at £75.00 (U.S. $144.60) — 605%.

The German-made 1978 Goebel *Hummel Annual* "Happy Pastime" (**22-G54-1.8**), ended 1981 priced in the U.S. at $117.00 — or 90% of issue price; in Canada at Can. $200.00 — 252%; and in England at £75.00 (U.S. $144.60) — 100%. The Finnish-made 1978 Arabia *Annual* "Lemminkainen's Chase" (**16-A69-1.3**), ended 1981 priced in the U.S. at $65.00 — or 77% of issue price; in Germany at DM182.00 (U.S. $81.15) — 104%; and in England at £40.00 (U.S. $77.10) — 122%.

The "world market" was also evident in reports of increased interest from countries previously considered beyond the realm of plate collecting, such as South Africa, Australia, and Japan. This was due in part to the aggressive marketing by Bing & Grøndahl and Royal Copenhagen in scores of countries around the world, as well as the growing number of local magazine and newspaper articles describing the phenomenal growth of plate collecting in North America over the past decade.

The 1980s — Decade of Promise

But as the 1970s ended, there was cause for concern about the health of the U.S. market. The sharp increase in the number of new issues in 1979 and the unprecedented six-month-long decline in the U.S. Market Bradex over the second half of the year were reminiscent of the gathering clouds of 1972. A few market watchers saw the prelude to a possible collapse.

Others noted, however, that the slide came off a two-year bull market; that despite it the Market Bradex (the Bradford Exchange index of overall market performance) had registered a net nine-point gain for the year; and that there were already signs that, far from panicking, collectors were quietly filling out their collections at bargain prices in anticipation of a resurgent market and continuing monetary inflation.

By the end of 1981, the market was stronger and healthier than ever before. More than five million collectors in the U.S. were active buying and selling and the U.S. Market Bradex rose to a record 358 during the 1981 trading period. More than 100 makers in 13 countries were producing new editions. In fact, virtually all of the world's great names in porcelain were now active in collector's plate manufacture.

With the existence of an American National Association of Limited Edition Dealers (NALED), and a stabilized secondary market as embodied by the Bradford Exchange in the United States and its subsidiary trading centers in other countries, it seems unlikely that the problems which led to the "crash of '72" would occur again.

In fact, several well-placed market analysts agreed that the Eighties could become the most prosperous era since Harald Bing created "Behind the Frozen Window" nearly a century ago.

16-A69-1.3
1978 Arabia *Kalevala*

Collector's plates: an art form of
remarkable variety (see page 21).
Top left "The Snow Maiden,"
top right "The Unicorn in Captivity,"
bottom left "Maria and Child,"
bottom right "Demure Madonna."

The World's Most Traded Art

by J. Roderick MacArthur

Director of the Board of Governors
of the Bradford Exchange

Writing the introduction to the *Bradford Book of Collector's Plates* has been a pleasure for me over the years. It gives me the chance to re-examine the dimensions of modern plate collecting, and I never fail to be a little amazed at the scope and variety of what has come to be literally the world's most traded art.

From its very first edition back in 1976, the *Bradford Book of Collector's Plates* has been *the* comprehensive guide to the modern plate market. Revised and updated each year, the *Bradford Book* is the only reference work of its kind that illustrates, documents, and reports on the more than 1,106 most actively traded plates on the U.S. market today.

Far more than a simple "picture book," the *Bradford Book* is the guide to one of the fastest growing markets in the world today and an invaluable tool for both seasoned and novice collectors. Some have compared it to a sort of illustrated market listing. But limited-edition collector's plates should be thought of as commodities — *not* securities — and art commodities at that.

The *Bradford Book* is organized to give you definitive information on all Bradex-listed plates (those currently listed on the exchange), including the country of origin, maker, series, year, complete plate title, artist, edition limit, issue price, and 1981 market performance. Indexing by Bradex number — the plate code number which identifies country of origin, maker, series, and position in the series — permits precise identification of every plate listed. For example, **14-B36-1.1** — Denmark (**14**); Bing & Grøndahl (**B36**); first series from the maker (**1.0**); first issue in the series (**0.1**) — is the Bradex number for the famous 1895 first issue in Bing & Grøndahl's *Christmas* series, "Behind the Frozen Window." (For a more complete explanation of the Bradex number system, see page 5.)

1981 Market Performance at a Glance

At a glance you can also compare a plate's original issue price with its 1981 high and low, and the exchange's own final 1981 closing price quotation, or "quote." This, of course, can be long out of date in 1982. For accurate current prices on this fast-paced market, refer to the *Bradford Exchange Current Quotations,* published bi-monthly.

Also included in this year's book is a 16-page listing of the over 3,500 limited-edition plates which are traded "over-the-counter." Over-the-counter issues (identified as OTC) are true limited-edition collector's plates, but they are not traded in sufficient volume to be listed on the U.S. exchange. Most over-the-counter plates, however, are traded on the

J. Roderick MacArthur

19

The Bradford Exchange North American headquarters

When people ask me to define a limited-edition collector's plate, I like to quote a simple definition from some years back: "A limited-edition collector's plate is a decorative plate produced in a limited edition for the purpose of being collected."

A collector's plate *is* an object created for an aesthetic purpose — be it fine art or decoration. But it is also a tangible possession that can have potential for dramatic secondary-market price appreciation. This potential stems from the one characteristic common to all limited-edition collector's plates: although they come in many sizes, illustrate many themes, and are made in various materials and shapes, they are *always* produced in limited editions.

Once the edition limit is reached, the edition is closed, never to reopen again, and the subsequent market price of plates from the edition is determined only by how much collectors are willing to pay. The fact that collector's plates are affordable art which can rise spectacularly on the secondary market has led to the phenomenal growth of the plate market in recent years.

By the early 1970s, collector's plates were gaining recognition as the "world's most traded art." Skeptics argued this point — citing other collectible industries or even the antique trade as generators of considerable buy and sell activity.

But a close look confirms that collector's plates occupy a unique position in the vast world of art. No other art form — regardless of style, medium, or popularity — is traded on a reasonably uniform market with the frequency and volume of collector's plates.

Paintings, lithographs, prints, and sculptures, are extensively collected, yet trading in the sense of uniform buy / sell transactions on an organized exchange simply does not exist. In the organized auctions many of these items are one-of-a-kind, or produced in such very small numbers that uniform trading is impossible and the frequency with which a given piece of art reaches the market is very low.

Today's thriving marketplace for collector's plates is unique in the community of art and *objets du vertu*. And the heart of

exchange, and can be obtained at prevailing market prices.

A few over-the-counter plates are Bradex-listed in other countries. A series may be actively traded on the German, English, or Canadian exchanges, for example, yet not qualify for Bradex-listing in the United States. However, most issues in the over-the-counter section have lost interest for the "mainstream" of collectors, and a few are "coterie plates" — plates made in such small editions that in today's vast market they remain unknown except to a very small number, or "coterie," of collectors.

A type of plate which you will never find in the *Bradford Book* is the "super-market plate." As the name implies, these plates are sold in supermarkets or are given away as premiums by merchants or banks. They are generally poorly made, have little artistic value, and are not issued in a strict limited edition. Nor will you find one of the many single-issue plates which have been made to commemorate the anniversary of your town, your school or your state.

Guide to the Heart of the Market

What you *will* find in the *Bradford Book* are the 1,106 plates which make up the heart of the U.S. limited-edition plate market — plates varied in artistry, theme, and material to suit the tastes of almost any collector.

the modern plate market is unquestionably the *Bradford Exchange Current Quotations* — the Bradex. Published bimonthly, it lists the more than 1,106 plates most actively traded today — plates from twelve countries, sixty-two makers and 136 series, appraises each plate's market performance at the close of each bi-monthly trading period, and registers the appropriate "high" and "low" offers and Bradford's closing price on the exchange (quote price).

A Remarkably Varied Art Form

Collector's plates may feature two-dimensional pictures or three-dimensional sculpture; they may be made in any one of a dozen countries; they come in a variety of sizes; but they are mainly only one shape — round. A few square plates have been introduced, but so far only three — the Rörstrand *Christmas* series (**76-R54-1**), the Royal Doulton *Beswick Christmas* series (**26-R62-1**) and Arabia's *Annual* series (**16-A69-1**) are traded with any regularity on the exchange.

The plates can be wafer-thin china (Belleek, Great Britain [**26-B18-0**]), or heavy sculptured stone (Studio Dante di Volteradici, Italy [**38-V90-0**] and Incolay Studios, U.S.A. [**84-I31-0**]). They can be metal such as silver, silverplate, copper or pewter, crystal (Lalique, France [**18-L3-0**], and Morgantown Crystal, U.S.A. [**84-M58-0**]), even wood (Anri, Italy [**38-A54-0**]). But most are some form of ceramic, from simple terra cotta to true hard-fire porcelain.

For more than half a century, collector's plates were issued almost exclusively in Christmas series and depicted winter and religious scenes. But in 1965, *"Deux Oiseaux"* (**18-L3-1.1**), from the famous French *cristallerie,* Lalique, broke that tradition: it was not porcelain, not blue-and-white, not Danish, not even a Christmas plate. An Art Nouveau-style interpretation of two entwined birds, it was not specifically designed as a Christmas gift item, but as the first in an annual series not tied to a specific season (the Lalique *Annual* series continued for twelve years to 1976). The plate almost immediately sold out, and its subsequent spectacular appreciation on the secondary market established limited-edition plates as true "collector's items."

Not surprisingly, Lalique's success spurred other makers to experiment with new themes. Bing & Grøndahl, makers of the very first collector's plate in 1895, introduced a *Mother's Day* series (**14-B36-3**) in 1969; the idea was quickly adopted by rival makers, Royal Copenhagen (**14-R59-2**) and Porsgrund (**54-P62-2**) among others. The U.S. Bicentennial provided the theme for several series in the early 1970s. In the latter half of the decade the field expanded dramatically to include series with themes from literature, cinema, history, the great masters, and even the whimsy of cartoons.

Arabia's *Annual series (***16-A69-1***)* recreates scenes from Finland's national epic poem, the *Kalevala.* Incolay Studios pays tribute to the great poets in its *Romantic Poets* collection (**84-I31-1**). Two Edwin M. Knowles China Company series are inspired by film classics: *The Wizard of Oz* (**84-K41-1**) and *Gone With the Wind* (**84-K41-3**). D'Arceau-Limoges produced a distinctive historical series with its *Women of the Century* collection (**18-D15-3**), a graphic chronology of a century of women's fashion. Works by Renoir, Raphael, and Leonardo da Vinci have all been reproduced on plates (**84-P29-4; 18-H8-2.1** and **2.3; 38-V22-6**). And Schmid's *Peanuts Christmas (***42-S12-1***)* and *Disney Christmas* (**42-S12-3**) series illustrate that there is even a place for the comics in the eclectic world of collector's plates.

Plate themes can be unconventional, as in Fairmont's *Classical American Beauties* (**84-F4-8**), or endearingly familiar as in Gorham's *Rockwell Four Seasons* (**84-G58-1**) and Knowles' *Csatari Grandparent Plate* series (**84-K41-4**). There are series set in locales all around the world: China (Artists of the World's *Children of Aberdeen* [**84-A72-1**]); Russia (*Heinrich's Russian Fairy Tales* [**22-H18-1**]); the American West (Fairmont's *DeGrazia Children* [**84-F4-4**]); Germany (Bareuther's *Father's Day* [**22-B7-2**]); and the Orient (Rosenthal's *Oriental Gold* [**22-R55-8**]). There are series with religious themes

26-W90-4.1
1977 Wedgwood
Blossoming of Suzanne

22-R55-1.1
1910 Rosenthal *Traditional Christmas* backstamp

(Königszelt Bavaria's *Hedi Keller Christmas* [**22-K46-1**]); patriotic themes (D'Arceau-Limoges' *Lafayette Legacy* [**18-D15-1**]); medieval themes (Haviland & Parlon's *The Lady and the Unicorn* [**18-H8-4**]); and nature themes (Pickard's *Lockhart Wildlife* [**84-P29-1**]).

The great potential of the collector's plate medium is one reason so many artists have been attracted to it. Such now-familiar artists as John McClelland, Edna Hibel, Ted DeGrazia, Bjørn Wiinblad, G.A. Hoover, Mary Vickers, Francisco Masseria, Raymond Kursár, Hedi Keller, and Joseph Csatari have each created works for the plate medium and become better known for this than for all their previous work. The range of styles is wide: from photographic realism to surrealism, from impressionism to primitivism, from classical sculpture to Tyrolean wood crafting.

Both Art and Craft

Collector's plates are a fusion of art and craft. Both the design on the plate and the technique used to render the design are forms of art. The quality of the plate itself — be it true hard-fire porcelain or true 24% lead crystal, for example — is of importance.

Serious collectors know, for instance, that all D'Arceau-Limoges plates must adhere to the two-century-old Grellet Standard, by which the quality of a plate is assessed in seven critical areas: whiteness, thickness, translucence, strength of body, unity of glaze, hardness of glaze, and color.

I'm fascinated by the craftsmanship of many plate series. Di Volteradici's work in ivory alabaster, the glass-work of Lalique, Orrefors, and Morgantown Crystal, the Damascene silver craft of Reed & Barton — all are disciplined skills to be admired as plate artistry.

The Backstamp

With the emphasis on craftsmanship, it's no wonder that makers are proud to fire their names onto their plates. Most fre-

quently, makers' names or trademarks appear on the reverse side — commonly known as "the backstamp."

Rosenthal of Germany was the first prominent manufacturer to use its name in bold type as its trademark and to include title, artist, and production information on the backs of plates. Their 1910 *Christmas* issue (**22-R55-1.1**) included the word *"handgemalt"* (handpainted), and the 1912 issue identified both the title ("Sternschnuppen," Shooting Stars) and artist (Paul Rieth).

The earliest Bing & Grøndahl plates carried only the famous maker's hallmark and the phrase "Made in Denmark"; in fact, it wasn't until 1944 that the plate title was included on the back of the plate as well. Similarly, Royal Copenhagen didn't identify plate titles on the backstamp until their 1954 *Christmas* plate, or credit the artist until a year later.

Today, the maker's hallmark is still the single most frequently seen mark on backstamps, but many makers now add a great deal more information. This information is of significance — but is often overlooked by the novice collector. Backstamps vary from series to series — even within series — and reflect the individuality of each edition. For example, the Gorham *Rockwell Four Seasons* plates (**84-G58-1**) contain a brief statement about Norman Rockwell's impact on American art. Mary Vicker's *Blossoming of Suzanne* series (**26-W90-4**) includes quotations from the artist. And both Anri's *Christmas* (**38-A54-1**) and Limoges-Turgot's *Durand's Children* (**18-L52-1**) have short descriptions of the plates' themes.

Backstamps are omitted from crystal plates because any markings on the reverse would show through the transparent plate body. The crystal Lalique *Annual* plates (**18-L3-1**) carry only the phrase "Lalique, France" etched as inconspicuously as possible on the border of the plate bases; Orrefors' *Annual Cathedral* plates (**76-O74-1**) identify only the maker, the year, the country and the fact that the plate is a limited-edition — all etched in small letters on the foot rim of the crystal plate body. The crystal *Yates' Country Ladies* (**84-M58-1**) plates from Morgantown Crystal incorporate the

backstamp information into the plate design, using thirty-one words to create a thin etched band around the circumference of the plate base.

Edition Limits and Market Value

The backstamp also reveals the way in which the plate edition is limited. Some manufacturers such as Anna-Perenna or the Hibel Studio announce the actual number of plates in the edition. Some, like Bing & Grøndahl, cloak their edition sizes in utmost secrecy — acknowledging only that an edition's production is cut off at the end of the year of issue. Still others limit the edition by the total number of firing days.

But however it is determined (and whether or not the plates are numbered), the edition limit is strictly observed; otherwise the plates are simply not true collector's plates. The fact that a finite number of plates are produced within the limits of any edition adds to the spirit of the hunt and the thrill of acquisition. It can also spark heated trading and unbridled speculation on the market as too many buyers go after too few plates in a "hot" new edition. With one exception*, *no plate in the Bradford Book or listed on the Bradford Exchange has ever been reissued once the edition closed.*†

Edition sizes can be large or small. Announced edition limits listed in the *Bradford Book* range from 500 plates for the 1971 Veneto Flair *Bellini* (**38-V22-1.1**) to 30,000 for the Haviland *Christmas* (**18-H6-1**). But the undisclosed editions are by far the largest, ranging from less than one thousand for the earliest plates into the hundreds of thousands for later ones.

When the plate market was just begin-ning, plates issued in small editions of 2,000 or less could command a strong following and trade up to incredible quote prices on the secondary market. Now, with the market expanding around the world and composed of several million collectors, such tiny editions generate comparatively little trading volume. In fact, I would tend to call any edition under 10,000 a "coterie plate," the one prominent exception being the Pickard *Children of Renoir* series (**84-P29-4**).

But don't let this discourage you from buying an issue from a small edition. Just remember that there is certainly no assurance that the plate will appreciate in value simply because the edition is small. A market "winner" is made when demand outstrips supply — and a very small plate edition does not automatically lead to heightened demand (in fact, it often discourages demand because of its resulting obscurity).

Plate series are either "closed-end" with a predetermined number of editions, or "open-end," to continue indefinitely. The D'Arceau-Limoges *Girls of the Seasons* series (**18-D15-4**) is a closed-end series of four annual plates. The Bing & Grøndahl *Christmas* series (**14-B36-1**) is

18-D15-4.1, 4.2, 4.3, 4.4
A closed-end series: D'Arceau-Limoges's *Les Jeunes Filles des Saisons,* opened in 1978 and closed in 1981.

---

* The one exception is the Rosenthal *Traditional Christmas* series (**22-R55-1**). Editions from 1910 to 1957 in this series were reopened briefly between 1969 and 1971, with all reissues identified by backstamps containing the reissue dates of manufacture. These plates are now Bradex-listed on the firm assurance by the maker that the practice ceased forever in 1971.

† In the very rare instance when a manufacturer has issued a plate with artwork that had previously appeared on another maker's plate, this "second-time" plate is *not* a collector's plate by definition.

The Bradford Exchange Trading Floor provides for the orderly trading of collector's plates.

$25.00; the Goebel *Hummel Annual* (**22-G54-1.1**) produced in 1971 at $25.00; the Rockwell Society *Heritage* (**84-R70-3.1**) issued in 1977 at $14.50 — have appreciated from 1,969% to 6,980% in market price, the result solely of collector demand.

And collector demand continued to grow at an explosive rate. In just the ten years from 1971 to 1981, the estimated number of collectors across the globe rose from 1.2 million to 6.8 million, with more than one-half million added in the past year alone. During the same period the estimated average number of daily transactions among the world's distributors, dealers, and individual collectors jumped from 2,900 to 22,880. From an obscure hobby in the early 1960s, plate collecting has become a boom.

The Orderly Market

Until recently, a collector searching for a plate from a scarce edition, or wishing to sell a plate from his collection, often was frustrated, simply because there were few ways to reach prospective traders. Dealers were willing, of course, to help locate a rare plate, and there were a few periodicals where an advertisement would be seen by other plate collectors. There were even occasional "finds" at auctions or in antique shops, or through personal contacts through collector's clubs. But for the most part, transactions among collectors were random and infrequent.

By the late 1960s, the vastly increased number of plate collectors demanded an organized market. With plate prices rising and falling dramatically according to the whims of collectors and dealers, and with more and more manufacturers entering the field, collectors needed a central source of information and place to go to buy or sell any of the hundreds of issues coming on the market.

The staff of the Bradford Exchange had monitored daily transactions for some time, and in September, 1973, with the publication of the first bi-monthly *Bradford Exchange Current Quotations* — or "Bradex" — current quotes on the most actively-traded issues became available to collectors across the United States on a routine basis.

open-end, with a new plate issued each year indefinitely.

As a general rule, the first plate in a series is most in demand. Some mistakenly call these plates "first editions." However, every limited-edition plate is a first edition since, by definition, there can be no "second edition." The first plate in a series is more properly called a "first issue."

Whatever the edition size, it is *only* collector demand which determines the success or failure of a plate on the market. Although people tend to forget this simple fact, it has proven true time and time again. The Lalique *Annual* (**18-L3-1.1**) which issued in 1965 at

A plate is listed on the Bradex *because of the volume of continued trading* — either past or expected — *not* because of its potential to increase in market price. A new plate that continues a series already traded is listed before trading begins, a new series from a maker whose other series are widely traded may be listed if demand is expected to carry over to the new series.

The market performance of twelve key indicator series selected from among the Bradex-listed series serves as a market barometer to both collectors and the industry at large. This "Market Bradex" — a sort of Dow Jones Index of plate market trends — is based on the quote price / issue price ratio of these key series. When the index goes down, it suggests a broad decline in market prices. When it rises, the market is in good health. The Market Bradex stood at 354 at the close of trading in 1981 — a year-to-date rise of twenty points since the close of 1980, a year in which the Market Bradex went down by 3 points.

The Standard Yardstick — the Eight-Point Checklist

At about the same time the first Bradex appeared, the exchange devised its Eight-Point Checklist to assist collectors in appraising plates on the market. No one can predict how a plate will perform on the market, and concern over potential market performance should never outweigh the collector's artistic preferences. But the checklist is helpful in determining a plate's market strengths and has become something of a standard yardstick since it was developed in 1972.

1. *Maker:* Is the maker known for its insistence on fine workmanship and continuity of its other plate series?
2. *Artistry:* Is it original art created especially for this plate by an artist of note? Is the subject one of broad, but not trite, appeal?
3. *Edition Size:* Is the edition clearly limited but not too limited to create a market? If the edition is closed, are dealers bidding in the secondary market?
4. *Collectibility:* Is it one, preferably the first, of a collectible periodic series or merely a single issue?
5. *Time of Acquisition:* Can you get it at the right time — at issue or while the price is still rising?
6. *Sponsorship:* Is it issued in association with a government or a prestigious institution?
7. *Commemorative Importance:* Does it commemorate a seasonal event or a historic event? If so, does it bring new insight to the event? Or is it an event in the history of the artist or maker?
8. *Material:* If made of ceramic, is it true hard-paste ("hard-fire") porcelain, bone china or fine china? If made of metal, is it solid gold or silver? If made of glass, is it genuine 24% lead crystal?

These eight points are listed in order of importance, but I would emphasize that for purposes of investment, Point Five — Time of Acquisition — is crucial. If you pay too much for a plate, it may take years to break even. Yet even at a price higher than issue price, a plate can be a bargain if its after-market appreciation is expected to continue.

In the early 1970s, even with the Eight-Point Checklist and the bi-monthly Bradex, there was still a need for an authoritative reference guide that collectors could rely on for complete information on the hundreds of plates that were being traded.

So, from 1974 until 1976, the staff of the Bradford Exchange researched and documented the phenomenon of limited-edition collector's plates — their history, their manufacturers, edition limits, and most importantly, their market performance. The result was the first *Bradford Book of Collector's Plates,* published in 1976.

Since then, our market analysts and staff researchers continue to revise, update, and expand the *Bradford Book* annually in order to make it the most up-to-date and most comprehensive guide to the modern plate market available anywhere. I hope that this 1982 edition gives you both the basic knowledge and the new insights into the world of collector's plates that serious collectors have, over the years, come to expect from the *Bradford Book.*

The 1981 Plate of the Year, "Little Boy Blue," (below), and the 1981 New Edition of the Year, "Hearts-a-Flutter" (see pages 28-29)

1981 – The Year in Review

Nineteen-eighty-one was a year of dynamic trading and enormous market expansion for limited-edition collector's plates. Some 510,000 new collectors entered the U.S. market in the 12-month reporting period — up 11.4% from 1980, to bring the total to just over 5,000,000. Attendance at the Platemakers Guild's traveling road shows and the South Bend convention set record highs. And exchange trading volume jumped 26.6% from 1980 to a record 2,287,063 transactions on the U.S. exchange. There were 82.4% more million-dollar-volume weeks recorded in 1981 than in the previous year.

The Market Bradex — the index of market performance according to twelve key indicator series which serves as a market barometer to both collectors and the industry at large* — closed the year at 354, down four points from October but up 20 points from 1980's final figure to establish a record year-end high. Analysts attributed the 20-point gain to the revitalization of the secondary market after the 1980 lull. Key factors were the increase in the number of collectors as well as a general renewed demand for back issues.

The demand for back issues was strong throughout the year. Advances outnumbered declines 527 to 155 by year's end. Total trading volume on the exchange alone exceeded 1980 figures in 10 out of 12 months, and dollar volume reached an all-time high — up 24.1% from the last year to stand at $55,892,995.

Chart of the Market Bradex, 1981

* The Market Bradex is based on the quote price / issue price ratio of the issues within these key series . . . Bing & Grøndahl *Christmas* (since 1965), Bing & Grøndahl *Mother's Day*, Royal Copenhagen *Christmas* (since 1965), Haviland *Christmas*, Goebel *Hummel Annual*, Schmid *Hummel Christmas*, Wedgwood *Christmas*, Royal Bayreuth *Mother's Day*, Gorham *Rockwell Four Seasons*, Haviland & Parlon *Tapestry I & II*, Studio Dante di Volteradici *Grand Opera*, Rockwell Society *Christmas*.

27

McClelland's Mother Goose Series Wins Again

The 1981 Plate of the Year — the single issue with the greatest price appreciation during the year — was "Little Boy Blue" (**84-R60-2.2**), to no one's great surprise. The 1980 issue in Reco's *McClelland's Mother Goose*, it rose 380% above its $22.50 issue price, to close 1981 at $108.00.

Runner-up for the Plate of the Year title was "Bedtime Story" (**84-K41-4.1**), the 1980 issue in Knowles' *Csatari Grandparent Plate* series. "Bedtime Story" started 1981 at $18.00, and was quoted at $58.00 by year's end, up 222.2%.

The success of Reco's *McClelland's Mother Goose* series (**84-R60-2**) — claiming the Plate of the Year title two years in a row — confirmed the almost universal appeal of children themes and attested to the continuing demand for the works of John McClelland, who had emerged as America's most popular child portraitist among plate collectors. Accordingly, analysts continued to watch "Little Miss Muffet" (**84-R60-2.3**), the 1981 issue in *McClelland's Mother Goose* series, closely — as well as "Tommy the Clown" (**84-R60-3.1**), the 1981 first issue in Reco's new *McClelland Children's Circus* collection.

Schmid Scores a First

Although Plate of the Year was expected, the 1981 New Edition of the Year — the plate which appreciated the most during its year of issue — was a complete surprise. This was "Hearts-a-Flutter" (**42-S12-7.5**), the 1981 Schmid *Peanuts Valentine's Day* issue. It was the first time a Schmid Peanuts plate had captured any titles. Released early in the year, "Hearts-a-Flutter" posted its first gain in August, up 71% from its $17.50 issue price to $30.00 — and closed the year at $37.00, up 111% over the course of the year.

A second surprise, and runner-up for New Edition of the Year, was "Freddie on the Green" (**84-C72-1.3**), the 1981 issue in Crown Parian's *Freddie the Freeloader* series. "Freddie on the Green" closed 1981 at $92.00, 53.3% above its issue price of $60.00 following an October-

84-R60-2.3
1981 Reco
McClelland's Mother Goose

84-C72-1.3
1981 Crown Parian
Freddie the Freeloader

84-R60-3.1
1981 Reco
McClelland Children's Circus

26-R62-11.2
1981 Royal Doulton
Portraits of Innocence

84-R70-3.3
1979 Rockwell Society *Heritage*

38-V90-1.6
1981 Studio Dante di Volteradici
Grand Opera

84-R70-3.5
1981 Rockwell Society *Heritage*

February spurt which sent it up 28 points to outrank Royal Doulton's "Adrien" (**26-R62-11.2**), second issue in their *Portraits of Innocence* series.

The year certainly started with a bang as the New Year's trading generated the most bullish January in exchange history. Total volume was up 58.3% from December 1980, and up 133.0% from January of 1980, as the normal post-holiday flurry of trading became something of a boom. "The Music Maker" (**84-R70-3.5**), the 1981 Rockwell Society *Heritage* issue, was far-and-away the most sought-after plate; it out-traded the second-ranked "After the Party" (**84-R70-2.6**), the 1981 Rockwell Society's *Mother's Day* issue, by four to one.

In February, the frantic pace slowed as the rush for confirmed orders of new 1981 plates ebbed and trading fell 5.9%. But total exchange activity remained ahead of February 1980 volume by 6.4%. Eight of the twelve key indicator series advanced, led by the di Volteradici *Grand Opera* series (**38-V90-1**), up 6.0%, to push the Market Bradex up 5 points to 339. Advances outnumbered declines 196 to 41, with the healthiest gains posted by "Lighthouse Keeper's Daughter" (**84-R70-3.3**), 1979 issue in the Rockwell Society's *Heritage* series, up 73.1% to $90.00, and "Panchito" (**26-R62-11.1**), the 1980 issue in Royal Doulton's *Portraits of Innocence* series, up 52.7% to $168.00. Of the few declining issues, "Swan and Cygnets" (**22-K4-2.6**), the 1976 Kaiser *Mother's Day* plate, suffered the heaviest loss, down 16.7% to $20.00.

Trading continued to slow through March, with total exchange volume down 13.9% from February's 186,749 transactions. Some doomsayers predicted that January's boom was ephemeral, and the large influx of new issues introduced at the Atlantic City China and Glass show in January would glut the market. However, the sluggish market trading was actually the result of a late release of many Mother's Day issues. Usually these sought-after plates are available by early March, and provide a strong sales impetus by mid-month. In 1981, many important Mother's Day plates — including the 1981 Rockwell Society's

Mother's Day series issue (**84-R70-2.6**) — did not enter the market in any quantity until mid-April.

First Quarter Volume: Up 16.6% Over 1980

First quarter figures showed dollar volume up 16.6% from the same period in 1980, and the quarter witnessed a record of eight million-dollar weeks. Total trading volume was up 5.5% from first quarter 1980, and up 22.0% from fourth quarter 1980. Further, the Market Bradex was finally on the move, rising 5 points to break the "deadlock of 1980," in which the Market Bradex had remained steady at 334 from June through December trading periods.

The health of the market was further confirmed by solid gains posted in April as trading volume climbed 12.9% from March levels. At the close of April trading, the Market Bradex stood at 348 — bypassing the previous Market Bradex high of 344, set in June, 1979. Overall, the year-to-date gain stood at a solid 14 points. Ten of the twelve key indicator series advanced, led by: Dante di Volteradici *Grand Opera* (**38-V90-1**), up 8.4%; Bing & Grøndahl *Christmas* (**14-B36-1**), up 4.9%; and Rockwell Society *Christmas* (**84-R70-1**), up 4.3%. Not one of the twelve key Bradex series posted a measurable decline.

Advances outnumbered declines in April, 271 to 23 — a record ratio of 12 to 1. Strongest gains were posted by "The Ship Builder" (**84-R70-3.4**), the 1980 issue in the Rockwell Society's *Heritage* series, up 68% to $42.00; "Freddie in the Bathtub" (**84-C72-1.1**), the 1979 issue in Crown Parian's *Freddie the Freeloader* series, up 66.7% to $200.00; and "Little Boy Blue" (**84-R60-2.2**), the 1980 issue in Reco's acclaimed *McClelland's Mother Goose* series, up 60% to $36.00 — its first gain over issue price.

This strengthening of the market continued. By the end of May, total exchange activity was up 40.4% from the same period in 1980, and by June, a record 198,391 transactions were completed in a single 30-day period — up 72.0% from the same period last year.

The Market Bradex closed June 30 at 351, up 3 points from April to set

84-K41-3.1
1978 Knowles *Gone With the Wind*

84-P29-5.1
1981 Pickard *Oleg Cassini's Most Beautiful Women of All Time*

84-K41-3.4
1981 Knowles *Gone With the Wind*

84-P29-6.1
1980 Pickard *Mother's Love*

yet another record. Nine of the twelve key indicator series advanced, and advances led declines, 148 to 34. The top gainer of the first half of 1981 was "Scarlett" (**84-K41-3.1**), the 1978 issue in Knowles' *Gone With the Wind* series, up 29.5% to $285.00.

The vigor of the collector's plate market in mid-summer 1981 was not confined to the exchange trading floor. Starting in April in Washington, D.C. (April 27-May 3), the Collector Platemakers Guild traveling mall shows gave collectors and non-collectors alike a brief look at the world of collector's plates in three cities where the shows had never been seen before.

Collector's Plates Go on the Road

Exhibits included some 200 new plates issued by Guild members; plate artist appearances; porcelain and fine china appraisals; a historical exhibit entitled "Firsts in Plate Collecting"; a presentation on how plates are made; and a Guild plate exchange. Actress Joan Fontaine, a collector herself, was on hand at the shows and served as a Guild spokesman. Ms. Fontaine was interviewed by newspapers and television stations in each city.

Guild officials estimate that 530,000 people attended the three shows in Washington, D.C., Detroit, Michigan, and Fort Lauderdale, Florida. Over 3,400 plates were registered at the three plate exchange events, and 1,460 were sold for a dollar volume of more than $100,000. The most actively traded plates were: "The Toy Maker" (**84-R70-3.1**), the 1977 issue in Rockwell Society's *Heritage* series; "The Cobbler" (**84-R70-3.2**), the 1978 issue in the same series; "The Lighthouse Keeper's Daughter" (**84-R70-3.3**), the 1979 issue in the series; and "Scarlett" (**84-K41-3.1**), the 1978 issue in Knowles' now-famous *Gone With the Wind* series.

The World Collector Platemakers Fair was held in New York City, June 27 through 29. Fair attendance of 4,391 was far lower than the previous year's attendance of 14,482 at the Los Angeles fair; yet the plate exchange drew heavy

traffic — 1,325 plates were registered, and 744 transactions were completed, totaling more than $65,000.

Pickard used the New York convention to unveil Oleg Cassini's "Helen of Troy" (**84-P29-5.1**), first issue in its *Oleg Cassini's Most Beautiful Women of All Time* collection. "Helen of Troy" was the first plate by a fashion designer.

At the New York fair, members of the Collector Platemakers Guild voted to replace the annual convention with the traveling mall shows.

From New York the collector's plate industry moved its attention to the Seventh International Plate Collectors Convention in South Bend, Indiana on July 9-12, sponsored by the Watson Collectors Club and the National Association of Limited Edition Dealers (NALED). An estimated 7,100 collectors attended — up 2,700 from the previous year. Of them, more than 3,000 attended the final judging of the Edwin M. Knowles China Co.-sponsored "Clark Gable Look-Alike Contest" promoting their highly-successful *Gone With the Wind* series (**84-K41-3**). And trading at the three-hour swap'n'sell set a record, with 2,529 plates registered and 1,449 transactions totaling more than $92,000.

NALED Awards Announced

The annual National Association of Limited Edition Dealers awards were also announced at South Bend: Francisco Masseria was named Artist of the Year; Pickard China (**84-P29-0**) was named Manufacturer of the Year; "Miracle" (**84-P29-6.1**), the 1980 issue in Pickard's *Mother's Love* series was voted Plate of the Year; and "Little Boy Blue" (**84-R60-2.2**), the 1980 issue in Reco's *McClelland's Mother Goose* series was named Collectible of the Year.

The heated trading at the New York and South Bend events was mirrored on the exchange as July trading volume of 191,000 units ran 11.4% ahead of the same period in 1980. By August, the Market Bradex stood at 355, up four more points from June. Nine of the twelve key indicators advanced; and advances outnumbered declines 233 to 51. The top gainer in late summer

was "Bell of Hope" (**84-F4-1.2**), the 1977 issue in Fairmont's *DeGrazia Holiday* series, up 150% to $125.00.

The growing success of DeGrazia issues led some market analysts to predict that DeGrazia might well earn the Plate of the Year title. DeGrazia series did well through the summer months. *DeGrazia Holiday* series (**84-F4-1**), as a whole, was up 45.5%; Fairmont's *DeGrazia Children* series (**84-F4-4**) rose 26.5%; and Gorham's *DeGrazia Children* (**84-G58-5**) gained 10.3%. As the year ended, however, even these spectacular gains could not compete with the other "hot" issues.

The plate that market analysts watched with growing wonder was "Hearts-a-Flutter" (**42-S12-7.5**), the 1981 Schmid *Peanuts Valentine's Day* issue in a series which had never shown spectacular gains before. First listed in February, in August "Hearts-a-Flutter" rose 71.4% above issue — from $17.50 to $30.00.

Another Rockwell Winner

But the most sought-after plate by the end of August was a new release, "Dreaming in the Attic" (**84-R70-4.1**), the first issue in the Rockwell Society's *Rockwell's Rediscovered Women* series. "Dreaming in the Attic" out-traded "The Music Maker" (**84-R70-3.5**), the 1981 issue in the Rockwell Society's *Heritage* series, by 223.3%, once more emphasizing the seemingly limitless appeal of Rockwell art to American collectors.

September's trading was up 8.2% from August, yet was no greater than the previous year's volume with 149,211 completed transactions on the exchange. Third quarter figures, however, showed year-to-date total exchange activity up 13% from the same period in 1980.

October proved a record-breaking month — with collector enthusiasm and industry activity pushing total trading volume to 344,000 units, 130.8% ahead of September's level. (This stands, at this writing, as the all-time one month trading volume record on the exchange.) Industry experts began speaking enthusiastically of a bullish year-end close as collectors eagerly vied for a number

84-F4-1.2
1977 Fairmont *DeGrazia Holiday*

84-R70-4.1
1981 Rockwell Society
Rockwell's Rediscovered Women

of new issues released in the fall. Of all the new releases, the Rockwell Society's *Rockwell's Rediscovered Women* first issue, "Dreaming in the Attic" (**84-R70-4.1**), quickly became the strongest trader.

At the end of October, ten of the twelve key indicator series advanced, pushing the Market Bradex to a record 358, while advances outnumbered declines 147 to 74. The top gainer was "Little Boy Blue" (**84-R60-2.2**), 1980 issue in Reco *McClelland's Mother Goose*, up 96.4% to $108.00. An obvious question arose: would "Little Boy Blue" now follow its predecessor, "Mary, Mary" (**84-R60-2.1**), and snare the Plate of the Year title?

On October 23, 1981, the prime-time NBC News Magazine aired a nationwide TV report on the plate collecting phenomenon. The program featured interviews with collectors and industry insiders at the Bradford Exchange and the South Bend convention. The Nielson Rating Service reported that the program was watched by over 7,905,000 viewers across the United States.

ALEA Disbands

Also in October, the American Limited Edition Association (ALEA) sponsored its annual convention in Columbus, Ohio (October 2-4). Attendance was a bitter disappointment to the organizers, although the swap'n'sell exchange met with some success. Of the 749 plates registered, 187, or 25%, were sold. The average sell price was $65.00. The low turn-out for the Columbus convention convinced members of the six-year-old association reluctantly to disband in November. Frank B. Knight, Executive Director of ALEA, announced that the organization had ". . . failed to gain sufficiently broad support to be considered a national organization or to justify its continuation."

But at the same time in November the market's upward spiral continued, with trading volume up 121.9% from the same period a year ago. December followed suit with total exchange activity running 37.8% ahead of December, 1980.

At year's end, in addition to the record volume of transactions, exchange dollar volume for the year had also reached an all-time high, up 24.1% from 1980, with 82.4% more million-dollar weeks — including two two-million-dollar-volume weeks. The Market Bradex closed the fourth quarter at 354.

After the Plate of the Year, "Little Boy Blue" (**84-R60-2.2**), and "Bedtime Story" (**84-K41-4.1**), the remaining top twenty gainers were: the 1980 Rockwell Society *Heritage*, "The Ship Builder" (**84-R70-3.4**), up 217.9% to $62.00; the 1979 Knowles *Gone With the Wind*, "Ashley" (**84-K41-3.2**), up 204.3% to $70.00; the 1980 Schmid *Raggedy Ann Annual*, "Sunshine Wagon" (**42-S12-9.1**), up 195.7% to $68.00; the 1979 Crown Parian *Freddie the Freeloader*, "Freddie in the Bathtub" (**84-C72-1.1**), up 185.7% to $300.00; 1979 Knowles *Americana Holidays*, "Thanksgiving" (**84-K41-2.2**), up 175% to $77.00; the 1978 Knowles *Gone With the Wind*, "Scarlett" (**84-K41-3.1**), up 163.6% to $290.00; and the 1977 Fairmont *DeGrazia Holiday*, "Bell of Hope" (**84-F4-1.2**), up 160% to $130.00.

Ranked tenth was "Waiting for Santa" (**42-S12-1.9**), the 1980 issue in Schmid's *Peanuts Christmas*, up 157.1% to $45.00, followed by "Mask Dancing" (**42-F78-1.4**), the 1980 Fukagawa *Warabe No Haiku* issue, up 150% to $105.00; "Mary, Mary" (**84-R60-2.1**), 1979 Reco *Mother Goose* issue, up 148.4% to $318.00; "Lighthouse Keeper's Daughter" (**84-R70-3.3**), 1979 Rockwell Society *Heritage* issue, up 140.4% to $125.00; "Flight into Egypt" (**22-K46-1.2**), the 1980 Königszelt Bavaria *Hedi Keller Christmas* plate, up 137.3% to $70.00; "Freddie's Shack" (**84-C72-1.2**), the 1980 Crown Parian *Freddie the Freeloader* issue, up 136.4% to $130.00; "Oliver's Birthday" (**22-A3-5.1**), 1979 Anna-Perenna *Uncle Tad's Cats* issue, up 133.3% to $175.00; "Becky & Baby" (**84-G58-6.2**), the 1977 Gorham *Sugar and Spice* issue, up 129.7% to $85.00; "Over the Rainbow" (**84-K41-1.1**), the 1977 Knowles *Wizard of Oz* plate, up 120% to $220.00; "Hearts-a-Flutter" (**42-S12-7.5**), the 1981 Schmid *Peanuts Valentine's Day* issue (New

42-S12-9.1
1980 Schmid *Raggedy Ann Annual*

22-A3-5.1
1979 Anna-Perenna *Uncle Tad's Cats*

84-K41-2.2
1979 Knowles *Americana Holidays*

84-K41-1.1
1977 Knowles *Wizard of Oz*

84-R60-2.1
1979 Reco
McClelland's Mother Goose

22-K46-1.2
1980 Königszelt Bavaria
Hedi Keller Christmas

Edition of the Year); and "The Adoration" (**22-K46-1.1**), the 1979 Königszelt Bavaria *Hedi Keller Christmas* issue, up 108.6% to $146.00.

The top issue in 1981 in trading volume was "The Music Maker" (**84-R70-3.5**), the 1981 Rockwell Society *Heritage* issue, which substantially out-traded runner-up "Dreaming in the Attic" (**84-R70-4.1**), the 1981 Rockwell Society *Rockwell's Rediscovered Women* issue.

The year's ten largest declines included the 1979 Dave Grossman *Annual*, "Leapfrog" (**42-G74-1.1**), down 27.7% to $47.00; the 1975 Wedgwood *Christmas* issue, "Tower Bridge" (**26-W90-1.7**), down 26.8% to $30.00; 1979 Kaiser *Christmas*, "Christmas Eve" (**22-K4-1.10**), down 26.7% to $22.00; 1972 Royal Copenhagen *Christmas*, "In the Desert" (**14-R59-1.65**) and the 1973 Kaiser *Mother's Day*, "Cats" (**22-K4-2.3**), each down 25% to $15.00 and $12.00 respectively.

The 1978 Wedgwood *Christmas*, "Horse Guards" (**26-W90-1.10**), ranked sixth among the year's declines, down 24% to $38.00; the 1978 Svend Jensen *Christmas* "Last Dream of Old Oak" (**14-J21-1.9**), the 1971 Royal Copenhagen *Mother's Day*, "American Mother" (**14-R59-2.1**), and the 1980 Goebel *Hummel Anniversary*, "Spring Dance" (**22-G54-3.2**), each down 22.2% to $21.00, $14.00, and $175.00 respectively; the 1977 Goebel *Hummel Annual*, "Apple Tree Boy" (**22-G54-1.7**), down 21.8% to $125.00; the 1979 Goebel *Hummel Annual*, "Singing Lesson" (**22-G54-1.9**), down 21.4% to $110.00; the 1974 Svend Jensen *Mother's Day*, "Daisies for Mother" (**14-J21-2.5**) and the 1980 Royal Copenhagen *Mother's Day*, "Outing with Mother" (**14-R59-2.10**), each down 20% to $20.00 and $30.00 respectively.

Lack of trading volume led to the delisting of five series from the Bradex at the close of 1981 trading. They were Haviland's *French Collection* (France), Lihs-Lindner's *A Child's Christmas* (Germany), Santa Clara's *Christmas* (Spain), Fairmont's *Irene Spencer Annual* (U.S.A.), and International's *Christmas* (U.S.A.).

22-H82-3.1
1982 Hutschenreuther
Love for All Seasons

84-F4-10.1
1981 Fairmont *Playful Memories*

84-K20-7.1
1980 Kern *Leaders of Tomorrow*

84-P29-7.1
1981 Pickard *Children of Mexico*

The trading volume of four series earned Bradex listing at year's end: Hutschenreuther's *Love for All Seasons* (Germany) (**22-H82-3**), Fairmont's *Playful Memories* (U.S.A.) (**84-F4-10**), Kern *Leaders of Tomorrow* (U.S.A.) (**84-K20-7**), and Pickard's *Children of Mexico* (U.S.A.) (**84-P29-7**).

A Winning Year

Overall, through the year spirited trading drew ever increasing numbers of new collectors into the market while hundreds of thousands were introduced to plate collecting through the activities of individual collectors' clubs, feature articles in such papers as the *New York Times* and *Chicago Tribune*, the Collector Platemakers Guild road shows, and for the first time, prime-time national television coverage.

The Market Bradex dipped slightly at year's end, down four points from the October reporting period, to close at 354. But most market observers seemed to think that the dip resulted from minor profit-taking among a few of the twelve key indicator series, that it was not representative of the market as a whole, and looked forward to another outstanding year in 1982.

Bradex-Listed Plates

The following gallery section of Bradex-listed plates is organized for quick location by numerical sequence according to Bradex number. (See page 5 for a full explanation of the Bradex numbering system.) Accompanying each full-color photograph of the more-than 1,100 Bradex-listed plates is definitive information including maker history, series and artist description, edition size, plus a full market price recap, including the issue price and high and low prices for 1981. In addition, full-color plate details — many at actual size — are featured throughout.

Porcelanas Verbano Argentina
Porcelana Granada

Since 1972, the Porcelana Granada series of Christmas plates has been made by one of Argentina's largest porcelain factories, Porcelanas Verbano. (The 1971 plate was produced in Cali, Colombia.) Porcelanas Verbano is a recognized producer of dinnerware and hand-painted pieces. The Christmas series, *Pax in Terra,* which chronologically illustrates the life of Christ, began in 1971 and is to run for fifteen years.

Thomas Fennell, Jr., designer of the first *Pax in Terra* issue, studied at the Cranbrook Academy of Art and the Boston Institute of Art. The current artist for the series is Gerry Sparks. Born in Chicago, she studied at the University of Miami School of Art under Eugene Massin, and has worked in oils, murals, ceramics, welded sculptures, and batik. Her works are displayed in the U.S., Bahamas, Greece, and Switzerland, and have won awards from the University of Miami and the Coconut Grove Society.

Pax in Terra (Peace on Earth)
Artist: As indicated
Porcelain decorated in cobalt blue
 underglaze
Diameter: 17.8 centimeters (7 inches)
Pierced foot rim
Edition size: As indicated
Numbered since 1972, without
 certificate

4-P61-1.4
1974 No Room at the Inn
Artist: Gerry Sparks/Edition: 5,000
Prices: Issue $15.00; 1981 High $18.00;
Low $16.00; Close $18.00; Up $2.00

4-P61-1.1

1971 The Annunciation
Artist: Tom Fennell, Jr./Edition: 9,300
Prices: Issue $12.00; 1981 High $21.00;
Low $15.00; Close $21.00; Up $6.00

4-P61-1.2

1972 Mary and Elizabeth
Artist: Gerry Sparks/Edition: 6,000
Prices: Issue $13.00; 1981 High $17.00;
Low $17.00; Close $17.00; No Change

4-P61-1.3

1973 Road to Bethlehem
Artist: Gerry Sparks/Edition: 5,000
Prices: Issue $14.00; 1981 High $17.00;
Low $17.00; Close $17.00; No Change

4-P61-1.5

1975 Shepherds in the Field
Artist: Gerry Sparks/Edition: 5,000
Prices: Issue $16.50; 1981 High $21.00;
Low $18.00; Close $21.00; Up $3.00

4-P61-1.6

1976 The Nativity
Artist: Gerry Sparks/Edition: 5,000
Prices: Issue $17.50; 1981 High $26.00;
Low $19.00; Close $26.00; Up $7.00

4-P61-1.7

1977 Three Kings
Artist: Gerry Sparks/Edition: 5,000
Prices: Issue $18.00; 1981 High $18.00;
Low $18.00; Close $18.00; No Change

4-P61-1.8

1978 Young Carpenter
Artist: Gerry Sparks/Edition: 5,000
Prices: Issue $18.00; 1981 High $26.00;
Low $20.00; Close $26.00; Up $6.00

4-P61-1.9

1979 Calling of Disciples
Artist: Gerry Sparks/Edition: 5,000
Prices: Issue $19.00; 1981 High $27.00;
Low $20.00; Close $27.00; Up $7.00

4-P61-1.10

1980 Loaves and Fishes
Artist: Gerry Sparks/Edition: 5,000
Prices: Issue $20.00; 1981 High $30.00;
Low $20.00; Close $30.00; Up $10.00

4-P61-1.11

1981 Suffer the Little Children
Artist: Gerry Sparks/Edition: 5,000
Prices: Issue $21.00; 1981 High $23.00;
Low $21.00; Close $23.00; Up $2.00

Maker had
no photo at
press time

4-P61-1.12

1982 Triumphal Entry
Artist: Gerry Sparks/Edition: 5,000
Issue price: Undetermined at press time

Behind the Frozen Window 14-B36-1.1
1895 Bing & Grøndahl *Christmas*
Detail from the world's first true
collector's plate

Bing & Grøndahl, Denmark's second oldest existing porcelain maker (after Royal Copenhagen), was established in 1853 by Frederick Vilhelm Grøndahl and Meyer and Jacob Bing. Grøndahl, a young sculptor previously employed by Royal Copenhagen, supplied the artistic talent while the Bing brothers provided financial backing. Although Grøndahl died before the manufactory's third year of operation, his name was retained in honor of his contribution. Bing & Grøndahl has continued under the leadership of the Bing family for five generations.

The world's first collector's plate, "Behind the Frozen Window," was issued by Bing & Grøndahl in 1895. This began its *Christmas* series which has been produced each year without interruption despite wars and economic crises. Plates in this series are now the most widely collected of all plates in the market. In 1969 Bing & Grøndahl issued the first Mother's Day plate, "Dog and Puppies." Besides limited-edition collector's plates, Bing & Grøndahl makes a variety of porcelain articles, including figurines and tableware. Many of their porcelain works can be found in museums around the world, and they have achieved the distinction of appointment to the royal courts of Denmark, Sweden, and Great Britain. This distinction is symbolized by the crown which is part of their trademark.

The artist for the very first collector's plate was Frans August Hallin, a Swede who moved to Copenhagen in 1885. After Harald Bing named him chief designer in 1895, Hallin created a distinctive item for the maker's Christmas giftware line — "Behind the Frozen Window." Its success assured his niche in history. He also designed the Christmas plates for 1896 and 1897. From 1897 until 1929 he served as manager of Bing & Grøndahl's exhibitions abroad, and in 1924 rose to the position of Assisting Director of the maker's artware line. Hallin retired in 1934 and died in Copenhagen in 1947.

Artist Henry Thelander's association with Bing & Grøndahl is unparalleled on the collector's plate market. The 1982 issue marks his twentieth consecutive design for the *Christmas* series. He also has designed every Bing & Grøndahl *Mother's Day* issue — fourteen in all. A self-taught artist, Thelander has spent his five-decade-long career living and working in Copenhagen, London, and Stockholm, benefiting from the variety of cultures and artistic influences. Known as the "equivalent of a poet laureate" in the field of Danish visual arts, he has designed government-sponsored postage stamps and posters. His celebrated series of paintings commemorating the kingdom's eight-hundredth anniversary is displayed in the Copenhagen town hall.

KONGELIG HOFLEVERANDØR

COPENHAGEN PORCELAIN

B&G

BING & GRØNDAHL

Christmas Series

Artist: As indicated

True underglaze-decorated porcelain hand-painted in Copenhagen blue on bas-relief

Diameter: 17.8 centimeters (7 inches)

Pierced foot rim

Edition size undisclosed, limited by year of issue

Not numbered, without certificate; individually initialed on back by each painter

14-B36-1.4
1898 Christmas Roses and Christmas Star
Artist: Fanny Garde
Prices: Issue $.75; 1981 High $725.00;
Low $725.00; Close $725.00; No Change

14-B36-1.1
1895 Behind the Frozen Window
Artist: Frans August Hallin
Prices: Issue $.50; 1981 High $4004.00;
Low $4000.00; Close $4004.00; Up $4.00

14-B36-1.2
1896 New Moon over Snow-covered Trees
Artist: Frans August Hallin
Prices: Issue $.50; 1981 High $2000.00;
Low $1950.00; Close $2000.00; Up $50.00

14-B36-1.3
1897 Christmas Meal of the Sparrows
Artist: Frans August Hallin
Prices: Issue $.75; 1981 High $1300.00;
Low $1300.00; Close $1300.00; No Change

14-B36-1.5
1899 The Crows Enjoying Christmas
Artist: Dahl Jensen
Prices: Issue $.75; 1981 High $1350.00;
Low $1290.00; Close $1350.00; Up $60.00

14-B36-1.6
1900 Church Bells Chiming in Christmas
Artist: Dahl Jensen
Prices: Issue $.75; 1981 High $760.00;
Low $760.00; Close $760.00; No Change

14-B36-1.7
1901 The Three Wise Men from the East
Artist: S. Sabra
Prices: Issue $1.00; 1981 High $400.00;
Low $380.00; Close $380.00; Down $20.00

14-B36-1.8

1902 Interior of a Gothic Church
Artist: Dahl Jensen
Prices: Issue $1.00; 1981 High $375.00;
Low $360.00; Close $360.00; Down $15.00

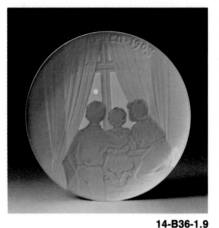

14-B36-1.9

1903 Happy Expectation of Children
Artist: Margrethe Hyldahl
Prices: Issue $1.00; 1981 High $275.00;
Low $275.00; Close $275.00; No Change

14-B36-1.10

1904 View of Copenhagen from
Frederiksberg Hill
Artist: Cathinka Olsen
Prices: Issue $1.00; 1981 High $125.00;
Low $120.00; Close $120.00; Down $5.00

14-B36-1.14

1908 St. Petri Church of Copenhagen
Artist: Povl Jorgensen
Prices: Issue $1.00; 1981 High $90.00;
Low $86.00; Close $86.00; No Change

14-B36-1.15

1909 Happiness over the Yule Tree
Artist: Aarestrup
Prices: Issue $1.50; 1981 High $106.00;
Low $100.00; Close $106.00; Up $6.00

14-B36-1.16

1910 The Old Organist
Artist: C. Ersgaard
Prices: Issue $1.50; 1981 High $95.00;
Low $90.00; Close $95.00; Up $5.00

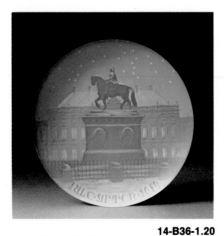

14-B36-1.20

1914 Royal Castle of Amalienborg,
Copenhagen
Artist: Th. Larsen
Prices: Issue $1.50; 1981 High $88.00;
Low $83.00; Close $88.00; Up $5.00

14-B36-1.21

1915 Chained Dog Getting Double Meal
on Christmas Eve
Artist: Dahl Jensen
Prices: Issue $1.50; 1981 High $140.00;
Low $120.00; Close $140.00; Up $20.00

14-B36-1.22

1916 Christmas Prayer of the Sparrows
Artist: J. Bloch Jorgensen
Prices: Issue $1.50; 1981 High $95.00;
Low $95.00; Close $95.00; No Change

14-B36-1.11
1905 Anxiety of the Coming Christmas Night
Artist: Dahl Jensen
Prices: Issue $1.00; 1981 High $155.00; Low $140.00; Close $155.00; Up $15.00

14-B36-1.12
1906 Sleighing to Church on Christmas Eve
Artist: Dahl Jensen
Prices: Issue $1.00; 1981 High $105.00; Low $105.00; Close $105.00; No Change

14-B36-1.13
1907 The Little Match Girl
Artist: E. Plockross
Prices: Issue $1.00; 1981 High $135.00; Low $120.00; Close $135.00; Up $15.00

14-B36-1.17
1911 First It Was Sung by Angels to Shepherds in the Fields
Artist: H. Moltke
Prices: Issue $1.50; 1981 High $95.00; Low $95.00; Close $95.00; No Change

14-B36-1.18
1912 Going to Church on Christmas Eve
Artist: Einar Hansen
Prices: Issue $1.50; 1981 High $95.00; Low $95.00; Close $95.00; No Change

14-B36-1.19
1913 Bringing Home the Yule Tree
Artist: Th. Larsen
Prices: Issue $1.50; 1981 High $102.00; Low $98.00; Close $102.00; Up $4.00

14-B36-1.23
1917 Arrival of the Christmas Boat
Artist: Achton Friis
Prices: Issue $1.50; 1981 High $90.00; Low $86.00; Close $90.00; Up $4.00

14-B36-1.24
1918 Fishing Boat Returning Home for Christmas
Artist: Achton Friis
Prices: Issue $1.50; 1981 High $90.00; Low $88.00; Close $88.00; Down $2.00

14-B36-1.25
1919 Outside the Lighted Window
Artist: Achton Friis
Prices: Issue $2.00; 1981 High $92.00; Low $88.00; Close $88.00; Down $2.00

14-B36-1.26

1920 Hare in the Snow
Artist: Achton Friis
Prices: Issue $2.00; 1981 High $85.00;
Low $74.00; Close $85.00; Up $7.00

14-B36-1.27

1921 Pigeons in the Castle Court
Artist: Achton Friis
Prices: Issue $2.00; 1981 High $72.00;
Low $68.00; Close $72.00; Up $4.00

14-B36-1.28

1922 Star of Bethlehem
Artist: Achton Friis
Prices: Issue $2.00; 1981 High $74.00;
Low $69.00; Close $72.00; Up $3.00

14-B36-1.32

1926 Churchgoers on Christmas Day
Artist: Achton Friis
Prices: Issue $2.50; 1981 High $75.00;
Low $75.00; Close $75.00; No Change

14-B36-1.33

1927 Skating Couple
Artist: Achton Friis
Prices: Issue $2.50; 1981 High $107.00;
Low $100.00; Close $107.00; Up $7.00

14-B36-1.34

1928 Eskimo Looking at Village Church
in Greenland
Artist: Achton Friis
Prices: Issue $2.50; 1981 High $75.00;
Low $67.00; Close $72.00; Up $5.00

14-B36-1.38

1932 Lifeboat at Work
Artist: H. Flugenring
Prices: Issue $2.50; 1981 High $88.00;
Low $86.00; Close $88.00; Up $2.00

14-B36-1.39

1933 The Korsor-Nyborg Ferry
Artist: H. Flugenring
Prices: Issue $3.00; 1981 High $64.00;
Low $64.00; Close $64.00; No Change

14-B36-1.40

1934 Church Bell in Tower
Artist: Immanuel Tjerne
Prices: Issue $3.00; 1981 High $69.00;
Low $64.00; Close $69.00; Up $5.00

14-B36-1.29
1923 Royal Hunting Castle, the Ermitage
Artist: Achton Friis
Prices: Issue $2.00; 1981 High $64.00;
Low $58.00; Close $64.00; Up $6.00

14-B36-1.30
1924 Lighthouse in Danish Waters
Artist: Achton Friis
Prices: Issue $2.50; 1981 High $72.00;
Low $72.00; Close $72.00; No Change

14-B36-1.31
1925 The Child's Christmas
Artist: Achton Friis
Prices: Issue $2.50; 1981 High $80.00;
Low $80.00; Close $80.00; No Change

14-B36-1.35
1929 Fox Outside Farm on Christmas Eve
Artist: Achton Friis
Prices: Issue $2.50; 1981 High $83.00;
Low $79.00; Close $80.00; Up $1.00

14-B36-1.36
1930 Yule Tree in Town Hall Square of
Copenhagen
Artist: H. Flugenring
Prices: Issue $2.50; 1981 High $110.00;
Low $103.00; Close $110.00; Up $7

14-B36-1.37
1931 Arrival of the Christmas Train
Artist: Achton Friis
Prices: Issue $2.50; 1981 High $80.00;
Low $78.00; Close $80.00; Up $2.00

14-B36-1.41
1935 Lillebelt Bridge Connecting Funen
with Jutland
Artist: Ove Larsen
Prices: Issue $3.00; 1981 High $68.00;
Low $58.00; Close $68.00; Up $10.00

14-B36-1.42
1936 Royal Guard Outside Amalienborg
Castle in Copenhagen
Artist: Ove Larsen
Prices: Issue $3.00; 1981 High $80.00;
Low $77.00; Close $78.00; Down $2.00

14-B36-1.43
1937 Arrival of Christmas Guests
Artist: Ove Larsen
Prices: Issue $3.00; 1981 High $85.00;
Low $75.00; Close $85.00; Up $10.00

14-B36-1.44

1938 Lighting the Candles
Artist: Immanuel Tjerne
Prices: Issue $3.00; 1981 High $136.00;
Low $130.00; Close $136.00; Up $6.00

14-B36-1.45

1939 Ole Lock-Eye, the Sandman
Artist: Immanuel Tjerne
Prices: Issue $3.00; 1981 High $175.00;
Low $150.00; Close $175.00; Up $15.00

14-B36-1.46

1940 Delivering Christmas Letters
Artist: Ove Larsen
Prices: Issue $4.00; 1981 High $170.00;
Low $170.00; Close $170.00; No Change

14-B36-1.50

1944 Sorgenfri Castle
Artist: Ove Larsen
Prices: Issue $5.00; 1981 High $130.00;
Low $130.00; Close $130.00; No Change

14-B36-1.51

1945 The Old Water Mill
Artist: Ove Larsen
Prices: Issue $5.00; 1981 High $145.00;
Low $140.00; Close $142.00; Down $1.00

14-B36-1.52

**1946 Commemoration Cross in Honor of
Danish Sailors Who Lost Their Lives
in World War II**
Artist: Margrethe Hyldahl
Prices: Issue $5.00; 1981 High $80.00;
Low $75.00; Close $80.00; Up $5.00

14-B36-1.56

1950 Kronborg Castle at Elsinore
Artist: Margrethe Hyldahl
Prices: Issue $5.50; 1981 High $158.00;
Low $157.00; Close $158.00; Up $1.00

14-B36-1.57

**1951 Jens Bang, New Passenger Boat
Running Between Copenhagen and
Aalborg**
Artist: Margrethe Hyldahl
Prices: Issue $6.00; 1981 High $100.00;
Low $93.00; Close $100.00; Up $7.00

14-B36-1.58

**1952 Old Copenhagen Canals at
Wintertime with Thorvaldsen
Museum in Background**
Artist: Borge Pramvig
Prices: Issue $6.00; 1981 High $80.00;
Low $75.00; Close $78.00; Up $3.00

14-B36-1.29
1923 Royal Hunting Castle, the Ermitage
Artist: Achton Friis
Prices: Issue $2.00; 1981 High $64.00;
Low $58.00; Close $64.00; Up $6.00

14-B36-1.30
1924 Lighthouse in Danish Waters
Artist: Achton Friis
Prices: Issue $2.50; 1981 High $72.00;
Low $72.00; Close $72.00; No Change

14-B36-1.31
1925 The Child's Christmas
Artist: Achton Friis
Prices: Issue $2.50; 1981 High $80.00;
Low $80.00; Close $80.00; No Change

14-B36-1.35
1929 Fox Outside Farm on Christmas Eve
Artist: Achton Friis
Prices: Issue $2.50; 1981 High $83.00;
Low $79.00; Close $80.00; Up $1.00

14-B36-1.36
1930 Yule Tree in Town Hall Square of
Copenhagen
Artist: H. Flugenring
Prices: Issue $2.50; 1981 High $110.00;
Low $103.00; Close $110.00; Up $7

14-B36-1.37
1931 Arrival of the Christmas Train
Artist: Achton Friis
Prices: Issue $2.50; 1981 High $80.00;
Low $78.00; Close $80.00; Up $2.00

14-B36-1.41
1935 Lillebelt Bridge Connecting Funen
with Jutland
Artist: Ove Larsen
Prices: Issue $3.00; 1981 High $68.00;
Low $58.00; Close $68.00; Up $10.00

14-B36-1.42
1936 Royal Guard Outside Amalienborg
Castle in Copenhagen
Artist: Ove Larsen
Prices: Issue $3.00; 1981 High $80.00;
Low $77.00; Close $78.00; Down $2.00

14-B36-1.43
1937 Arrival of Christmas Guests
Artist: Ove Larsen
Prices: Issue $3.00; 1981 High $85.00;
Low $75.00; Close $85.00; Up $10.00

14-B36-1.44

1938 Lighting the Candles
Artist: Immanuel Tjerne
Prices: Issue $3.00; 1981 High $136.00;
Low $130.00; Close $136.00; Up $6.00

14-B36-1.45

1939 Ole Lock-Eye, the Sandman
Artist: Immanuel Tjerne
Prices: Issue $3.00; 1981 High $175.00;
Low $150.00; Close $175.00; Up $15.00

14-B36-1.46

1940 Delivering Christmas Letters
Artist: Ove Larsen
Prices: Issue $4.00; 1981 High $170.00;
Low $170.00; Close $170.00; No Change

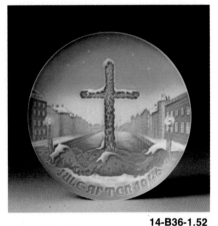

14-B36-1.50

1944 Sorgenfri Castle
Artist: Ove Larsen
Prices: Issue $5.00; 1981 High $130.00;
Low $130.00; Close $130.00; No Change

14-B36-1.51

1945 The Old Water Mill
Artist: Ove Larsen
Prices: Issue $5.00; 1981 High $145.00;
Low $140.00; Close $142.00; Down $1.00

14-B36-1.52

1946 Commemoration Cross in Honor of
Danish Sailors Who Lost Their Lives
in World War II
Artist: Margrethe Hyldahl
Prices: Issue $5.00; 1981 High $80.00;
Low $75.00; Close $80.00; Up $5.00

14-B36-1.56

1950 Kronborg Castle at Elsinore
Artist: Margrethe Hyldahl
Prices: Issue $5.50; 1981 High $158.00;
Low $157.00; Close $158.00; Up $1.00

14-B36-1.57

1951 Jens Bang, New Passenger Boat
Running Between Copenhagen and
Aalborg
Artist: Margrethe Hyldahl
Prices: Issue $6.00; 1981 High $100.00;
Low $93.00; Close $100.00; Up $7.00

14-B36-1.58

1952 Old Copenhagen Canals at
Wintertime with Thorvaldsen
Museum in Background
Artist: Borge Pramvig
Prices: Issue $6.00; 1981 High $80.00;
Low $75.00; Close $78.00; Up $3.00

14-B36-1.47
1941 Horses Enjoying Christmas Meal in Stable
Artist: Ove Larsen
Prices: Issue $4.00; 1981 High $335.00;
Low $305.00; Close $335.00; Up $30.00

14-B36-1.48
1942 Danish Farm on Christmas Night
Artist: Ove Larsen
Prices: Issue $4.00; 1981 High $150.00;
Low $140.00; Close $140.00; Down $10.00

14-B36-1.49
1943 The Ribe Cathedral
Artist: Ove Larsen
Prices: Issue $5.00; 1981 High $172.00;
Low $172.00; Close $172.00; No Change

14-B36-1.53
1947 Dybbol Mill
Artist: Margrethe Hyldahl
Prices: Issue $5.00; 1981 High $100.00;
Low $85.00; Close $100.00; Up $15.00

14-B36-1.54
1948 Watchman, Sculpture of Town Hall, Copenhagen
Artist: Margrethe Hyldahl
Prices: Issue $5.50; 1981 High $70.00;
Low $70.00; Close $70.00; No Change

14-B36-1.55
1949 Landsoldaten, 19th Century Danish Soldier
Artist: Margrethe Hyldahl
Prices: Issue $5.50; 1981 High $80.00;
Low $73.00; Close $78.00; Up $5.00

14-B36-1.59
1953 Royal Boat in Greenland Waters
Artist: Kjeld Bonfils
Prices: Issue $7.00; 1981 High $78.00;
Low $70.00; Close $78.00; Up $8.00

14-B36-1.60
1954 Birthplace of Hans Christian Andersen, with Snowman
Artist: Borge Pramvig
Prices: Issue $7.50; 1981 High $105.00;
Low $96.00; Close $105.00; Up $9.00

14-B36-1.61
1955 Kalundborg Church
Artist: Kjeld Bonfils
Prices: Issue $8.00; 1981 High $102.00;
Low $102.00; Close $102.00; No Change

14-B36-1.62

1956 Christmas in Copenhagen
Artist: Kjeld Bonfils
Prices: Issue $8.50; 1981 High $155.00;
Low $155.00; Close $155.00; No Change

14-B36-1.63

1957 Christmas Candles
Artist: Kjeld Bonfils
Prices: Issue $9.00; 1981 High $155.00;
Low $155.00; Close $155.00; No Change

14-B36-1.64

1958 Santa Claus
Artist: Kjeld Bonfils
Prices: Issue $9.50; 1981 High $115.00;
Low $102.00; Close $115.00; Up $13.00

14-B36-1.68

1962 Winter Night
Artist: Kjeld Bonfils
Prices: Issue $11.00; 1981 High $86.00;
Low $65.00; Close $86.00; Up $21.00

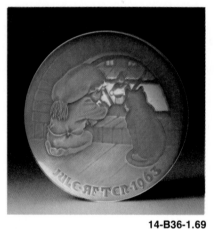

14-B36-1.69

1963 The Christmas Elf
Artist: Henry Thelander
Prices: Issue $11.00; 1981 High $145.00;
Low $100.00; Close $145.00; Up $45.00

14-B36-1.70

1964 The Fir Tree and Hare
Artist: Henry Thelander
Prices: Issue $11.50; 1981 High $60.00;
Low $46.00; Close $60.00; Up $14.00

14-B36-1.74

1968 Christmas in Church
Artist: Henry Thelander
Prices: Issue $14.00; 1981 High $48.00;
Low $40.00; Close $48.00; Up $8.00

14-B36-1.75

1969 Arrival of Christmas Guests
Artist: Henry Thelander
Prices: Issue $14.00; 1981 High $33.00;
Low $27.00; Close $32.00; Up $5.00

14-B36-1.76

1970 Pheasants in the Snow at Christmas
Artist: Henry Thelander
Prices: Issue $14.50; 1981 High $25.00;
Low $23.00; Close $23.00; Down $2.00

14-B36-1.65

1959 Christmas Eve
Artist: Kjeld Bonfils
Prices: Issue $10.00; 1981 High $140.00;
Low $136.00; Close $140.00; Up $4.00

14-B36-1.66

1960 Danish Village Church
Artist: Kjeld Bonfils
Prices: Issue $10.00; 1981 High $190.00;
Low $175.00; Close $190.00; Up $15.00

14-B36-1.67

1961 Winter Harmony
Artist: Kjeld Bonfils
Prices: Issue $10.50; 1981 High $120.00;
Low $100.00; Close $120.00; Up $20.00

14-B36-1.71

1965 Bringing Home the Christmas Tree
Artist: Henry Thelander
Prices: Issue $12.00; 1981 High $60.00;
Low $56.00; Close $60.00; Up $4.00

14-B36-1.72

1966 Home for Christmas
Artist: Henry Thelander
Prices: Issue $12.00; 1981 High $55.00;
Low $51.00; Close $55.00; Up $4.00

14-B36-1.73

1967 Sharing the Joy of Christmas
Artist: Henry Thelander
Prices: Issue $13.00; 1981 High $50.00;
Low $40.00; Close $45.00; Up $5.00

14-B36-1.77

1971 Christmas at Home
Artist: Henry Thelander
Prices: Issue $15.00; 1981 High $23.00;
Low $18.00; Close $20.00; Up $2.00

14-B36-1.78

1972 Christmas in Greenland
Artist: Henry Thelander
Prices: Issue $16.50; 1981 High $19.00;
Low $13.00; Close $19.00; Up $5.00

14-B36-1.79

1973 Country Christmas
Artist: Henry Thelander
Prices: Issue $19.50; 1981 High $30.00;
Low $24.00; Close $30.00; Up $6.00

14-B36-1.80

1974 Christmas in the Village
Artist: Henry Thelander
Prices: Issue $22.00; 1981 High $20.00;
Low $14.00; Close $20.00; Up $6.00

14-B36-1.81

1975 The Old Water Mill
Artist: Henry Thelander
Prices: Issue $27.50; 1981 High $26.00;
Low $22.00; Close $26.00; Up $4.00

14-B36-1.82

1976 Christmas Welcome
Artist: Henry Thelander
Prices: Issue $27.50; 1981 High $32.00;
Low $27.00; Close $32.00; Up $5.00

14-B36-1.85

1979 White Christmas
Artist: Henry Thelander
Prices: Issue $36.50; 1981 High $40.00;
Low $28.00; Close $40.00; Up $12.00

14-B36-1.86

1980 Christmas in the Woods
Artist: Henry Thelander
Prices: Issue $42.50; 1981 High $45.00;
Low $42.50; Close $45.00; Up $2.50

14-B36-1.87

1981 Christmas Peace
Artist: Henry Thelander
Prices: Issue $49.50; 1981 High $49.50;
Low $49.50; Close $49.50; No Change

Mother's Day Series

Artist: Henry Thelander
True underglaze-decorated porcelain
hand-painted in Copenhagen blue
on bas-relief
Diameter: 15.2 centimeters (6 inches)
Pierced foot rim
Edition size undisclosed, limited by
year of issue
Not numbered, without certificate;
individually initialed on back by each
painter

14-B36-3.1

1969 Dog and Puppies
Artist: Henry Thelander
Prices: Issue $9.75; 1981 High $510.00;
Low $480.00; Close $500.00; Up $20.00

14-B36-3.2

1970 Bird and Chicks
Artist: Henry Thelander
Prices: Issue $10.00; 1981 High $46.00;
Low $42.00; Close $43.00; Up $1.00

14-B36-1.83

1977 Copenhagen Christmas
Artist: Henry Thelander
Prices: Issue $29.50; 1981 High $32.00;
Low $30.00; Close $32.00; Up $2.00

14-B36-1.84

1978 A Christmas Tale
Artist: Henry Thelander
Prices: Issue $32.00; 1981 High $38.00;
Low $34.00; Close $35.00; Down $3.00

14-B36-1.88

1982 The Christmas Tree
Artist: Henry Thelander
Issue price: $54.50

14-B36-3.3

1971 Cat and Kitten
Artist: Henry Thelander
Prices: Issue $11.00; 1981 High $20.00;
Low $18.00; Close $20.00; Up $2.00

14-B36-3.4

1972 Mare and Foal
Artist: Henry Thelander
Prices: Issue $12.00; 1981 High $20.00;
Low $17.00; Close $20.00; Up $3.00

14-B36-3.5

1973 Duck and Ducklings
Artist: Henry Thelander
Prices: Issue $13.00; 1981 High $22.00;
Low $16.00; Close $22.00; Up $6.00

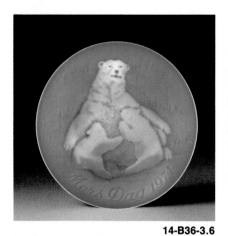

14-B36-3.6

1974 Bear and Cubs
Artist: Henry Thelander
Prices: Issue $16.50; 1981 High $20.00;
Low $18.00; Close $18.00; Down $2.00

14-B36-3.7

1975 Doe and Fawns
Artist: Henry Thelander
Prices: Issue $19.50; 1981 High $19.00;
Low $17.00; Close $19.00; Up $1.00

14-B36-3.8

1976 Swan Family
Artist: Henry Thelander
Prices: Issue $22.50; 1981 High $23.00;
Low $20.00; Close $23.00; Up $3.00

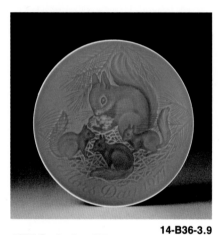

14-B36-3.9

1977 Squirrel and Young
Artist: Henry Thelander
Prices: Issue $23.50; 1981 High $28.00;
Low $25.00; Close $28.00; Up $3.00

14-B36-3.10

1978 Heron
Artist: Henry Thelander
Prices: Issue $24.50; 1981 High $26.00;
Low $25.00; Close $25.00; Down $1.00

14-B36-3.11

1979 Fox and Cubs
Artist: Henry Thelander
Prices: Issue $27.50; 1981 High $33.00;
Low $28.00; Close $33.00; Up $3.00

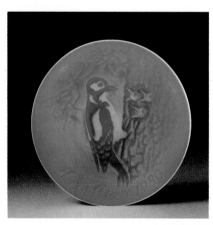

14-B36-3.12

1980 Woodpecker and Young
Artist: Henry Thelander
Prices: Issue $29.50; 1981 High $36.00;
Low $29.50; Close $36.00; Up $6.50

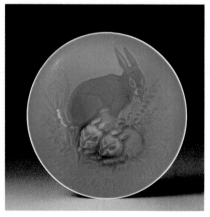

14-B36-3.13

1981 Hare and Young
Artist: Henry Thelander
Prices: Issue $36.50; 1981 High $39.00;
Low $36.50; Close $39.00; Up $2.50

14-B36-3.14

1982 Lioness and Cubs
Artist: Henry Thelander
Issue price: $39.50

Franklin's Tale 26-L46-1.2
1982 Longton Crown *Canterbury Tales*
Detail showing how artist G.A. Hoover's
colors are enhanced by the plate medium
of fine English bone china

Grande Copenhagen plates are produced at the Eslau porcelain factory near Copenhagen. Grande Copenhagen began its *Christmas* series of plates depicting Danish winter scenes in 1975.

Artists for Grande Copenhagen *Christmas* plates prior to 1980 are undisclosed. The artist for the 1980, 1981, and 1982 issues is Frode Bahnsen of Aarhus, Jutland, Denmark. Bahnsen studied sculpture, ceramics, and drawing at the Copenhagen Royal Academy of Art, and subsequently worked for the Royal Mint in Copenhagen, rising to the position of head sculptor in 1968. Among the many places where his works have been exhibited are the Charlottenborg Art Exhibition in Copenhagen, F.I.D.M.E. (Federal International Danish Medal Exhibitions), and the National Museum of Copenhagen. In 1978 he was titled knight of Dannebrog by the Queen of Denmark.

Christmas Series

Artist: As indicated
True underglaze-decorated porcelain
 hand-painted in Copenhagen blue
 on bas-relief
Diameter: 18.4 centimeters (7¼ inches)
Pierced foot rim
Edition size undisclosed, limited by
 year of issue
Not numbered, without certificate;
 individually initialed on back by
 each painter

14-G65-1.1

1975 Alone Together
Artist: Undisclosed
Prices: Issue $24.50; 1981 High $25.00;
Low $25.00; Close $25.00; No Change

14-G65-1.5

1979 Pheasants in the Snow
Artist: Undisclosed
Prices: Issue $34.50; 1981 High $34.50;
Low $34.50; Close $34.50; No Change

14-G65-1.2

1976 Christmas Wreath
Artist: Undisclosed
Prices: Issue $24.50; 1981 High $28.00;
Low $25.00; Close $28.00; Up $3.00

14-G65-1.3

1977 Fishwives at Gammelstrand
Artist: Undisclosed
Prices: Issue $26.50; 1981 High $31.00;
Low $31.00; Close $31.00; No Change

14-G65-1.4

1978 Hans Christian Andersen
Artist: Undisclosed
Prices: Issue $32.50; 1981 High $33.00;
Low $30.00; Close $33.00; Up $3.00

14-G65-1.6

1980 The Snow Queen in the Tivoli
Artist: Frode Bahnsen
Prices: Issue $39.50; 1981 High $39.50;
Low $39.50; Close $39.50; No Change

14-G65-1.7

1981 Little Match Girl in Nyhavn
Artist: Frode Bahnsen
Prices: Issue $42.50; 1981 High $42.50;
Low $42.50; Close $42.50; No Change

14-G65-1.8

No information available at press time

Svend Jensen plates are made by the Désirée porcelain factory near Copenhagen and are the result of an association between art consultant Svend Jensen and porcelain expert H.C. Torbal. In 1970 they issued the first limited-edition plates in two Svend Jensen annual collections — a *Christmas* series based on Hans Christian Andersen fairy tales, and a *Mother's Day* series.

Copenhagen-born Mads Stage received his training at the Royal Danish Academy of Arts and won several prizes for his illustrations of Danish literary works. His perceptive, though child-like style has brought him a wide following, both in Denmark and in the United States. Svend Otto was inspired by such Danish masters as Eckersberg, Marstrand, and Skovgard, and studied at the Kunsthaandvaerkerskolen in the School of Art, Craft and Design; Bizzie Hoyers Malerskole; and the St. Martin's School of Arts in London. His works have been published in ten countries on three continents, and he won the 1978 Gold Medal for best illustration of Hans Christian Andersen stories. Edvard Eriksen is perhaps the greatest Danish sculptor of this century. Born in Copenhagen, Eriksen studied wood carving between 1895-99 under the tutelage of Soph. Petersen at the Royal Danish Academy of Arts, and later worked in fine marble. In 1906 he received the Gold Medal from the Danish Royal Academy, and most of his creations remain in the Charlottenborg museum. His masterpiece is "The Little Mermaid," situated in Copenhagen harbor as a greeting to all incoming ships. This was sculpted in 1913, inspired by the Hans Christian Andersen fairy tale. Nulle Oigaard, a prominent Danish watercolorist, studied at the Royal Danish Academy of Arts and at the Julien Academie in Paris. He was greatly influenced by the painter Alex Klingsor and his initial efforts were in book and magazine illustrations. In 1977 Oigaard won an award from the Danish Society of Arts and Crafts, and the honored work was exhibited at the museum for art and industry, the Kunstindustrimuseet. Other institutions displaying Oigaard works include the Galarie Gammelstrand and France's Musée Chateau d'Anessy. Maggi Baaring studied at the Folmer Bonnens painting school in 1928 and later at Illums Bolighus. Her early career was spent as a commercial and fashion artist, and her accomplishments include theatre and revue decorations and interior design of cinemas. Her works are displayed at Illums Bolighus and in New York and Denver. Her literary illustrations include De Maupassant's collected works and the novels of Sagan, Coward, Colette, and Maugham.

DENMARK

Svend Jensen

Christmas Series

Artist: As indicated. Artist's name appears on back

True underglaze-decorated porcelain hand-painted in Copenhagen blue on bas-relief

Diameter: 17.8 centimeters (7 inches)

Pierced foot rim

Edition size undisclosed, limited by year of issue

Not numbered, without certificate; individually initialed on back by each painter

14-J21-1.4

1973 The Fir Tree
Artist: Svend Otto
Prices: Issue $22.00; 1981 High $31.00; Low $30.00; Close $31.00; Up $1.00

14-J21-1.1

1970 Hans Christian Andersen House
Artist: Gerhard Sausmark
Prices: Issue $14.50; 1981 High $70.00;
Low $60.00; Close $70.00; Up $10.00

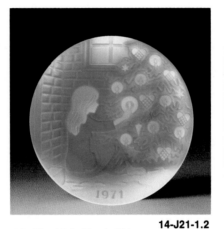

14-J21-1.2

1971 The Little Match Girl
Artist: Mads Stage
Prices: Issue $15.00; 1981 High $34.00;
Low $31.00; Close $34.00; Up $3.00

14-J21-1.3

1972 Little Mermaid of Copenhagen
Artist: Rights from family of Edvard Eriksen,
sculptor
Prices: Issue $16.50; 1981 High $37.00;
Low $28.00; Close $37.00; Up $9.00

14-J21-1.5

1974 The Chimney Sweep
Artist: Svend Otto
Prices: Issue $25.00; 1981 High $30.00;
Low $30.00; Close $30.00; No Changse

14-J21-1.6

1975 The Ugly Duckling
Artist: Svend Otto
Prices: Issue $27.50; 1981 High $25.00;
Low $17.00; Close $25.00; Up $7.00

14-J21-1.7

1976 The Snow Queen
Artist: Mads Stage
Prices: Issue $27.50; 1981 High $26.00;
Low $24.00; Close $24.00; Down $2.00

14-J21-1.8

1977 The Snowman
Artist: Svend Otto
Prices: Issue $29.50; 1981 High $22.00;
Low $22.00; Close $22.00; No Change

14-J21-1.9

1978 The Last Dream of the Old Oak Tree
Artist: Svend Otto
Prices: Issue $32.00; 1981 High $27.00;
Low $21.00; Close $21.00; Down $6.00

14-J21-1.10

1979 The Old Street Lamp
Artist: Svend Otto
Prices: Issue $36.50; 1981 High $36.00;
Low $34.00; Close $34.00; Down $2.00

Mother's Day Series

Artist: As indicated. Artist's name
appears on back
True underglaze-decorated porcelain
hand-painted in Copenhagen blue
on bas-relief
Diameter: 17.8 centimeters (7 inches)
Edition size undisclosed, limited by
year of issue
Not numbered, with certificate since
1977; individually initialed on back
by each painter

14-J21-2.1

1970 Bouquet for Mother
Artist: Maggi Baaring
Prices: Issue $14.50; 1981 High $62.00;
Low $52.00; Close $62.00; Up $10.00

14-J21-2.5

1974 Daisies for Mother
Artist: Mads Stage
Prices: Issue $25.00; 1981 High $25.00;
Low $20.00; Close $20.00; Down $5.00

14-J21-2.6

1975 Surprise for Mother
Artist: Mads Stage
Prices: Issue $27.50; 1981 High $18.00;
Low $16.00; Close $18.00; Up $2.00

14-J21-1.11

1980 Willie Winky
Artist: Svend Otto
Prices: Issue $42.50; 1981 High $42.50;
Low $42.50; Close $42.50; No Change

14-J21-1.12

1981 The Uttermost Parts of the Sea
Artist: Svend Otto
Prices: Issue $49.50; 1981 High $49.50;
Low $49.50; Close $49.50; No Change

14-J21-1.13

1982 Twelve by the Mailcoach
Artist: Svend Otto
Issue price: $54.50

14-J21-2.2

1971 Mother's Love
Artist: Nulle Oigaard
Prices: Issue $15.00; 1981 High $26.00;
Low $24.00; Close $24.00; Down $2.00

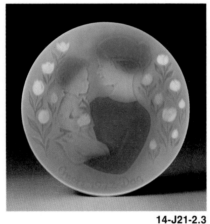

14-J21-2.3

1972 Good Night
Artist: Mads Stage
Prices: Issue $16.50; 1981 High $25.00;
Low $19.00; Close $25.00; Up $6.00

14-J21-2.4

1973 Flowers for Mother
Artist: Mads Stage
Prices: Issue $20.00; 1981 High $28.00;
Low $28.00; Close $28.00; No Change

14-J21-2.7

1976 The Complete Gardener
Artist: Mads Stage
Prices: Issue $27.50; 1981 High $20.00;
Low $18.00; Close $20.00; Up $2.00

14-J21-2.8

1977 Little Friends
Artist: Mads Stage
Prices: Issue $29.50; 1981 High $20.00;
Low $17.00; Close $17.00; Down $3.00

14-J21-2.9

1978 Dreams
Artist: Mads Stage
Prices: Issue $32.00; 1981 High $30.00;
Low $24.00; Close $30.00; Up $6.00

14-J21-2.10

1979 Promenade
Artist: Mads Stage
Prices: Issue $36.50; 1981 High $30.00;
Low $28.00; Close $28.00; Down $2.00

14-J21-2.11

1980 Nursery Scene
Artist: Mads Stage
Prices: Issue $42.50; 1981 High $42.50;
Low $42.50; Close $42.50; No Change

14-J21-2.12

1981 Daily Duties
Artist: Mads Stage
Prices: Issue $49.50; 1981 High $49.50;
Low $49.50; Close $49.50; No Change

14-J21-2.13

1982 My Best Friend
Artist: Mads Stage
Issue price: $54.50

Vainamoinen's Sowing 16-A69-1.1
1976 Arabia *Annual*
Detail from the first collector's plate made
in Finland, one of the few square plates

The Royal Copenhagen Porcelain Manufactory, Denmark's oldest existing porcelain maker, was established by Franz Henrich Muller with the support of Denmark's queen dowager, Juliane Marie, in January 1775. Since the 1760s, members of the Danish royal family had been interested in the white hard-paste porcelain made in China, but it was not until 1772 that Muller, a Danish pharmacist and chemist, was able to duplicate the fine porcelain. In 1779 "The Danish Porcelain Factory," as Royal Copenhagen was then called, came under royal control.

The Danish Court controlled the firm from 1779 to 1867, a period in its history that is still symbolized by the crown in its trademark. The three wavy lines under the crown, part of the factory trademark since 1775, pay tribute to Denmark's tradition as a seafaring nation and represent Denmark's three ancient waterways: the Sound, the Great Belt, and the Little Belt. In 1867 the factory was sold and has continued under private ownership. It is still a supplier to the royal court in Denmark.

The first Royal Copenhagen *Christmas* plate was issued in 1908, and the series has continued every year since then. For the first three years the plates were six inches in diameter. Beginning with the 1911 issue, they were changed to the seven-inch size. From the beginning, the motif for each year's *Christmas* plate has been selected from suggestions submitted by employees of the Royal Copenhagen factory. Until 1941, small quantities of plates in the *Christmas* series were created with the word "Christmas" translated into other languages to meet the demand from non-Danish collectors. The Royal Copenhagen *Mother's Day* series was started in 1971.

Christian Thomsen, designer of the first Royal Copenhagen collector's plate, served an apprenticeship as a woodcarver before joining the firm in 1898. His porcelain creations won a silver medal in a Milan exhibit in 1908 and a gold medal in a Brussels exhibit in 1910. His work now hangs in the Museum of Decorative Arts in Copenhagen. Arnold Krog innovated the famed cobalt-blue underglaze design technique which has become a tradition in Danish plate making. He worked for Royal Copenhagen from 1884 to 1916, rising to art director and taking the Grand Prix for decorative art in Paris in 1900. Krog's most famous creation is his fountain located in The Hague, The Netherlands. Artist Kai Lange has been with Royal Copenhagen since the age of seventeen and, after more than half a century with the firm, is regarded as one of the most knowledgeable artists working in the porcelain medium today. The first Kai Lange design selected for the annual *Christmas* plate was for the 1940 issue, and since 1963 every plate, except the 1976 issue, has been a Kai Lange creation. Kamma Svenson, artist for the first two *Mother's Day* issues, has gained a world following for her illustrations of Danish literary scenes. Since 1950 she has worked as an illustrator for *Politiken,* one of the two largest Copenhagen newspapers. Her work, "Russian Dolls," was reproduced as a UNICEF Christmas card. The Royal Academy of Fine Arts has sponsored numerous exhibitions of her work. Ib Spang Olsen, artist for the *Mother's Day* series, is a recipient of the Danish Children's Book Prize.

Royal Copenhagen

Christmas Series

Artist: As indicated. Artist's name
  appears on back since 1955
True underglaze-decorated porcelain
  hand-painted in Copenhagen blue
  on bas-relief
Diameter: 15.2 centimeters (6 inches)
  for 1908 to 1910; 17.8 centimeters
  (7 inches) thereafter
Pierced foot rim
Edition size unannounced, limited by
  year of issue
Not numbered, without certificate;
  individually initialed on back by each
  painter

14-R59-1.4

1911 Danish Landscape
Artist: Oluf Jensen
Prices: Issue $1.00; 1981 High $150.00;
Low $130.00; Close $150.00; Up $20.00

14-R59-1.1

1908 Madonna and Child
Artist: Chr. Thomsen
Prices: Issue $1.00; 1981 High $1900.00;
Low $1885.00; Close $1900.00; Up $15.00

14-R59-1.2

1909 Danish Landscape
Artist: St. Ussing
Prices: Issue $1.00; 1981 High $190.00;
Low $170.00; Close $170.00; Down $10.00

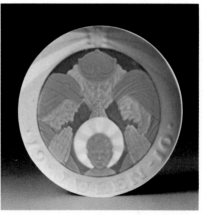

14-R59-1.3

1910 The Magi
Artist: Chr. Thomsen
Prices: Issue $1.00; 1981 High $155.00;
Low $145.00; Close $145.00; Down $4.00

14-R59-1.5

1912 Elderly Couple by Christmas Tree
Artist: Chr. Thomsen
Prices: Issue $1.00; 1981 High $170.00;
Low $165.00; Close $165.00; Down $5.00

14-R59-1.6

1913 Spire of Frederik's Church,
   Copenhagen
Artist: A. Boesen
Prices: Issue $1.50; 1981 High $138.00;
Low $135.00; Close $138.00; Up $3.00

14-R59-1.7

1914 Sparrows in Tree at Church of the
   Holy Spirit, Copenhagen
Artist: A. Boesen
Prices: Issue $1.50; 1981 High $135.00;
Low $130.00; Close $135.00; Up $5.00

14-R59-1.8

1915 Danish Landscape
Artist: A. Krog
Prices: Issue $1.50; 1981 High $206.00;
Low $180.00; Close $185.00; Up $5.00

14-R59-1.9

1916 Shepherd in the Field on Christmas Night
Artist: Ricard Böcher
Prices: Issue $1.50; 1981 High $95.00;
Low $90.00; Close $95.00; Up $5.00

14-R59-1.10

1917 Tower of Our Savior's Church, Copenhagen
Artist: Oluf Jensen
Prices: Issue $2.00; 1981 High $83.00;
Low $80.00; Close $83.00; Up $3.00

14-R59-1.14

1921 Aabenraa Marketplace
Artist: Oluf Jensen
Prices: Issue $2.00; 1981 High $75.00;
Low $73.00; Close $75.00; Up $2.00

14-R59-1.15

1922 Three Singing Angels
Artist: Ellinor Selschau
Prices: Issue $2.00; 1981 High $79.00;
Low $73.00; Close $73.00; Down $1.00

14-R59-1.16

1923 Danish Landscape
Artist: Oluf Jensen
Prices: Issue $2.00; 1981 High $78.00;
Low $76.00; Close $78.00; Up $2.00

14-R59-1.20

1927 Ship's Boy at the Tiller on Christmas Night
Artist: Benjamin Olsen
Prices: Issue $2.00; 1981 High $160.00;
Low $130.00; Close $160.00; Up $26.00

14-R59-1.21

1928 Vicar's Family on Way to Church
Artist: G. Rode
Prices: Issue $2.00; 1981 High $78.00;
Low $73.00; Close $78.00; Up $5.00

14-R59-1.22

1929 Grundtvig Church, Copenhagen
Artist: Oluf Jensen
Prices: Issue $2.00; 1981 High $78.00;
Low $72.00; Close $78.00; Up $6.00

14-R59-1.11
1918 Sheep and Shepherds
Artist: Oluf Jensen
Prices: Issue $2.00; 1981 High $96.00;
Low $93.00; Close $96.00; Up $3.00

14-R59-1.12
1919 In the Park
Artist: Oluf Jensen
Prices: Issue $2.00; 1981 High $96.00;
Low $93.00; Close $96.00; Up $3.00

14-R59-1.13
1920 Mary with the Child Jesus
Artist: G. Rode
Prices: Issue $2.00; 1981 High $87.00;
Low $78.00; Close $87.00; Up $9.00

14-R59-1.17
**1924 Christmas Star over the Sea and
Sailing Ship**
Artist: Benjamin Olsen
Prices: Issue $2.00; 1981 High $108.00;
Low $103.00; Close $105.00; Up $2.00

14-R59-1.18
**1925 Street Scene from Christianshavn,
Copenhagen**
Artist: Oluf Jensen
Prices: Issue $2.00; 1981 High $88.00;
Low $80.00; Close $88.00; Up $8.00

14-R59-1.19
**1926 View of Christianshavn Canal,
Copenhagen**
Artist: Ricard Böcher
Prices: Issue $2.00; 1981 High $83.00;
Low $79.00; Close $83.00; Up $4.00

14-R59-1.23
**1930 Fishing Boats on the Way to the
Harbor**
Artist: Benjamin Olsen
Prices: Issue $2.50; 1981 High $92.00;
Low $86.00; Close $90.00; Down $2.00

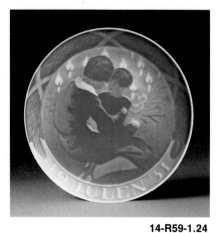

14-R59-1.24
1931 Mother and Child
Artist: G. Rode
Prices: Issue $2.50; 1981 High $96.00;
Low $86.00; Close $96.00; Up $10.00

14-R59-1.25
**1932 Frederiksberg Gardens with Statue
of Frederik VI**
Artist: Oluf Jensen
Prices: Issue $2.50; 1981 High $85.00;
Low $78.00; Close $85.00; Up $7.00

14-R59-1.26

1933 The Great Belt Ferry
Artist: Benjamin Olsen
Prices: Issue $2.50; 1981 High $118.00;
Low $102.00; Close $118.00; Up $16.00

14-R59-1.27

1934 The Hermitage Castle
Artist: Oluf Jensen
Prices: Issue $2.50; 1981 High $122.00;
Low $122.00; Close $122.00; No Change

14-R59-1.28

1935 Fishing Boat off Kronborg Castle
Artist: Benjamin Olsen
Prices: Issue $2.50; 1981 High $142.00;
Low $139.00; Close $141.00; Down $1.00

14-R59-1.32

1939 Expeditionary Ship in Pack-Ice of Greenland
Artist: Sv. Nic. Nielsen
Prices: Issue $3.00; 1981 High $255.00;
Low $255.00; Close $255.00; No Change

14-R59-1.33

1940 The Good Shepherd
Artist: Kai Lange
Prices: Issue $3.00; 1981 High $380.00;
Low $370.00; Close $380.00; No Change

14-R59-1.34

1941 Danish Village Church
Artist: Th. Kjolner
Prices: Issue $3.00; 1981 High $400.00;
Low $400.00; Close $400.00; No Change

14-R59-1.38

1945 A Peaceful Motif
Artist: Ricard Böcher
Prices: Issue $4.00; 1981 High $360.00;
Low $360.00; Close $360.00; No Change

14-R59-1.39

1946 Zealand Village Church
Artist: Nils Thorsson
Prices: Issue $4.00; 1981 High $155.00;
Low $155.00; Close $155.00; No Change

14-R59-1.40

1947 The Good Shepherd
Artist: Kai Lange
Prices: Issue $4.50; 1981 High $210.00;
Low $195.00; Close $195.00; Down $15.00

14-R59-1.29
1936 Roskilde Cathedral
Artist: Ricard Böcher
Prices: Issue $2.50; 1981 High $138.00;
Low $128.00; Close $138.00; Up $10.00

14-R59-1.30
1937 Christmas Scene in Main Street,
Copenhagen
Artist: Nils Thorsson
Prices: Issue $2.50; 1981 High $145.00;
Low $130.00; Close $145.00; Up $15.00

14-R59-1.31
1938 Round Church in Osterlars on
Bornholm
Artist: Herne Nielsen
Prices: Issue $3.00; 1981 High $293.00;
Low $279.00; Close $293.00; Up $14.00

14-R59-1.35
1942 Bell Tower of Old Church in Jutland
Artist: Nils Thorsson
Prices: Issue $4.00; 1981 High $420.00;
Low $420.00; Close $420.00; No Change

14-R59-1.36
1943 Flight of Holy Family to Egypt
Artist: Nils Thorsson
Prices: Issue $4.00; 1981 High $532.00;
Low $520.00; Close $532.00; Up $12.00

14-R59-1.37
1944 Typical Danish Winter Scene
Artist: Viggo Olsen
Prices: Issue $4.00; 1981 High $160.00;
Low $155.00; Close $160.00; Up $2.00

14-R59-1.41
1948 Nodebo Church at Christmastime
Artist: Th. Kjolner
Prices: Issue $4.50; 1981 High $172.00;
Low $155.00; Close $172.00; Up $17.00

14-R59-1.42
1949 Our Lady's Cathedral, Copenhagen
Artist: Hans H. Hansen
Prices: Issue $5.00; 1981 High $169.00;
Low $150.00; Close $169.00; Up $19.00

14-R59-1.43
1950 Boeslunde Church, Zealand
Artist: Viggo Olsen
Prices: Issue $5.00; 1981 High $200.00;
Low $200.00; Close $200.00; No Change

14-R59-1.44
1951 Christmas Angel
Artist: Ricard Böcher
Prices: Issue $5.00; 1981 High $330.00;
Low $315.00; Close $330.00; Up $15.00

14-R59-1.45
1952 Christmas in the Forest
Artist: Kai Lange
Prices: Issue $5.00; 1981 High $130.00;
Low $130.00; Close $130.00; No Change

14-R59-1.46
1953 Frederiksberg Castle
Artist: Th. Kjolner
Prices: Issue $6.00; 1981 High $115.00;
Low $110.00; Close $115.00; Up $5.00

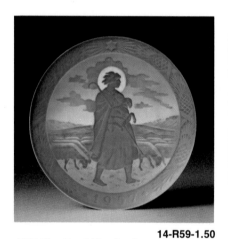

14-R59-1.50
1957 The Good Shepherd
Artist: Hans H. Hansen
Prices: Issue $8.00; 1981 High $120.00;
Low $110.00; Close $120.00; Up $10.00

14-R59-1.51
1958 Sunshine over Greenland
Artist: Hans H. Hansen
Prices: Issue $9.00; 1981 High $145.00;
Low $137.00; Close $145.00; Up $8.00

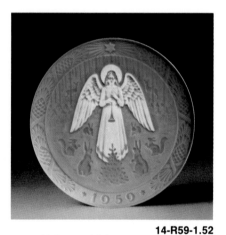

14-R59-1.52
1959 Christmas Night
Artist: Hans H. Hansen
Prices: Issue $9.00; 1981 High $145.00;
Low $142.00; Close $142.00; Down $3.00

14-R59-1.56
1963 Hojsager Mill
Artist: Kai Lange
Prices: Issue $11.00; 1981 High $98.00;
Low $93.00; Close $98.00; Up $5.00

14-R59-1.57
1964 Fetching the Christmas Tree
Artist: Kai Lange
Prices: Issue $11.00; 1981 High $77.00;
Low $70.00; Close $77.00; Up $7.00

14-R59-1.58
1965 Little Skaters
Artist: Kai Lange
Prices: Issue $12.00; 1981 High $78.00;
Low $70.00; Close $74.00; Up $4.00

14-R59-1.47

1954 Amalienborg Palace, Copenhagen
Artist: Kai Lange
Prices: Issue $6.00; 1981 High $140.00;
Low $140.00; Close $140.00; No Change

14-R59-1.48

1955 Fano Girl
Artist: Kai Lange
Prices: Issue $7.00; 1981 High $225.00;
Low $219.00; Close $225.00; Up $6.00

14-R59-1.49

1956 Rosenborg Castle, Copenhagen
Artist: Kai Lange
Prices: Issue $7.00; 1981 High $180.00;
Low $175.00; Close $180.00: No Change

14-R59-1.53

1960 The Stag
Artist: Hans H. Hansen
Prices: Issue $10.00; 1981 High $195.00;
Low $185.00; Close $192.00; Down $3.00

14-R59-1.54

1961 Training Ship Danmark
Artist: Kai Lange
Prices: Issue $10.00; 1981 High $190.00;
Low $180.00; Close $190.00; Up $10.00

14-R59-1.55

1962 The Little Mermaid at Wintertime
Artist: Undisclosed
Prices: Issue $11.00; 1981 High $220.00;
Low $200.00; Close $220.00; Up $20.00

14-R59-1.59

1966 Blackbird at Christmastime
Artist: Kai Lange
Prices: Issue $12.00; 1981 High $55.00;
Low $51.00; Close $54.00; Down $1.00

14-R59-1.60

1967 The Royal Oak
Artist: Kai Lange
Prices: Issue $13.00; 1981 High $48.00;
Low $45.00; Close $45.00; Down $1.00

14-R59-1.61

1968 The Last Umiak
Artist: Kai Lange
Prices: Issue $13.00; 1981 High $37.00;
Low $31.00; Close $31.00; Down $1.00

14-R59-1.62

1969 The Old Farmyard
Artist: Kai Lange
Prices: Issue $14.00; 1981 High $36.00;
Low $33.00; Close $36.00; Up $3.00

14-R59-1.63

1970 Christmas Rose and Cat
Artist: Kai Lange
Prices: Issue $14.00; 1981 High $36.00;
Low $33.00; Close $33.00; No Change

14-R59-1.64

1971 Hare in Winter
Artist: Kai Lange
Prices: Issue $15.00; 1981 High $24.00;
Low $21.00; Close $23.00; Down $1.00

14-R59-1.68

1975 Queen's Palace
Artist: Kai Lange
Prices: Issue $27.50; 1981 High $22.00;
Low $20.00; Close $20.00; Down $2.00

14-R59-1.69

1976 Danish Watermill
Artist: Sven Vestergaard
Prices: Issue $27.50; 1981 High $43.00;
Low $39.00; Close $41.00; Up $2.00

14-R59-1.70

1977 Immervad Bridge
Artist: Kai Lange
Prices: Issue $32.00; 1981 High $28.00;
Low $26.00; Close $26.00; No Change

14-R59-1.74

1981 Admiring the Christmas Tree
Artist: Kai Lange
Prices: Issue $52.50; 1981 High $52.50;
Low $52.50; Close $52.50; No Change

14-R59-1.75

1982 Waiting for Christmas
Artist: Kai Lange
Issue price: $54.50

14-R59-1.65

1972 In the Desert
Artist: Kai Lange
Prices: Issue $16.00; 1981 High $20.00;
Low $15.00; Close $15.00; Down $5.00

14-R59-1.66

1973 Train Homeward Bound for Christmas
Artist: Kai Lange
Prices: Issue $22.00; 1981 High $28.00;
Low $26.00; Close $27.00; Down $1.00

14-R59-1.67

1974 Winter Twilight
Artist: Kai Lange
Prices: Issue $22.00; 1981 High $22.00;
Low $19.00; Close $19.00; Down $1.00

14-R59-1.71

1978 Greenland Scenery
Artist: Kai Lange
Prices: Issue $35.00; 1981 High $34.00;
Low $33.00; Close $34.00; Up $1.00

14-R59-1.72

1979 Choosing the Christmas Tree
Artist: Kai Lange
Prices: Issue $42.50; 1981 High $47.00;
Low $40.00; Close $47.00; Up $7.00

14-R59-1.73

1980 Bringing Home the Christmas Tree
Artist: Kai Lange
Prices: Issue $49.50; 1981 High $60.00;
Low $49.50; Close $53.00; Up $3.50

Mother's Day Series

Artist: As indicated
True underglaze-decorated porcelain
 hand-painted in Copenhagen blue
 on bas-relief
Diameter: 15.9 centimeters (6¼ inches)
Pierced foot rim
Edition size unannounced, limited by
 year of issue
Not numbered, without certificate;
 individually initialed on back by each
 painter

14-R59-2.1

1971 American Mother
Artist: Kamma Svensson
Prices: Issue $12.50; 1981 High $18.00;
Low $14.00; Close $14.00; Down $4.00

14-R59-2.5

1975 Bird in Nest
Artist: Arne Ungermann
Prices: Issue $20.00; 1981 High $21.00;
Low $18.00; Close $21.00; Up $3.00

14-R59-2.6

1976 Mermaids
Artist: Arne Ungermann
Prices: Issue $20.00; 1981 High $18.00;
Low $18.00; Close $18.00; No Change

14-R59-2.10

1980 An Outing with Mother
Artist: Ib Spang Olsen
Prices: Issue $37.50; 1981 High $37.50;
Low $30.00; Close $30.00; Down $7.50

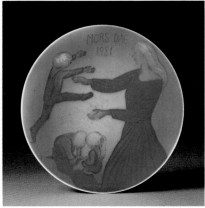

14-R59-2.11

1981 Reunion
Artist: Ib Spang Olsen
Prices: Issue $39.00; 1981 High $39.00;
Low $39.00; Close $39.00; No Change

14-R59-2.2

1972 Oriental Mother
Artist: Kamma Svensson
Prices: Issue $14.00; 1981 High $10.00;
Low $9.00; Close $9.00; Down $1.00

14-R59-2.3

1973 Danish Mother
Artist: Arne Ungermann
Prices: Issue $16.00; 1981 High $18.00;
Low $16.00; Close $18.00; Up $2.00

14-R59-2.4

1974 Greenland Mother
Artist: Arne Ungermann
Prices: Issue $16.50; 1981 High $20.00;
Low $17.00; Close $20.00; Up $3.00

14-R59-2.7

1977 The Twins
Artist: Arne Ungermann
Prices: Issue $24.00; 1981 High $28.00;
Low $24.00; Close $26.00; Up $2.00

14-R59-2.8

1978 Mother and Child
Artist: Ib Spang Olsen
Prices: Issue $26.00; 1981 High $24.00;
Low $24.00; Close $24.00; No Change

14-R59-2.9

1979 A Loving Mother
Artist: Ib Spang Olsen
Prices: Issue $29.50; 1981 High $37.00;
Low $30.00; Close $30.00; Down $4.00

14-R59-2.12

1982 The Children's Hour
Artist: Ib Spang Olsen
Issue price: $39.00

ARABIA
FINLAND

In 1873 Arabia was founded as a subsidiary of the Swedish firm Rörstrand (see Sweden, Rörstrand). The factory was located on the outskirts of Helsinki, a site chosen in hopes of supplying the growing markets for ceramics in Finland and the Russian Empire. Early products included dinner services, pitchers, and mugs, almost all based on Rörstrand designs.

In 1884 Arabia was reorganized as a Finnish company, Arabia Aktiefabrik, and developed its own designs from that time on. The company won a gold medal at the Paris World Exhibition in 1900, and is the only pottery producing both household and art ceramics in Finland today.

To celebrate the one-hundredth anniversary of the firm in 1973, Arabia produced a limited-edition anniversary plate. Its success, in turn, led to the introduction in 1976 of an annual limited-edition series based on the Finnish national epic, the *Kalevala*.

Born in Hollola, Finland, Raija Uosikkinen is widely recognized as a master ceramicist. She studied at the Institute of Industrial Arts in Helsinki. In 1947 she joined the Arabia design department, and in 1952 she received a grant scholarship from the Arabia-Decora factory to study in Germany. She has taken subsequent study trips to Australia, England, Turkey, and Indonesia. A 1954 Helsinki exhibit was exclusively devoted to her creations. Her work, a distinctive contemporary folk art style, has also been exhibited at Brussels (1958), Milan (1960), and Sacramento (1961), where she won the prestigious Gold Medal.

Kalevala Series

Artist: Raija Uosikkinen
Stoneware
Diameter: 19 centimeters square
   (7½ inches square)
Pierced foot rim
Edition size undisclosed
Not numbered, without certificate

16-A69-1.4

1979 Kullervo's Revenge
Artist: Raija Uosikkinen
Prices: Issue $39.50; 1981 High $39.50;
Low $39.50; Close $39.50; No Change

16-A69-1.1

1976 Vainamoinen's Sowing
Artist: Raija Uosikkinen
Prices: Issue $30.00; 1981 High $165.00;
Low $130.00; Close $165.00; Up $35.00

16-A69-1.2

1977 Aino's Fate
Artist: Raija Uosikkinen
Prices: Issue $30.00; 1981 High $68.00;
Low $60.00; Close $60.00; Down $8.00

16-A69-1.3

1978 Lemminkainen's Chase
Artist: Raija Uosikkinen
Prices: Issue $39.00; 1981 High $70.00;
Low $65.00; Close $65.00; Down $5.00

16-A69-1.5

1980 Vainamoinen's Rescue
Artist: Raija Uosikkinen
Prices: Issue $45.00; 1981 High $70.00;
Low $45.00; Close $70.00; Up $25.00

16-A69-1.6

1981 Vainamoinen's Magic
Artist: Raija Uosikkinen
Prices: Issue $49.50; 1981 High $49.50;
Low $49.50; Close $49.50; No Change

16-A69-1.7

No information available at press time

The hallmark of Henri d'Arceau L. & Fils is one of the most prestigious in the famous porcelain center of Limoges. The firm, which claims to adhere to the original "Grellet Standard" of 1768 for handcraftsmanship, is today directed by Gerard Boyer, a descendant of the founder.

The firm was commissioned by L'Association l'Esprit de Lafayette to produce the six-plate bicentennial series *Collection Le Patrimoine de Lafayette (Lafayette Legacy Collection)*, 1973-1975, which chronicles the role of the Marquis de Lafayette in America's War of Independence. The D'Arceau-Limoges *Christmas* series, *Noël Vitrail*, begun in 1975, was inspired by the stained-glass windows of the cathedral at Chartres. *Les Femmes du Siècle (Women of the Century)*, a twelve-plate series commissioned by the Chambre Syndicale de la Couture Parisienne, began in 1976. This series, recognized by the United Nations, depicts Western women's fashions from 1865 to 1965. Introduced in 1978 was *Les Jeunes Filles des Saisons (Girls of the Seasons)*, and in 1979 *Les Très Riches Heures (The Very Rich Hours)*, which adapts its artwork from an early fifteenth-century illuminated manuscript. In 1980, the firm, in collaboration with La Société de Paris et Son Histoire, issued Louis Dali's *Les Douze Sites Parisiens de Louis Dali (The Twelve Parisian Places of Louis Dali)* series, a collection of the artist's unique impressions of the famous city.

Among the artists who have designed works for D'Arceau-Limoges are the late André Restieau, world authority on the techniques of re-creating medieval stained glass coloration in porcelain; neo-Classicist Guy Cambier, winner of numerous awards from the Prix de la Jeune Peinture Méditerranée in 1955 to the Médaille d'or au Prix Leonardo da Vinci in 1972; and François Ganeau, resident consultant to the Theatre Comedie Française. In 1980 the noted Impressionist Louis Dali, a Fellow of the Salon de l'Ecole Francaise and the Salon des Independants, joined D'Arceau-Limoges artists with his *Les Douze Sites Parisiens de Louis Dali* series.

Collection Le Patrimoine de Lafayette
(The Lafayette Legacy Collection)

Artist: André Restieau. Artist's signature appears on front, initials on back
Overglaze-decorated porcelain
Diameter: 21.6 centimeters (8½ inches)
Attached back hanger
Edition size undisclosed, limited by announced period of issue
Numbered with certificate

18-D15-1.1
1973 The Secret Contract
Artist: André Restieau
Prices: Issue $14.82; 1981 High $48.00;
Low $48.00; Close $48.00; No Change

18-D15-1.2
1973 The Landing at North Island
Artist: André Restieau
Prices: Issue $19.82; 1981 High $53.00;
Low $53.00; Close $53.00; No Change

18-D15-1.3
1974 The Meeting at City Tavern
Artist: André Restieau
Prices: Issue $19.82; 1981 High $48.00;
Low $48.00; Close $48.00; No Change

18-D15-1.4
1974 The Battle of Brandywine
Artist: André Restieau
Prices: Issue $19.82; 1981 High $59.00;
Low $55.00; Close $55.00; Down $4.00

18-D15-1.5
1975 The Messages to Franklin
Artist: André Restieau
Prices: Issue $19.82; 1981 High $67.00;
Low $65.00; Close $65.00; Down $2.00

18-D15-1.6
1975 The Siege at Yorktown
Artist: André Restieau
Prices: Issue $19.82; 1981 High $51.00;
Low $51.00; Close $51.00; No Change

Noël Vitrail (Stained-glass Christmas)

Artist: André Restieau. Artist's signature
  appears on front, initials on back
Overglaze-decorated porcelain
Diameter: 21 centimeters (8¼ inches)
Attached back hanger
Edition size undisclosed, limited by
  announced period of issue
Numbered with certificate

18-D15-2.1
1975 La Fuite en Egypte (Flight into Egypt)
Artist: André Restieau
Prices: Issue $24.32; 1981 High $114.00;
Low $110.00; Close $110.00; Down $4.00

18-D15-2.5
1979 L'Adoration des Rois
  (The Adoration of Kings)
Artist: André Restieau
Prices: Issue $26.81; 1981 High $30.00;
Low $30.00; Close $30.00; No Change

Les Femmes du Siècle

(The Women of the Century)

Artist: François Ganeau. Artist's
  signature appears on front, initials on
  back
Overglaze-decorated porcelain
Diameter: 21.6 centimeters (8½ inches)
Attached back hanger
Edition size undisclosed, limited by
  announced period of issue
Numbered with certificate

18-D15-3.1
1976 Scarlet en Crinoline
Artist: François Ganeau
Prices: Issue $17.67; 1981 High $39.00;
Low $39.00; Close $39.00; No Change

18-D15-3.2
1976 Sarah en Tournure
Artist: François Ganeau
Prices: Issue $22.74; 1981 High $32.00;
Low $32.00; Close $32.00; No Change

18-D15-2.2
1976 Dans la Crêche (In the Manger)
Artist: André Restieau
Prices: Issue $24.32; 1981 High $34.00;
Low $30.00; Close $30.00; Down $4.00

18-D15-2.3
1977 Le Refus d'Hèbergement
(No Room at the Inn)
Artist: André Restieau
Prices: Issue $24.32; 1981 High $35.00;
Low $31.00; Close $35.00; Up $4.00

18-D15-2.4
1978 La Purification (The Purification)
Artist: André Restieau
Prices: Issue $26.81; 1981 High $28.00;
Low $28.00; Close $28.00; No Change

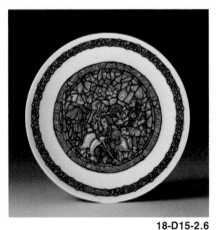

18-D15-2.6
1980 Joyeuse Nouvelle
(Tidings of Great Joy)
Artist: André Restieau
Prices: Issue $28.74; 1981 High $28.74;
Low $28.74; Close $28.74; No Change

18-D15-2.7
1981 Guides par l'Etoile
(Guided by the Star)
Artist: André Restieau
Prices: Issue $28.74; 1981 High $28.74;
Low $28.74; Close $28.74; No Change

18-D15-2.8
No information available at press time

18-D15-3.3
1976 Colette, la Femme Sportive
Artist: François Ganeau
Prices: Issue $22.74; 1981 High $29.00;
Low $29.00; Close $29.00; No Change

18-D15-3.4
1976 Léa, la Femme Fleur
Artist: François Ganeau
Prices: Issue $22.74; 1981 High $28.00;
Low $28.00; Close $28.00; No Change

18-D15-3.5
1977 Albertine, la Femme Liane
Artist: François Ganeau
Prices: Issue $22.74; 1981 High $28.00;
Low $28.00; Close $28.00; No Change

18-D15-3.6

1977 Edith, la Femme Pratique
Artist: François Ganeau
Prices: Issue $22.74; 1981 High $28.00;
Low $28.00; Close $28.00; No Change

18-D15-3.7

1977 Daisy, la Garçonne
Artist: François Ganeau
Prices: Issue $22.74; 1981 High $28.00;
Low $28.00; Close $28.00; No Change

18-D15-3.8

1977 Marlène, la Vamp
Artist: François Ganeau
Prices: Issue $22.74; 1981 High $28.00;
Low $28.00; Close $28.00; No Change

18-D15-3.11

1979 Françoise en Pantalon
Artist: François Ganeau
Prices: Issue $22.74; 1981 High $28.00;
Low $28.00; Close $28.00; No Change

18-D15-3.12

1979 Brigitte en Mini-jupe
Artist: François Ganeau
Prices: Issue $22.74; 1981 High $28.00;
Low $28.00; Close $28.00: No Change

Les Jeunes Filles des Saisons
(The Girls of the Seasons)

Artist: Guy Cambier. Artist's signature
   appears on front
Overglaze-decorated porcelain banded
   in gold
Diameter: 24.8 centimeters (9¾ inches)
No hanger
Edition size limited to 15,000
Numbered with certificate

18-D15-4.1

1978 La Jeune Fille d'Eté (Summer Girl)
Artist: Guy Cambier
Prices: Issue $105.00; 1981 High $125.00;
Low $125.00; Close $125.00; No Change

18-D15-3.9

1978 Hélène, l'Intrépide
Artist: François Ganeau
Prices: Issue $22.74; 1981 High $28.00;
Low $28.00; Close $28.00; No Change

18-D15-3.10

1978 Sophie, la Féminité Retrouvée
Artist: François Ganeau
Prices: Issue $22.74; 1981 High $28.00;
Low $28.00; Close $28.00; No Change

18-D15-4.2

1979 La Jeune Fille d'Hiver (Winter Girl)
Artist: Guy Cambier
Prices: Issue $105.00; 1981 High $105.00;
Low $105.00; Close $105.00; No Change

18-D15-4.3

**1980 La Jeune Fille du Printemps
(Spring Girl)**
Artist: Guy Cambier
Prices: Issue $105.00; 1981 High $105.00;
Low $105.00; Close $105.00; No Change

18-D15-4.4

**1981 La Jeune Fille d'Automne
(Autumn Girl)**
Artist: Guy Cambier
Prices: Issue $105.00; 1981 High $105.00;
Low $105.00; Close $105.00; No Change

Les Très Riches Heures
(The Very Rich Hours Series)

Artist: Jean Dutheil. Artist's signature
  appears on back
Overglaze-decorated porcelain
Diameter: 24.8 centimeters (9¾ inches)
Attached back hanger
Edition size unannounced
Numbered with certificate

18-D15-5.1
1979 Janvier (January)
Artist: Jean Dutheil
Prices: Issue $75.48; 1981 High $75.48;
Low $75.48; Close $75.48; No Change

18-D15-5.2
1980 Avril (April)
Artist: Jean Dutheil
Prices: Issue $75.48; 1981 High $75.48;
Low $75.48; Close $75.48; No Change

Les Douze Sites Parisiens
de Louis Dali
(The Twelve Parisian Places
of Louis Dali)

Artist: Louis Dali. Artist's signature
  appears on front
Overglaze-decorated porcelain
Diameter: 21 centimeters (8¼ inches)
Attached back hanger
Edition size undisclosed, limited by
  announced period of issue
Numbered with certificate

18-D15-6.1
1980 L'Arc de Triomphe
      (The Arch of Triumph)
Artist: Louis Dali
Prices: Issue $22.94; 1981 High $22.94;
Low $22.94; Close $22.94; No Change

18-D15-6.4
1981 L'Église Saint-Pierre et le Sacré-
      Coeur de Montmartre (St. Peter's
      Church and Sacred Heart Basilica)
Artist: Louis Dali
Prices: Issue $26.83; 1981 High $26.83;
Low $26.83; Close $26.83; No Change

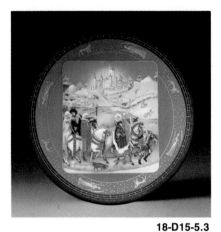

18-D15-5.3

1981 Août (August)
Artist: Jean Dutheil
Prices: Issue $75.48; 1981 High $75.48;
Low $75.48; Close $75.48; No Change

18-D15-5.4

1982 Juin (June)
Artist: Jean Dutheil
Issue price: $75.48

18-D15-6.2

1981 La Cathedrale Notre-Dame
(Notre Dame Cathedral)
Artist: Louis Dali
Prices: Issue $24.94; 1981 High $24.94;
Low $24.94; Close $24.94; No Change

18-D15-6.3

1981 La Place de la Concorde
(Concord Place)
Artist: Louis Dali
Prices: Issue $24.94; 1981 High $24.94;
Low $24.94; Close $24.94; No Change

18-D15-6.5

1982 Le Marché aux Fleurs et la
Conciergerie (The Flower Market
and the Conciergerie)
Artist: Louis Dali
Issue price $26.83

18-D15-6.6

1982 La Pointe du Vert Galant et le Pont
Neuf (Vert Galant Point and the New
Bridge)
Artist: Louis Dali
Issue price: $26.83

Haviland

In 1839 David Haviland of New York City became the first American importer of Limoges porcelain made from white kaolin clay. When, in 1842, he realized that French factories would not adjust methods to meet the tastes of his American market, Haviland established his own pottery in Limoges.

In 1892 his son, Theodore, left the firm but remained in Limoges to set up Theodore Haviland & Company for production of porcelain dinnerware and decorative pieces. In the 1930s, Theodore Haviland & Company opened an American Haviland factory to produce tableware; the firm also bought the original Haviland & Company established by David Haviland.

All Haviland collector's plates are produced in Limoges, France. *The Twelve Days of Christmas* series, begun in 1970, is based on the carol of the same title. The five-plate *Bicentennial* series, introduced in 1972, commemorates events leading to the American Declaration of Independence.

And 1979 marked the beginning of the *Mille et Une Nuits* series based on the literary classic *One Thousand One Arabian Nights*.

Adept in a variety of styles, French painter Remy Hétreau is the principal artist for Haviland collector's plates, with two distinctively different series to his credit — from historical chronicle to delightful yuletide fantasy. Noted watercolorist Liliane Tellier, creator of the *Mille et Une Nuits* series, has an extensive following among connoisseurs of the medium. A native Parisienne, she studied watercolor and gouache at L'Ecole Camondo in Paris and refined her techniques in Sweden. Later she worked for the International Society for Education through Art as a consultant to UNESCO.

The Twelve Days of Christmas Series

Artist: Remy Hétreau. Artist's signature appears on back
Overglaze-decorated porcelain
Diameter: 21.3 centimeters (8⅜ inches)
No hanger
Edition size limited to announced quantity of 30,000
Not numbered, without certificate

18-H6-1.4

1973 Four Colly Birds
Artist: Remy Hétreau
Prices: Issue $28.50; 1981 High $45.00;
Low $33.00; Close $42.00; Up $9.00

18-H6-1.1

1970 A Partridge in a Pear Tree
Artist: Remy Hétreau
Prices: Issue $25.00; 1981 High $200.00;
Low $190.00; Close $190.00; Down $6.00

18-H6-1.2

1971 Two Turtle Doves
Artist: Remy Hétreau
Prices: Issue $25.00; 1981 High $64.00;
Low $60.00; Close $60.00; Down $1.00

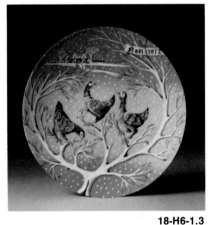

18-H6-1.3

1972 Three French Hens
Artist: Remy Hétreau
Prices: Issue $27.50; 1981 High $25.00;
Low $21.00; Close $25.00; Up $2.00

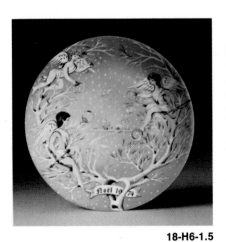

18-H6-1.5

1974 Five Golden Rings
Artist: Remy Hétreau
Prices: Issue $30.00; 1981 High $28.00;
Low $25.00; Close $25.00; Down $3.00

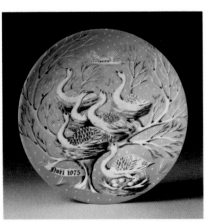

18-H6-1.6

1975 Six Geese A'Laying
Artist: Remy Hétreau
Prices: Issue $32.50; 1981 High $32.00;
Low $32.00; Close $32.00; No Change

18-H6-1.7

1976 Seven Swans A'Swimming
Artist: Remy Hétreau
Prices: Issue $38.00; 1981 High $38.00;
Low $30.00; Close $38.00; Up $8.00

18-H6-1.8

1977 Eight Maids A'Milking
Artist: Remy Hétreau
Prices: Issue $40.00; 1981 High $50.00;
Low $42.00; Close $50.00; Up $8.00

18-H6-1.9

1978 Nine Ladies Dancing
Artist: Remy Hétreau
Prices: Issue $45.00; 1981 High $42.00;
Low $40.00; Close $40.00; Down $2.00

18-H6-1.10

1979 Ten Lords A'Leaping
Artist: Remy Hétreau
Prices: Issue $50.00; 1981 High $50.00;
Low $46.00; Close $50.00; Up $2.00

Bicentennial Series

Artist: Remy Hétreau. Artist's signature
  appears on back
Overglaze-decorated porcelain
Diameter: 24.8 centimeters (9¾ inches)
No hanger
Edition size limited to announced
  quantity of 10,000
Not numbered, without certificate

18-H6-2.1

1972 Burning of the Gaspee
Artist: Remy Hétreau
Prices: Issue $39.95; 1981 High $40.00;
Low $36.00; Close $37.00; Down $1.00

18-H6-2.2

1973 Boston Tea Party
Artist: Remy Hétreau
Prices: Issue $39.95; 1981 High $43.00;
Low $40.00; Close $43.00; Up $3.00

Mille et Une Nuits

(1001 Arabian Nights)
Artist/Designer: Liliane Tellier
  Signature appears on front
Porcelain banded in gold
Diameter: 24.1 centimeters (9½ inches)
No hanger
Edition size: As indicated
Numbered with certificate

18-H6-4.1

1979 Le Cheval Magique
(The Magic Horse)
Artist/Designer: Liliane Tellier
Edition size unannounced
Prices: Issue $54.50; 1981 High $54.50;
Low $54.50; Close $54.50; No Change

18-H6-4.2

1980 Aladin et la Lampe Merveilleuse
(Aladin and the Wonderful Lamp)
Artist/Designer: Liliane Tellier
Edition size undisclosed, limited by announced
period of issue.
Prices: Issue $54.50; 1981 High $54.50;
Low $54.50; Close $54.50; No Change

18-H6-1.11

1980 Eleven Pipers Piping
Artist: Remy Hétreau
Prices: Issue $55.00; 1981 High $60.00;
Low $55.00; Close $55.00; No Change

18-H6-1.12

1981 Twelve Drummers Drumming
Artist: Remy Hétreau
Prices: Issue $60.00; 1981 High $60.00;
Low $60.00; Close $60.00; No Change

18-H6-2.3

1974 First Continental Congress
Artist: Remy Hétreau
Prices: Issue $39.95; 1981 High $35.00;
Low $27.00; Close $35.00; Up $8.00

18-H6-2.4

1975 Ride of Paul Revere
Artist: Remy Hétreau
Prices: Issue $40.00; 1981 High $42.00;
Low $40.00; Close $42.00; Up $2.00

18-H6-2.5

1976 The Declaration of Independence
Artist: Remy Hétreau
Prices: Issue $48.00; 1981 High $50.00;
Low $46.00; Close $50.00; Up $4.00

Maker had
no photo at
press time

18-H6-4.3

1981 Scheherazade
Artist/Designer: Liliane Tellier
Issue Price $54.50

18-H6-4.4

No information available at press time

Haviland & Parlon

Haviland & Parlon is a chapter in the intricate Haviland porcelain story. In 1853 Robert Haviland left New York City to work for his brother David Haviland in Limoges (see France, Haviland). In 1870 Robert's son Charles Field Haviland also established a porcelain factory in Limoges and used "Ch. Field Haviland" as his trade name. After he retired in 1881, the firm was known by several different names until 1942, when Robert Haviland (Robert's great-grandson) purchased it. The firm is now known as Robert Haviland & C. Parlon but retains the "Ch. Field Haviland" trademark.

The *Tapestry* series, begun in 1971, reproduced six scenes from the French medieval tapestries, "The Hunt of the Unicorn," now hanging in the Cloisters of New York's Metropolitan Museum of Art. The *Christmas* series of famous Renaissance Madonnas began in 1972, and a second *Tapestry* series of six plates began in 1977, reproducing scenes from "The Lady and the Unicorn" tapestries hanging in the Cluny Museum in Paris.

Designs for the *Christmas* series are taken from works by the great masters as indicated.

Tapestry Series

Artist: Unknown. Reproduced from French medieval tapestries
Overglaze-decorated porcelain banded in gold
Diameter: 25.4 centimeters (10 inches)
No hanger
Edition size limited to announced quantity of 10,000
Not numbered, without certificate

18-H8-1.1
1971 The Unicorn in Captivity
Artist: Unknown
Prices: Issue $35.00; 1981 High $206.00;
Low $190.00; Close $198.00; Up $8.00

18-H8-1.2
1972 Start of the Hunt
Artist: Unknown
Prices: Issue $35.00; 1981 High $84.00;
Low $75.00; Close $84.00; Up $9.00

18-H8-1.3
1973 Chase of the Unicorn
Artist: Unknown
Prices: Issue $35.00; 1981 High $145.00;
Low $130.00; Close $145.00; Up $15.00

18-H8-1.4
1974 End of the Hunt
Artist: Unknown
Prices: Issue $37.50; 1981 High $132.00;
Low $112.00; Close $132.00; Up $20.00

18-H8-1.5
1975 The Unicorn Surrounded
Artist: Unknown
Prices: Issue $40.00; 1981 High $75.00;
Low $65.00; Close $75.00; Up $10.00

18-H8-1.6
1976 The Unicorn Is Brought to the Castle
Artist: Unknown
Prices: Issue $42.50; 1981 High $62.00;
Low $50.00; Close $62.00; Up $12.00

Christmas Series

Artist: As indicated
Overglaze-decorated porcelain banded
  in gold
Diameter 25.4 centimeters (10 inches)
No hanger
Edition size: As indicated
Numbered without certificate

18-H8-2.1

1972 Madonna and Child
Artist: Raphael/Edition: 5,000
Prices: Issue $35.00; 1981 High $150.00;
Low $145.00; Close $145.00; Down $3.00

18-H8-2.2

1973 Madonnina
Artist: Feruzzi/Edition: 5,000
Prices: Issue $40.00; 1981 High $100.00;
Low $97.00; Close $100.00; Up $3.00

18-H8-2.5

1976 Madonna and Child
Artist: Botticelli/Edition: 7,000
Prices: Issue $45.00; 1981 High $60.00;
Low $59.00; Close $60.00; Up $1.00

18-H8-2.6

1977 Madonna and Child
Artist: Bellini/Edition: 7,500
Prices: Issue $48.00; 1981 High $52.00;
Low $48.00; Close $52.00; Up $4.00

18-H8-2.3

1974 Cowper Madonna and Child
Artist: Raphael/Edition: 5,000
Prices: Issue $42.50; 1981 High $100.00;
Low $75.00; Close $75.00; Down $15.00

18-H8-2.4

1975 Madonna and Child
Artist: Murillo/Edition: 7,500
Prices: Issue $42.50; 1981 High $56.00;
Low $56.00; Close $56.00; No Change

18-H8-2.7

1978 Madonna and Child
Artist: Fra Filippo Lippi/Edition: 7,500
Prices: Issue $48.00; 1981 High $48.00;
Low $48.00; Close $48.00; No Change

18-H8-2.8

1979 Madonna of the Eucharist
Artist: Botticelli/Edition: 7,500
Prices: Issue $49.50; 1981 High $72.00;
Low $55.00; Close $72.00; Up $17.00

Lady and the Unicorn Series

Artist: Unknown. Reproduced from
 French medieval tapestries
Overglaze-decorated porcelain banded
 in gold
Diameter: 25.4 centimeters (10 inches)
No hanger
Edition size: As indicated
Not numbered, without certificate

18-H8-4.1

1977 To My Only Desire
Artist: Unknown/Edition: 20,000
Prices: Issue $45.00; 1981 High $86.00;
Low $80.00; Close $86.00; Up $6.00

18-H8-4.2

1978 Sight
Artist: Unknown/Edition: 20,000
Prices: Issue $45.00; 1981 High $52.00;
Low $48.00; Close $48.00; Down$2.00

18-H8-4.3

1979 Sound
Artist: Unknown/Edition: 20,000
Prices: Issue $47.50; 1981 High $53.00;
Low $53.00; Close $53.00; No Change

18-H8-4.4

1980 Touch
Artist: Unknown/Edition: 15,000
Prices: Issue $52.50; 1981 High $102.00;
Low $60.00; Close $102.00; Up $42.00

18-H8-4.5

1981 Scent
Artist: Unknown/Edition: 10,000
Prices: Issue $59.00; 1981 High $59.00;
Low $59.00; Close $59.00; No Change

Maker had
no photo at
press time

18-H8-4.6

1982 Taste
Artist: Unknown/Edition: 10,000
Issue price: $59.00

Chase of the Unicorn 18-H8-1.3
1972 Haviland & Parlon *Tapestry I*
Detail showing the exceptional fidelity of
the collector's plate to the original medieval
masterpiece

Réné Lalique, founder of the firm that bears his name, began his career as a goldsmith and jeweler in the late nineteenth century. His clients included such notables as Sarah Bernhardt and the dealers Cartier and Boucheron.

In 1902 his interests turned to glassmaking and he acquired a small glassworks at Clairfontaine, France. In 1909 he opened a glass factory near Paris where he produced bottles for the leading Parisian *parfumeurs,* and in 1918 he opened the present Lalique factory in Alsace. Here he began to produce glass items in the Art Deco style. His designs, usually created in pressed glass, are noted for the frosted and satin effects of the glass. Until his death in 1945, Lalique produced numerous commercial glass objects such as perfume bottles, vases, and figurines.

Upon Réné's death in 1945, his son Marc — himself a noted artist — inherited the firm and served as its president until his death in 1977. The firm is currently headed by Marc's daughter, Marie-Claude. As Lalique's chief designer she created the *Annual* series of Lalique crystal collector's plates which began in 1965 and ended in 1976.

The third generation in a distinguished family of artists, Madame Lalique is known for her versatility, being an accomplished painter, sculptor, glass-blower, and jewelry designer. She is a graduate of the Grand Chaumiere and L'Ecole Normale Superiore des Arts Decoratifs de Paris where she concentrated in the painting medium until her teacher, André Arbus, developed her appreciation of the Decorative Arts.

Annual Series

Artist: Marie-Claude Lalique
Full lead crystal with incised designs
Diameter: 21.6 centimeters (8½ inches)
No hanger
Edition size: As indicated. Announced between 5,000 and 8,000 from 1967 to 1975
Not numbered, without certificate; engraved "Lalique-France" on back

18-L3-1.4
1968 Gazelle Fantaisie (Gazelle Fantasy)
Artist: Marie-Claude Lalique
Prices: Issue $25.00; 1981 High $125.00; Low $125.00; Close $125.00; No Change

18-L3-1.1

1965 Deux Oiseaux (Two Birds)
Artist: Marie-Claude Lalique /Edition: 2,000
Prices: Issue $25.00; 1981 High $1825.00;
Low $1770.00; Close $1770.00; Down $55.00

18-L3-1.2

1966 Rose de Songerie (Dream Rose)
Artist: Marie-Claude Lalique /Edition: 5,000
Prices: Issue $25.00; 1981 High $350.00;
Low $325.00; Close $350.00; Up $25.00

18-L3-1.3

1967 Ballet de Poisson (Fish Ballet)
Artist: Marie-Claude Lalique
Prices: Issue $25.00; 1981 High $294.00;
Low $290.00; Close $290.00; No Change

18-L3-1.5

1969 Papillon (Butterfly)
Artist: Marie-Claude Lalique
Prices: Issue $30.00; 1981 High $120.00;
Low $115.00; Close $120.00; No Change

18-L3-1.6

1970 Paon (Peacock)
Artist: Marie-Claude Lalique
Prices: Issue $30.00; 1981 High $120.00;
Low $120.00; Close $120.00; No Change

18-L3-1.7

1971 Hibou (Owl)
Artist: Marie-Claude Lalique
Prices: Issue $35.00; 1981 High $95.00;
Low $90.00; Close $95.00; Up $5.00

18-L3-1.8

1972 Coquillage (Shell)
Artist: Marie-Claude Lalique
Prices: Issue $40.00; 1981 High $80.00;
Low $75.00; Close $80.00; Up $5.00

18-L3-1.9

1973 Petit Geai (Jayling)
Artist: Marie-Claude Lalique
Prices: Issue $42.50; 1981 High $73.00;
Low $70.00; Close $70.00; Down $3.00

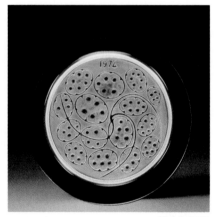

18-L3-1.10

1974 Sous d'Argent (Silver Pennies)
Artist: Marie-Claude Lalique
Prices: Issue $47.50; 1981 High $65.00;
Low $58.00; Close $58.00; Down $4.00

18-L3-1.11

1975 Duo de Poisson (Fish Duet)
Artist: Marie-Claude Lalique
Prices: Issue $50.00; 1981 High $68.00;
Low $65.00; Close $68.00; Up $3.00

18-L3-1.12

1976 Aigle (Eagle)
Artist: Marie-Claude Lalique
Prices: Issue $60.00; 1981 High $160.00;
Low $155.00; Close $158.00; Up $3.00

Deux Oiseaux 18-L3-1.1
1965 Lalique *Annual*
Detail showing incised design on the first
lead crystal collector's plate

The porcelain house of Limoges-Turgot draws upon a tradition of porcelain making which began with A.-R.-J. Turgot, Baron de l'Aulne, Louis XVI's administrator for the Limousin province of which Limoges was the capital. When kaolin clay, the key ingredient in true hard-fire porcelain, was discovered in 1768 at the nearby town of Saint-Yrieix, it was largely due to Turgot's efforts that the Limoges porcelain industry was established and achieved world renown.

Les Enfants de Durand, (Durand's Children Collection), began in 1978 and is the first proprietary series by Limoges-Turgot.

The late artist, Paul Durand, achieved an international reputation for his illustrations of such children's classics as *The Three Musketeers,* and *Treasure Island.* His art was personally chosen by General Charles de Gaulle to illustrate his 1969 Christmas message to French children.

Les Enfants de Durand
(Durand's Children Collection)

Artist: Paul Durand. Artist's signature
   appears on front
Overglaze-decorated porcelain
Diameter: 20.3 centimeters (8 inches)
Attached back hanger
Edition size undisclosed, limited by
   year of issue
Numbered with certificate

18-L52-1.1
1978 Marie-Ange
Artist: Paul Durand
Prices: Issue $36.40; 1981 High $40.00;
Low $37.00; Close $40.00; Up $3.00

18-L52-1.2
1979 Emilie et Philippe
Artist: Paul Durand
Prices: Issue $36.40; 1981 High $45.00;
Low $40.00; Close $45.00; Up $5.00

18-L52-1.3
1980 Christiane et Fifi
Artist: Paul Durand
Prices: Issue $36.40; 1981 High $55.00;
Low $36.40; Close $55.00; Up $18.60

18-L52-1.4
1980 Cecile et Raoul
Artist: Paul Durand
Prices: Issue $36.40; 1981 High $55.00;
Low $36.40; Close $55.00; Up $18.60

Named for Anna Perenna, the Roman goddess associated with health, abundance, and the rebirth of spring, Anna-Perenna, Inc. was founded in 1977 by its president, Klaus D. Vogt, exclusively to produce high-quality limited-edition plates in hard-paste porcelain.

The *Triptych* series, inspired by the portable altar-pieces of the Middle Ages, began in 1979 with a three-plate set which reinterprets ancient Byzantine religious motifs. In 1979, Anna-Perenna introduced *Romantic Loves,* a four-plate series celebrating great romantic loves of history. Their four-plate series, *Uncle Tad's Cats,* began in 1979 and ended in 1981.

Frank Russell and Gertrude Barrer, the creators of the *Triptych* and the *Romantic Loves* series, are husband-and-wife co-workers who have blended their talents to become a successful art-producing team. They met at the Art Student's League in New York and, after five years of going their separate ways, reunited in New York's art center, Greenwich Village, working jointly in photography, lithographs, frescoes, serigraphs, ceramics, and sculpture. Their work has been exhibited at the Art Institute of Chicago and the Whitney Museum of American Art, and hangs in the private collections of Cyrus Vance, Helmut Schmidt, and the U.N. Interfaith Chapel in New York. In 1980, their "Byzantine Triptych" was presented by Munich's Cardinal Ratzinger to Pope John Paul II during his pilgrimage to West Germany. Thaddeus Krumeich ("Uncle Tad") is master of the style known as *trompe l'oeil,* which he calls "magic realism." He has had shows throughout the United States, is represented in such private collections as those of Mrs. Paul Mellon, "Doc" Severinson, and His Excellency Seydou Traori, Mali Ambassador to the United States, and his work was selected for use in the 1980-81 series of UNICEF greeting cards.

The Triptych Series

Artist: Frank Russell and Gertrude Barrer. Artists' signatures appear on front
Hard-paste porcelain with hinged frame
Diameter: plates one and three, 21.6 cm. (8½ in.); plate two, 24.8 cm. (9¾ in.); overall triptych, 88.9 cm. x 45.7 cm. (35 in x 18 in.) for 1979 set; 83.8 cm. x 38.1 cm. (33 in x 15 in.) for 1980 set
Attached back hanger
Edition size: As indicated
Individually hand-numbered with certificate

A triptych is a set of three panels hinged side by side, bearing paintings or carvings usually on a religious theme and often used as a portable altarpiece.

1979 Gabriel

22-A3-3.1-1

1979 Madonna and Child

22-A3-3.1-2

1979 Michael

22-A3-3.1-3

The Byzantine Triptych
Artist: Frank Russell and Gertrude Barrer
Edition: 5,000 sets
Prices: Issue $325.00; 1981 High $335.00;
Low $325.00; Close $335.00; Up $10.00

1980 Saul

22-A3-3.2-1

1980 David

22-A3-3.2-2

1980 Solomon

22-A3-3.2-3

The Jerusalem Triptych
Artist: Frank Russell and Gertrude Barrer
Edition: 5,000 sets
Prices: Issue $350.00; 1981 High $350.00;
Low $350.00; Close $350.00; No Change

No information available at press time

22-A3-3.3-2

22-A3-3.3-3

Romantic Loves Series

Artist: Frank Russell and Gertrude Barrer. Artists' signatures appear on front
Hard-paste porcelain banded in gold
Diameter: 25 centimeters (9⅞ inches)
Attached back hanger
Edition size limited to 7,500
Individually hand-numbered with certificate

22-A3-4.1

1979 Romeo and Juliet
Artist: Frank Russell and Gertrude Barrer
Prices: Issue $95.00; 1981 High $95.00;
Low $95.00; Close $95.00; No Change

Uncle Tad's Cats Series

Artist: Thaddeus Krumeich
Artist's signature appears on front
Hard-paste porcelain
Diameter: 24.8 centimeters (9¾ inches)
Attached back hanger
Edition size limited to 5,000
Individually hand-numbered with certificate

22-A3-5.1

1979 Oliver's Birthday
Artist: Thaddeus Krumeich
Prices: Issue $75.00; 1981 High $175.00;
Low $75.00; Close $175.00; Up $100.00

22-A3-4.2

1980 Lancelot and Guinevere
Artist: Frank Russell and Gertrude Barrer
Prices: Issue $95.00; 1981 High $95.00;
Low $95.00; Close $95.00; No Change

22-A3-4.3

1981 Helen and Paris
Artist: Frank Russell and Gertrude Barrer
Prices: Issue $95.00; 1981 High $95.00;
Low $95.00; Close $95.00; No Change

22-A3-4.4

1982 Lovers of the Taj Mahal
Artist: Frank Russell and Gertrude Barrer
Issue price: $95.00

22-A3-5.2

1980 Peaches and Cream
Artist: Thaddeus Krumeich
Prices: Issue $75.00; 1981 High $90.00;
Low $75.00; Close $87.00; Up $12.00

22-A3-5.3

1981 Princess Aurora, Queen of the Night
Artist: Thaddeus Krumeich
Prices: Issue $80.00; 1981 High $90.00;
Low $80.00; Close $90.00; Up $10.00

22-A3-5.4

1981 Walter's Window
Artist: Thaddeus Krumeich
Prices: Issue $85.00; 1981 High $85.00;
Low $85.00; Close $85.00; No Change

The Bareuther & Company porcelain factory began to produce dinnerware, vases, and giftware in 1867. The small shop was established with a porcelain kiln and an annular brick kiln by sculptor Johann Matthaeus Ries. In 1884 Ries's son sold the shop to Oskar Bareuther who continued to produce fine tableware.

To observe the one-hundredth anniversary of the factory in 1967, Bareuther began a series of limited-edition *Christmas* plates. A *Father's Day* series, depicting the great castles of Germany, was started in 1969.

Hans Mueller, born in Waldsassen, Bavaria, was the son of a Bareuther artist. He studied engraving and painting at the porcelain academy in Selb, and in 1952 joined Bareuther as a porcelain painter. He was promoted to chief designer for the firm in 1968.

Christmas Series

Artist: Hans Mueller, except 1971
Porcelain decorated in cobalt blue underglaze
Diameter: 20.3 centimeters (8 inches)
Pierced foot rim
Edition size limited to announced quantity of 10,000
Not numbered, without certificate

22-B7-1.4

1970 Chapel in Oberndorf
Artist: Hans Mueller
Prices: Issue $12.50; 1981 High $18.00;
Low $18.00; Close $18.00; No Change

22-B7-1.1

1967 Stiftskirche
Artist: Hans Mueller
Prices: Issue $12.00; 1981 High $130.00;
Low $120.00; Close $130.00; Up $10.00

22-B7-1.2

1968 Kappl
Artist: Hans Mueller
Prices: Issue $12.00; 1981 High $42.00;
Low $36.00; Close $42.00; Up $6.00

22-B7-1.3

1969 Christkindlesmarkt
Artist: Hans Mueller
Prices: Issue $12.00; 1981 High $22.00;
Low $20.00; Close $22.00; Up $2.00

22-B7-1.5

1971 Toys for Sale
From drawing by Ludwig Richter
Prices: Issue $12.75; 1981 High $22.00;
Low $19.00; Close $19.00; Down $1.00

22-B7-1.6

1972 Christmas in Munich
Artist: Hans Mueller
Prices: Issue $14.50; 1981 High $50.00;
Low $48.00; Close $48.00; Down $2.00

22-B7-1.7

1973 Christmas Sleigh Ride
Artist: Hans Mueller
Prices: Issue $15.00; 1981 High $28.00;
Low $27.00; Close $28.00; Up $1.00

22-B7-1.8

1974 Church in the Black Forest
Artist: Hans Mueller
Prices: Issue $19.00; 1981 High $28.00;
Low $28.00; Close $28.00; No Change

22-B7-1.9

1975 Snowman
Artist: Hans Mueller
Prices: Issue $21.50; 1981 High $27.00;
Low $25.00; Close $27.00; Up $2.00

22-B7-1.10

1976 Chapel in the Hills
Artist: Hans Mueller
Prices: Issue $23.50; 1981 High $35.00;
Low $32.00; Close $35.00; Up $3.00

22-B7-1.13

1979 Winter Day
Artist: Hans Mueller
Prices: Issue $35.00; 1981 High $42.00;
Low $30.00; Close $42.00; Up $12.00

22-B7-1.14

1980 Miltenberg
Artist: Hans Mueller
Prices: Issue $37.50; 1981 High $50.00;
Low $37.50; Close $50.00; Up $12.50

22-B7-1.15

1981 Walk in the Forest
Artist: Hans Mueller
Prices: Issue $39.50; 1981 High $39.50;
Low $39.50; Close $39.50; No Change

22-B7-1.11

1977 Story Time
Artist: Hans Mueller
Prices: Issue $24.50; 1981 High $29.00;
Low $27.00; Close $29.00; Up $2.00

22-B7-1.12

1978 Mittenwald
Artist: Hans Mueller
Prices: Issue $27.50; 1981 High $34.00;
Low $30.00; Close $34.00; Up $4.00

22-B7-1.16

1982 Bad Wimpfen
Artist: Hans Mueller
Issue price: $39.50

Father's Day Series

Artist: Hans Mueller
Porcelain decorated in cobalt blue
  underglaze
Diameter: 20.3 centimeters (8 inches)
Pierced foot rim
Edition size limited to announced
  quantity of 2,500
Not numbered, without certificate

22-B7-2.1

1969 Castle Neuschwanstein
Artist: Hans Mueller
Prices: Issue $10.50; 1981 High $55.00;
Low $50.00; Close $53.00; Up $3.00

22-B7-2.2

1970 Castle Pfalz
Artist: Hans Mueller
Prices: Issue $12.50; 1981 High $22.00;
Low $19.00; Close $20.00; Up $1.00

22-B7-2.6

1974 Wurzburg Castle
Artist: Hans Mueller
Prices: Issue $19.00; 1981 High $50.00;
Low $40.00; Close $50.00; Up $10.00

22-B7-2.7

1975 Castle Lichtenstein
Artist: Hans Mueller
Prices: Issue $21.50; 1981 High $34.00;
Low $26.00; Close $34.00; Up $8.00

22-B7-2.11

1979 Castle Rheinstein
Artist: Hans Mueller
Prices: Issue $35.00; 1981 High $27.00;
Low $27.00; Close $27.00; No Change

22-B7-2.12

1980 Castle Cochum
Artist: Hans Mueller
Prices: Issue $37.50; 1981 High $37.50;
Low $37.50; Close $37.50; No Change

22-B7-2.3

1971 Castle Heidelberg
Artist: Hans Mueller
Prices: Issue $12.75; 1981 High $19.00;
Low $17.00; Close $19.00; Up $2.00

22-B7-2.4

1972 Castle Hohenschwangau
Artist: Hans Mueller
Prices: Issue $14.50; 1981 High $18.00;
Low $17.00; Close $18.00; Up $1.00

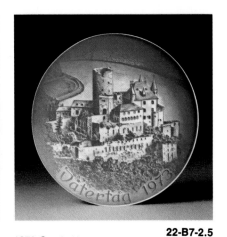

22-B7-2.5

1973 Castle Katz
Artist: Hans Mueller
Prices: Issue $15.00; 1981 High $23.00;
Low $23.00; Close $23.00; No Change

22-B7-2.8

1976 Castle Hohenzollern
Artist: Hans Mueller
Prices: Issue $23.50; 1981 High $33.00;
Low $33.00; Close $33.00; No Change

22-B7-2.9

1977 Castle Eltz
Artist: Hans Mueller
Prices: Issue $24.50; 1981 High $27.00;
Low $25.00; Close $27.00; Up $2.00

22-B7-2.10

1978 Castle Falkenstein
Artist: Hans Mueller
Prices: Issue $27.50; 1981 High $28.00;
Low $25.00; Close $28.00; Up $3.00

22-B7-2.13

1981 Castle Gutenfels
Artist: Hans Mueller
Prices: Issue $39.50; 1981 High $39.50;
Low $39.50; Close $39.50; No Change

22-B7-2.14

1982 Castle Zwingenberg
Artist: Hans Mueller
Issue price: $39.50

Berlin Design

Berlin Design's limited-edition plates, mugs, and other collectibles are manufactured by the Kaiser Porcelain Company (see Germany, Kaiser), and are identified by the distinctive bear-and-crown symbol of the city of Berlin.

The *Christmas* series, introduced in 1970, depicts Yule festivities in German towns.

Artists for Berlin Design plates are not disclosed.

Christmas Series

Artist: Undisclosed
Porcelain decorated in cobalt blue
  underglaze
Diameter: 19.7 centimeters (7¾ inches)
Pierced foot rim
Edition size: As indicated
Not numbered, without certificate

22-B20-1.4
1973 Christmas in Wendelstein
Artist: Undisclosed/Edition: 20,000
Prices: Issue $20.00; 1981 High $27.00;
Low $25.00; Close $27.00; Up $2.00

22-B20-1.1

1970 Christmas in Bernkastel
Artist: Undisclosed/Edition: 4,000
Prices: Issue $14.50; 1981 High $155.00;
Low $128.00; Close $155.00; Up $27.00

22-B20-1.2

1971 Christmas in Rothenburg on Tauber
Artist: Undisclosed/Edition: 20,000
Prices: Issue $14.50; 1981 High $26.00;
Low $23.00; Close $26.00; Up $3.00

22-B20-1.3

1972 Christmas in Michelstadt
Artist: Undisclosed/Edition: 20,000
Prices: Issue $15.00; 1981 High $25.00;
Low $20.00; Close $25.00; Up $5.00

22-B20-1.5

1974 Christmas in Bremen
Artist: Undisclosed/Edition: 20,000
Prices: Issue $25.00; 1981 High $30.00;
Low $24.00; Close $30.00; Up $6.00

22-B20-1.6

1975 Christmas in Dortland
Artist: Undisclosed/Edition: 20,000
Prices: Issue $30.00; 1981 High $25.00;
Low $25.00; Close $25.00; No Change

22-B20-1.7

1976 Christmas Eve in Augsburg
Artist: Undisclosed/Edition: 20,000
Prices: Issue $32.00; 1981 High $25.00;
Low $25.00; Close $25.00; No Change

22-B20-1.8
1977 Christmas Eve in Hamburg
Artist: Undisclosed/Edition: 20,000
Prices: Issue $32.00; 1981 High $32.00;
Low $28.00; Close $32.00; Up $4.00

22-B20-1.9
1978 Christmas Market at the Berlin Cathedral
Artist: Undisclosed/Edition: 20,000
Prices: Issue $36.00; 1981 High $36.00;
Low $34.00; Close $36.00; Up $2.00

22-B20-1.10
1979 Christmas Eve in Greetsiel
Artist: Undisclosed/Edition: 20,000
Prices: Issue $47.50; 1981 High $48.00;
Low $46.00; Close $48.00; Up $2.00

22-B20-1.11
1980 Christmas Eve in Miltenberg
Artist: Undisclosed/Edition: 20,000
Prices: Issue $55.00; 1981 High $58.00;
Low $50.00; Close $58.00; Up $8.00

22-B20-1.12
1981 Christmas Eve in Hahnenklee
Artist: Undisclosed
Prices: Issue $55.00; 1981 High $55.00;
Low $55.00; Close $55.00; No Change

22-B20-1.13
1982 Christmas Eve in Wasserburg
Artist: Undisclosed
Issue price: $55.00

Gabriel 22-A3-3.1-1
Madonna and Child 22-A3-3.1-2
Michael 22-A3-3.1-3
1979 Anna-Perenna *Byzantine Triptych*
Details of the three plates in the first
collector's plate triptych.

Kirke Platten

Danish Church

Danish Church plates, formerly called Roskilde Church plates, are produced by a division of Bareuther & Company (see Germany, Bareuther). The *Church* series, started in 1968, is of famous Danish churches.

Artists for Danish Church plates are not disclosed.

Church Series

Artist: Undisclosed
Porcelain decorated in cobalt blue underglaze
Diameter: 19.7 centimeters (7¾ inches)
Pierced foot rim
Edition size undisclosed, limited by year of issue
Not numbered, without certificate

22-D5-1.4

1971 Ejby Church
Artist: Undisclosed
Prices: Issue $13.00; 1981 High $20.00;
Low $16.00; Close $20.00; Up $4.00

22-D5-1.1

1968 Roskilde Cathedral
Artist: Undisclosed
Prices: Issue $12.00; 1981 High $23.00;
Low $23.00; Close $23.00; No Change

22-D5-1.2

1969 Ribe Cathedral
Artist: Undisclosed
Prices: Issue $13.00; 1981 High $13.00;
Low $11.00; Close $11.00; Down $2.00

22-D5-1.3

1970 Marmor Church
Artist: Undisclosed
Prices: Issue $13.00; 1981 High $12.00;
Low $10.00; Close $12.00; Up $2.00

22-D5-1.5

1972 Kalundborg Church
Artist: Undisclosed
Prices: Issue $13.00; 1981 High $30.00;
Low $21.00; Close $30.00; Up $9.00

22-D5-1.6

1973 Grundtvig Church
Artist: Undisclosed
Prices: Issue $15.00; 1981 High $20.00;
Low $18.00; Close $20.00; Up $2.00

22-D5-1.7

1974 Broager Church
Artist: Undisclosed
Prices: Issue $15.00; 1981 High $18.00;
Low $18.00; Close $18.00; No Change

22-D5-1.8

1975 Sct. Knuds Church
Artist: Undisclosed
Prices: Issue $18.00; 1981 High $22.00;
Low $19.00; Close $22.00; Up $3.00

22-D5-1.9

1976 Osterlars Church
Artist: Undisclosed
Prices: Issue $22.00; 1981 High $25.00;
Low $21.00; Close $25.00; Up $4.00

22-D5-1.10

1977 Budolfi Church
Artist: Undisclosed
Prices: Issue $15.95; 1981 High $30.00;
Low $23.00; Close $30.00; Up $7.00

22-D5-1.11

1978 Haderslev Cathedral
Artist: Undisclosed
Prices: Issue $19.95; 1981 High $18.00;
Low $16.00; Close $18.00; Up $2.00

22-D5-1.12

1979 Holmens Church
Artist: Undisclosed
Prices: Issue $19.95; 1981 High $37.00;
Low $20.00; Close $37.00; Up $17.00

22-D5-1.13

1980 Sct. Bendts Church
Artist: Undisclosed
Prices: Issue $24.00; 1981 High $24.00;
Low $24.00; Close $24.00; No Change

Maker had
no photo at
press time

22-D5-1.14

1981 Vor Frue Church
Artist: Undisclosed
Issue price: $32.50

22-D5-1.15

No information available at press time

Maria and Child **22-R55-2.1**
1971 Rosenthal *Christmas*
Detail showing artist Bjørn Wiinblad's use of
eighteen ceramic colors

The Dresden trademark was originated in 1971 by Porzellanfabrik Tirschenreuth in honor of the famous early porcelain-making region of that name. Porzellanfabrik Tirschenreuth was established in the Dresden-Meissen area in 1838. In 1927, the firm merged with Lorenz Hutschenreuther A G and moved to Selb, Bavaria.

Dresden introduced its *Mother's Day* series in 1972. It ended in 1977.

Hans Waldheimer, the German wildlife and landscape artist noted for his strong compositional unity, created the series.

Mother's Day Series

Artist: Hans Waldheimer
Porcelain centers decorated in cobalt blue underglaze; white baroque rims in relief, trimmed with matte gold edges
Diameter: 19 centimeters (7½ inches)
Attached back hanger
Edition size: As indicated
Not numbered, without certificate

22-D68-2.1

1972 Doe and Fawns
Artist: Hans Waldheimer/Edition: 8,000
Prices: Issue $15.00; 1981 High $16.00;
Low $16.00; Close $16.00; No Change

22-D68-2.2

1973 Mare and Colt
Artist: Hans Waldheimer/Edition: 6,000
Prices: Issue $16.00; 1981 High $26.00;
Low $22.00; Close $26.00; Up $4.00

22-D68-2.3

1974 Tiger and Cub
Artist: Hans Waldheimer/Edition: 5,000
Prices: Issue $20.00; 1981 High $25.00;
Low $23.00; Close $25.00; Up $1.00

22-D68-2.4

1975 Dachshund Family
Artist: Hans Waldheimer/Edition: 5,000
Prices: Issue $24.00; 1981 High $32.00;
Low $30.00; Close $32.00; Up $2.00

22-D68-2.5

1976 Mother Owl and Young
Artist: Hans Waldheimer/Edition: 5,000
Prices: Issue $26.00; 1981 High $34.00;
Low $30.00; Close $34.00; Up $4.00

22-D68-2.6

1977 Chamois
Artist: Hans Waldheimer/Edition: 5,000
Prices: Issue $28.00; 1981 High $28.00;
Low $28.00; Close $28.00; No Change

W. Goebel Porzellanfabrik was established in 1871 in Oeslau by Franz-Detleff Goebel and his son William. Headed by Wilhelm Goebel, who represents the fifth generation of the founding family, Goebel produces handcrafted figurines, plates, dinnerware, and gift items.

In 1935 Goebel introduced the famous M. I. Hummel figurines based on sketches by the Franciscan nun. In 1971, to celebrate the one-hundredth anniversary of the firm, Goebel inaugurated an *Annual* series of limited-edition plates with the M. I. Hummel designs.

The Hummel *Anniversary* series began in 1975, with a new plate to be issued every five years.

The late Sister Maria Innocentia Hummel (1909-1946), in her years at the Franciscan convent at Siessen, produced stylized drawings of children — quite often with a religious theme — which Goebel has translated into both porcelain figurines and bas-relief stoneware plates.

Hummel Annual Series

Artist: Sister M. I. Hummel
   Artist's signature appears on front
Stoneware with hand-painted bas-relief
Diameter: 19 centimeters (7½ inches)
Pierced foot rim
Edition size undisclosed, limited by
   year of issue
Not numbered, without certificate

22-G54-1.1

1971 Heavenly Angel
Artist: Sister M. I. Hummel
Prices: Issue $25.00; 1981 High $960.00;
Low $930.00; Close $930.00; Down $30.00

22-G54-1.2

1972 Hear Ye, Hear Ye
Artist: Sister M. I. Hummel
Prices: Issue $30.00; 1981 High $120.00;
Low $100.00; Close $115.00; Up $15.00

22-G54-1.3

1973 Globe Trotter
Artist: Sister M. I. Hummel
Prices: Issue $32.50; 1981 High $280.00;
Low $260.00; Close $260.00; Down $15.00

22-G54-1.4

1974 Goose Girl
Artist: Sister M. I. Hummel
Prices: Issue $40.00; 1981 High $137.00;
Low $120.00; Close $120.00; Down $17.00

22-G54-1.5

1975 Ride into Christmas
Artist: Sister M. I. Hummel
Prices: Issue $50.00; 1981 High $120.00;
Low $105.00; Close $105.00; Down $10.00

22-G54-1.6

1976 Apple Tree Girl
Artist: Sister M. I. Hummel
Prices: Issue $50.00; 1981 High $107.00;
Low $98.00; Close $98.00; Down $2.00

22-G54-1.7

1977 Apple Tree Boy
Artist: Sister M. I. Hummel
Prices: Issue $50.00; 1981 High $180.00;
Low $125.00; Close $125.00; Down $35.00

22-G54-1.8

1978 Happy Pastime
Artist: Sister M. I. Hummel
Prices: Issue $65.00; 1981 High $135.00;
Low $117.00; Close $117.00; Down $8.00

22-G54-1.9

1979 Singing Lesson
Artist: Sister M. I. Hummel
Prices: Issue $90.00; 1981 High $150.00;
Low $110.00; Close $110.00; Down $30.00

22-G54-1.10

1980 School Girl
Artist: Sister M. I. Hummel
Prices: Issue $100.00; 1981 High $100.00;
Low $85.00; Close $85.00; Down $15.00

22-G54-1.11

1981 Umbrella Boy
Artist: Sister M. I. Hummel
Prices: Issue $100.00; 1981 High $100.00;
Low $100.00; Close $100.00; No Change

22-G54-1.12

1982 Umbrella Girl
Artist: Sister M. I. Hummel
Issue price: $100.00

Hummel Anniversary Series

Artist: Sister M. I. Hummel
  Artist's signature appears on front
Stoneware with hand-painted bas-relief
Diameter: 25.4 centimeters (10 inches)
Pierced foot rim
Edition size undisclosed, limited by
  year of issue
Not numbered, without certificate

22-G54-3.1

1975 Stormy Weather
Artist: Sister M. I. Hummel
Prices: Issue $100.00; 1981 High $380.00;
Low $325.00; Close $325.00; Down $55.00

22-G54-3.2

1980 Spring Dance
Artist: Sister M. I. Hummel
Prices: Issue $225.00; 1981 High $225.00;
Low $175.00; Close $175.00; Down $50.00

Heavenly Angel 22-G54-1.1
1971 Goebel *Hummel Annual*
Hand-painted stoneware bas-relief
distinguishes one of the most sought-after
of all collector's plates

HEINRICH
PORZELLAN

The history of Heinrich Porzellan dates from the opening by Franz Heinrich of a porcelain-painting studio in 1896 in Selb, Bavaria, near the Czechoslovakian border. In 1901, Heinrich established his own porcelain factory, Heinrich & Co., which produced fine table- and giftware. The firm remained under the control of the Heinrich family until 1976, when it was purchased by Villeroy & Boch. Heinrich creations are now distributed worldwide through Villeroy & Boch's marketing channels.

In 1980, Heinrich began a series of porcelain plates entitled *Russian Fairy Tales.*

Russian artist Boris Vasil'evich Zvorykin was born in Moscow in 1872 and was one of the last great book illustrators of Czarist Russia. He was also noted for his murals in the Cathedral at Simferopol. Forced to leave Russia during the 1917 revolution, Zvorykin settled in Paris in 1920 and became an integral figure in an expatriate movement to retain the cultural heritage of Imperial Russia. He elaborately illustrated four books of Russian fairy tales. These books eventually found an American audience when Jacqueline Kennedy Onassis edited the manuscripts and published them under the title *The Firebird and Other Russian Fairy Tales.*

Russian Fairy Tales Series

Artist: Boris Zvorykin
Hard-paste porcelain banded in gold
Diameter: 21 centimeters (8¼ inches)
No hanger
Edition size limited to 27,500
Not numbered, with certificate

22-H18-1.1

1980 The Snow Maiden
Artist: Boris Zvorykin
Prices: Issue $70.00; 1981 High $70.00;
Low $70.00; Close $70 00; No Change

22-H18-1.2

**1980 The Snow Maiden at the Court of
Tsar Berendei**
Artist: Boris Zvorykin
Prices: Issue $70.00; 1981 High $70.00;
Low $70.00; Close $70.00; No Change

22-H18-1.3

**1980 The Snow Maiden and Lel the
Shepherd Boy**
Artist: Boris Zvorykin
Prices: Issue $70.00; 1981 High $70.00;
Low $70.00; Close $70.00; No Change

22-H18-1.4

1981 The Red Knight
Artist: Boris Zvorykin
Prices: Issue $70.00; 1981 High $70.00;
Low $70.00; Close $70.00; No Change

22-H18-1.5

1981 Vassilissa and Her Stepsisters
Artist: Boris Zvorykin
Prices: Issue $70.00; 1981 High $70.00;
Low $70.00; Close $70.00; No Change

22-H18-1.6

1981 Vassilissa Is Presented to the Tsar
Artist: Boris Zvorykin
Prices: Issue $70.00; 1981 High $70.00;
Low $70.00; Close $70.00; No Change

22-H18-1.7
1982 In Search of the Firebird
Artist: Boris Zvorykin
Issue price: $70.00

22-H18-1.8
1982 Ivan and Tsarevna on the Grey Wolf
Artist: Boris Zvorykin
Issue price: $70.00

22-H18-1.9
1982 The Wedding of Tsarevna Elena the
Fair
Artist: Boris Zvorykin
Issue price: $70.00

Vassilissa and Her Stepsisters
22-H18-1.5
1981 Heinrich/Villeroy & Boch
Russian Fairy Tales
The opulent, lavish border pattern is based
on traditional Russian decorative motifs

HIBEL
STUDIO

Hibel Studio was founded in 1976. Headquartered in Riviera Beach, Florida, the studio specializes in original stone lithographs, lithographs on porcelain, and limited-edition collector's plates. All artwork is approved by Edna Hibel, and plates are made by Kaiser Porcelain and Rosenthal China (see Germany, Kaiser, Rosenthal).

Hibel Studio began its first series of collector's plates, the *David* series, in 1979. The four-plate series, with artwork by Edna Hibel, is based on the biblical story of King David.

Edna Hibel, at twenty-two, became the youngest living artist to have a painting in a major American museum when the Boston Museum purchased one of her canvases in 1939. She is an elected member of the Royal Society of Arts in London, and is the only living female artist with a U.S. museum devoted to her works. In 1979, she gave a one-woman show at the Monaco Fine Arts Gallery under the patronage of Prince Rainier and Princess Grace and won the "International Year of the Child" award in the United States. She held an internationally acclaimed show in 1980 at Castle Mainau in Germany sponsored by Count and Countess Lennart Bernadotte.

David Series

Artist: Edna Hibel. Artist's signature appears on front
Porcelain highlighted and banded in gold
Diameter: 25.7 centimeters (10⅛ inches)
Pierced foot rim
Edition size limited to 5,000
Numbered with certificate

Maker had
no photo at
press time

22-H31-1.1
1979 The Wedding of David and
   Bathsheba
Artist: Edna Hibel
Prices: Issue $250.00; 1981 High $310.00;
Low $280.00; Close $300.00; Up $20.00

22-H31-1.2
1980 David, Bathsheba and Solomon
Artist: Edna Hibel
Prices: Issue $275.00; 1981 High $275.00;
Low $275.00; Close $275.00; No Change

1981 David the King
Artist: Edna Hibel
Issue price: $275.00

22-H31-1.3

22-H31-1.4
No information available at press time

HUTSCHENREUTHER
GERMANY

Hutschenreuther has produced limited edition collector's plates since 1973, when they introduced their *Canada Christmas* series (not U.S. Bradex-listed). The *Love for All Seasons* series began in 1982 and will depict six scenes of medieval romance as portrayed by the artist team of Charlotte and William Hallett.

Charlotte and William Hallett have worked together in a variety of artistic media, including silver, crystal, and painting. Charlotte studied fine art at the University of Bridgeport in Connecticut, and William Hallett graduated from the Vesper George School of Art in Boston. As a husband-and-wife artistic team, the Halletts have held numerous shows of their works, and list private individuals, major corporations, and royal families among their collectors.

Love for All Seasons Series

Artist: Charlotte and William Hallett.
  Artists' signatures appear on back
Hard-paste porcelain with gold design
  on border
Diameter: 20.3 centimeters (8 inches)
Attached back hanger
Edition size limited to 10,000
Not numbered, without certificate

22-H82-3.1

22-H82-3.2

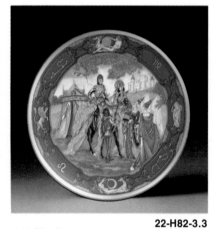

22-H82-3.3

1982 The Minstrel Song
Artist: Charlotte and William Hallett
Issue price: $125.00

1982 Affection
Artist: Charlotte and William Hallett
Issue price: $125.00

1982 The Tournament
Artist: Charlotte and William Hallett
Issue price: $125.00

KAISER

Kaiser porcelain dates to 1872 when porcelain painter August Alboth set up his own workshop in Coburg. When he retired in 1899, his son Ernst moved the pottery to Bavaria. Marriage united the Alboth and Kaiser families in 1922, resulting in the ALKA trademark — a combination of the first two letters of both names.

In 1938 the firm purchased the old Bavarian pottery of Silbermann Brothers, which had been awarded a royal diploma in 1882 for its "magnificent" cobalt blue underglaze. The company opened its modern factory in Staffelstein in 1953 and in 1970 the trademark was changed to Kaiser Porcelain.

Long a producer of porcelain coffee sets, dinnerware, and figurines, Kaiser introduced its first series of limited-edition plates, the *Christmas* series, in 1970. The *Mother's Day* series began in 1971, and to observe the company's own centennial, the *Anniversary* series began a year later.

Born in Karlsbad, Bohemia, Toni Schoener descended from a long family line of porcelain painters. He served his apprenticeship with Porzellanfabrik Altrohlau and Rosenthal Studios as a youth and studied at the Karlsbad School of Arts. Upon graduation, he returned to Porzellanfabrik Altrohlau where he became chief designer. After the ravages of World War II closed all German porcelain factories, Schoener devoted his talent to restoring war-damaged fresco paintings in cathedrals and churches. When stability returned, Schoener joined Kaiser Porcelain as chief designer. He retired officially in 1975, but continued to design plates for Kaiser until his death in 1978. Hungarian-born artist Nori Peter studied at the Academy of Fine Arts in Budapest. She fled Hungary to Canada following the uprising of 1956 and became fascinated by the native Eskimo and their habitat. She has gained wide acclaim for her paintings of their life.

Christmas Series

Artist: As indicated
Porcelain decorated in cobalt blue underglaze
Diameter: 19 centimeters (7½ inches)
Pierced foot rim
Edition size undisclosed, limited by year of issue except 1974
Not numbered, without certificate

22-K4-1.4

1973 Holy Night
Artist: Toni Schoener
Prices: Issue $18.00; 1981 High $42.00;
Low $40.00; Close $42.00; Up $2.00

22-K4-1.1

1970 Waiting for Santa Claus
Artist: Toni Schoener
Prices: Issue $12.50; 1981 High $40.00;
Low $35.00; Close $40.00; Up $5.00

22-K4-1.2

1971 Silent Night
Artist: Kurt Bauer
Prices: Issue $13.50; 1981 High $20.00;
Low $19.00; Close $20.00; Up $1.00

22-K4-1.3

1972 Welcome Home
Artist: Kurt Bauer
Prices: Issue $16.50; 1981 High $17.00;
Low $15.00; Close $15.00; Down $2.00

22-K4-1.5

1974 Christmas Carolers
Artist: Kurt Bauer / Edition: 8,000
Prices: Issue $25.00; 1981 High $34.00;
Low $29.00; Close $34.00; Up $5.00

22-K4-1.6

1975 Bringing Home the Christmas Tree
Artist: Joann Northcott
Prices: Issue $25.00; 1981 High $23.00;
Low $16.00; Close $23.00; Up $7.00

22-K4-1.7

1976 Christ the Saviour Is Born
Artist: Carlo Maratta
Prices: Issue $25.00; 1981 High $24.00;
Low $20.00; Close $24.00; Up $4.00

22-K4-1.8

1977 The Three Kings
Artist: Toni Schoener
Prices: Issue $25.00; 1981 High $17.00;
Low $17.00; Close $17.00; No Change

22-K4-1.9

1978 Shepherds in the Field
Artist: Toni Schoener
Prices: Issue $30.00; 1981 High $28.00;
Low $28.00; Close $28.00; No Change

22-K4-1.10

1979 Christmas Eve
Artist: H. Blum
Prices: Issue $32.00; 1981 High $30.00;
Low $22.00; Close $22.00; Down $8.00

Mother's Day Series

Artist: As indicated
Porcelain decorated in cobalt blue
  underglaze
Diameter: 19 centimeters (7½ inches)
Pierced foot rim
Edition size undisclosed, limited by
  year of issue except 1974
Not numbered, without certificate

22-K4-2.1

1971 Mare and Foal
Artist: Toni Schoener
Prices: Issue $13.00; 1981 High $37.00;
Low $34.00; Close $34.00; Down $1.00

22-K4-2.5

1975 German Shepherd
Artist: Toni Schoener
Prices: Issue $25.00; 1981 High $50.00;
Low $40.00; Close $50.00; Up $10.00

22-K4-2.6

1976 Swan and Cygnets
Artist: Toni Schoener
Prices: Issue $25.00; 1981 High $24.00;
Low $20.00; Close $20.00; Down $4.00

22-K4-1.11
1980 Joys of Winter
Artist: H. Blum
Prices: Issue $40.00; 1981 High $40.00;
Low $33.00; Close $33.00; Down $7.00

22-K4-1.12
1981 Most Holy Night
Artist: Kurt Bauer
Prices: Issue $40.00; 1981 High $40.00;
Low $40.00; Close $40.00; No Change

22-K4-1.13
1982 Bringing Home the Christmas Tree
Artist: Kurt Bauer.
Issue price: $40.00

22-K4-2.2
1972 Flowers for Mother
Artist: Toni Schoener
Prices: Issue $16.50; 1981 High $18.00;
Low $17.00; Close $17.00; Down $1.00

22-K4-2.3
1973 Cats
Artist: Toni Schoener
Prices: Issue $17.00; 1981 High $16.00;
Low $12.00; Close $12.00; Down $4.00

22-K4-2.4
1974 Fox
Artist: Toni Schoener / Edition: 7,000
Prices: Issue $22.00; 1981 High $16.00;
Low $14.00; Close $14.00; Down $2.00

22-K4-2.7
1977 Mother Rabbit and Young
Artist: Toni Schoener
Prices: Issue $25.00; 1981 High $16.00;
Low $16.00; Close $16.00; No Change

22-K4-2.8
1978 Hen and Chicks
Artist: Toni Schoener
Prices: Issue $30.00; 1981 High $16.00;
Low $16.00; Close $16.00; No Change

22-K4-2.9
1979 A Mother's Devotion
Artist: Nori Peter
Prices: Issue $32.00; 1981 High $26.00;
Low $24.00; Close $24.00; Down $2.00

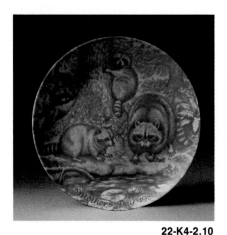

22-K4-2.10

1980 Raccoon Family
Artist: Joann Northcott
Prices: Issue $40.00; 1981 High $40.00;
Low $40.00; Close $40.00; No Change

22-K4-2.11

1981 Safe Near Mother
Artist: H. Blum
Prices: Issue $40.00; 1981 High $40.00;
Low $40.00; Close $40.00; No Change

22-K4-2.12

1982 Pheasant Family
Artist: Kurt Bauer
Issue price: $40.00

Anniversary Series

Artist: As indicated
Porcelain decorated in cobalt blue
    underglaze
Diameter: 19 centimeters (7½ inches)
Pierced foot rim
Edition size undisclosed, limited by
    year of issue except 1974 and 1975
Not numbered, without certificate

22-K4-3.1

1972 Love Birds
Artist: Toni Schoener
Prices: Issue $16.50; 1981 High $16.00;
Low $14.00; Close $14.00; Down $2.00

22-K4-3.2

1973 In the Park
Artist: Toni Schoener
Prices: Issue $18.00; 1981 High $17.00;
Low $16.00; Close $16.00; Down $1.00

22-K4-3.6

1977 A Simple Gift
Artist: Toni Schoener
Prices: Issue $25.00; 1981 High $21.00;
Low $19.00; Close $21.00; Up $2.00

22-K4-3.7

1978 Viking Toast
Artist: Toni Schoener
Prices: Issue $30.00; 1981 High $30.00;
Low $30.00; Close $30.00; No Change

22-K4-3.8

1979 Romantic Interlude
Artist: H. Blum
Prices: Issue $32.00; 1981 High $34.00;
Low $30.00; Close $30.00; Down $4.00

22-K4-3.3

1974 Canoeing Down River
Artist: Toni Schoener/Edition 7,000
Prices: Issue $22.00; 1981 High $33.00;
Low $27.00; Close $27.00; Down $1.00

22-K4-3.4

1975 Tender Moment
Artist: Kurt Bauer/Edition: 7,000
Prices: Issue $25.00; 1981 High $31.00;
Low $28.00; Close $31.00; Up $3.00

22-K4-3.5

1976 Serenade for Lovers
Artist: Toni Schoener
Prices: Issue $25.00; 1981 High $30.00;
Low $27.00; Close $30.00; Up $3.00

22-K4-3.9

1980 Love at Play
Artist: H. Blum
Prices: Issue $40.00; 1981 High $40.00;
Low $40.00; Close $40.00; No Change

22-K4-3.10

1981 Rendezvous
Artist: H. Blum
Prices: Issue $40.00; 1981 High $40.00;
Low $40.00; Close $40.00; No Change

22-K4-3.11

1982 The Betrothal
Artist: Kurt Bauer
Issue price: $40.00

KÖNIGSZELT
BAVARIA

Königszelt Bavaria entered the collector's plate market in 1979 with the first issue in its *Hedi Keller Christmas* series, more than a century after the creation of the first porcelain bearing the hallmark of Königszelt of Silesia. The likeness of Wilhelm I (1797-1888), king of Prussia and first sovereign of a united Germany, is incorporated in the hallmark of Königszelt Bavaria – a tribute to his early patronage under which Bavarian porcelain began its rise to prominence among the porcelain creations of the world. In 1981 the *Grimm's Fairy Tales* series began in commemoration of the two-hundredth anniversary of the Grimm brothers' birth.

Hedi Keller was born in Tuttlingen, a village near the Black Forest. She studied for three years at the Kunstakademie in Stuttgart, learning about the great masters – Titian, Rembrandt, and Brueghel – but later was influenced by Van Gogh and the French Impressionists, who discarded conventional ideas to seek a more personalized style. Her work has been exhibited in galleries in Berlin, Munich, and Dusseldorf. Charles Gehm, a graduate of the Columbus Art School, is a prominent member of the Society of Illustrators and has gained a wide audience through his cover designs for Saul Bellow books.

Hedi Keller Christmas Series

Artist: Hedi Keller. Artist's signature
    appears on front
Overglaze-decorated porcelain
Diameter: 24.1 centimeters (9½ inches)
Attached back hanger
Edition size unannounced
Numbered with certificate

22-K46-1.1
1979 The Adoration
Artist: Hedi Keller
Prices: Issue $29.50; 1981 High $150.00;
Low $70.00; Close $146.00; Up $76.00

22-K46-1.2
1980 Flight into Egypt
Artist: Hedi Keller
Prices: Issue $29.50; 1981 High $70.00;
Low $29.50; Close $70.00; Up $40.50

22-K46-1.3
1981 Return into Galilee
Artist: Hedi Keller
Prices: Issue $29.50; 1981 High $32.00;
Low $29.50; Close $32.00; Up $2.50

22-K46-1.4
No information available at press time

Grimm's Fairy Tales Series

Artist: Charles Gehm. Artist's signature
  appears on front
Overglaze-decorated porcelain
Diameter: 19.7 centimeters (7¾ inches)
Attached back hanger and pierced
  foot rim
Edition size undisclosed, limited by
  period of issue
Numbered with certificate

22-K46-2.1

1981 Rumpelstilzchen
Artist: Charles Gehm
Prices: Issue $23.00; 1981 High $23.00;
Low $23.00; Close $23.00; No Change

22-K46-2.2

1982 Rapunzel
Artist: Charles Gehm
Issue price: $25.00

Maker had
no photo at
press time

22-K46-2.3

1982 Hansel and Gretel
Artist: Charles Gehm
Issue price: $25.00

Adoration **22-K46-1.1**
1979 Koenigszelt-Bavaria
Hedi Keller Christmas
Detail showing artist Hedi Keller's distinctive
naiv style

Lihs-Lindner

The Lindner porcelain factory was established by Ernst Lindner in the 1930s in Kueps, Bavaria. Collector's plates by Lihs-Lindner were the product of collaboration between Lindner and Helmut H. Lihs of Long Beach, California. Lihs provided motifs and sketches which were finished by Lindner's artist, Josef Neubauer. Lindner also produces bells, vases, and various porcelain items.

The *Christmas* series started in 1972 and ended in 1977.

Joseph Neubauer, a native of Bavaria, is prominent among German porcelain artists as a master of *Volkskunst* (folk art).

Christmas Series

Artist: Josef Neubauer
Porcelain decorated in cobalt blue underglaze and 24k gold applied overglaze
Diameter: 19 centimeters (7½ inches)
Pierced foot rim
Edition size: As indicated
Numbered, with certificate since 1976

22-L31-1.1

1972 Little Drummer Boy
Artist: Josef Neubauer/Edition: 6,000
Prices: Issue $25.00; 1981 High $71.00;
Low $60.00; Close $60.00; Down $11.00

22-L31-1.2

1973 The Little Carolers
Artist: Josef Neubauer/Edition: 6,000
Prices: Issue $25.00; 1981 High $16.00;
Low $14.00; Close $14.00; Down $2.00

22-L31-1.3

1974 Peace on Earth
Artist: Josef Neubauer/Edition: 6,000
Prices: Issue $25.00; 1981 High $30.00;
Low $30.00; Close $30.00; No Change

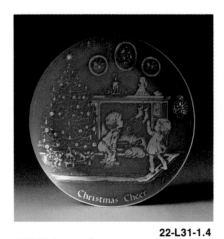

22-L31-1.4

1975 Christmas Cheer
Artist: Josef Neubauer/Edition: 6,000
Prices: Issue $30.00; 1981 High $29.00;
Low $26.00; Close $29.00; Up $3.00

22-L31-1.5

1976 The Joy of Christmas
Artist: Josef Neubauer/Edition: undisclosed
Prices: Issue $30.00; 1981 High $22.00;
Low $20.00; Close $20.00; Down $2.00

22-L31-1.6

1977 Have a Holly-Jolly Christmas
Artist: Josef Neubauer/Edition: undisclosed
Prices: Issue $30.00; 1981 High $23.00;
Low $20.00; Close $20.00; Down $3.00

Philipp Rosenthal, Sr. began his business in 1879 in the town of Selb in Bavaria. He initially purchased "white ware" from various porcelain manufacturers in Selb (including Hutschenreuther) and painted it with his own designs.

In 1895 he established his own factory in Kronach where he produced fine porcelain signed *Rosenthal* on the back, making him one of the first porcelain makers to use his name rather than a symbol. Philipp died in 1937 and the business was taken over by his son, Philipp, Jr., who still heads the firm.

Rosenthal's *Traditional Christmas* series began in 1910 and ended with the 1974 issue. From 1969 to 1971 some of the earlier plates were reissued in small quantities (no more than 500 per reissue). Reissued plates, regardless of the year depicted, have a post-1957 backstamp and their foot rims are not pierced. After 1971, the firm discontinued the practice of reissuing plates from previous years, and each Rosenthal collector's plate is now produced only during its current year. The *Traditional Christmas* now qualify as limited editions. The *Classic Rose Christmas* series was introduced in 1974 bearing Rosenthal's Classic Rose Collection backstamp.

In 1971 Rosenthal began the first of its Studio-Linie collections with the Wiinblad *Christmas* series. These plates carry intricate modern designs partially hand painted in as many as eighteen colors and are embellished with platinum and 18k gold. The *Nobility of Children* series and the *Oriental Gold* series also began in 1976 and carried Rosenthal's Classic Rose Collection backstamp. Both series ended in 1979.

Danish artist Bjørn Wiinblad graduated from the Royal Academy of Art in 1944 and worked for Nymølle Art Fajance Factory from 1946 to 1956. His creations attracted the attention of Philipp Rosenthal, Jr., who, after extensive negotiation, persuaded Wiinblad to design works for the German maker. He was assigned to create products for the Studio-Linie, a high-quality/high-price line of Rosenthal ware. His distinctive collector's plates are world renowned, and the "Lotus" pattern of dinnerware he designed won the 1965 American Interior Design Award. Wiinblad today divides his time among his Rosenthal studio at Selb, his private workshop in Kongens Lyngby near Copenhagen, and the Nymølle Art Fajance Factory, which he now owns. His works now hang in the Museum of Decorative Art in Copenhagen, the Museum of Decorative Art in Bergen, Norway, the Faenza Museum in Italy, and the National Museum of Sweden in Stockholm. Edna Hibel, at twenty-two, became the youngest living artist to have a painting in a major American museum when the Boston Museum purchased one of her canvases in 1939. She is an elected member of the Royal Society of Arts in London, and is the only living female artist with a U.S. museum devoted to her works. In 1979, she gave a one-woman show at the Monaco Fine Arts Gallery under the patronage of Prince Rainier and Princess Grace and won the "International Year of the Child" award in the United States. She held an internationally acclaimed show in 1980 at Castle Mainau in Germany sponsored by Count and Countess Lennart Bernadotte.

Traditional Christmas Series

Artist: As indicated. Artist's name
  appears on back
Overglaze-decorated porcelain, many
  in series have gold inner rim and
  lettering
Diameter: 21.6 centimeters (8½ inches)
Pierced foot rim until 1971, attached
  back hanger thereafter
Edition size: Undisclosed
Not numbered, without certificate

22-R55-1.1

1910 Winter Peace
Artist: Jul V. Guldbrandson
Issue price: Unknown

22-R55-1.2

1911 The Three Wise Men
Artist: Heinrich Vogoler
Issue price: Unknown

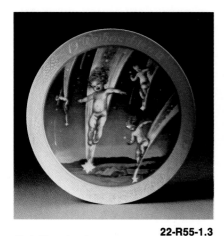

22-R55-1.3

1912 Shooting Stars
Artist: Paul Rieth
Issue price: Unknown

22-R55-1.4

1913 Christmas Lights
Artist: Julius Dietz
Issue price: Unknown

22-R55-1.5

1914 Christmas Song
Artist: Prof. L. V. Zumbusch
Issue price: Unknown

22-R55-1.6

1915 Walking to Church
Artist: Jul V. Guldbrandson
Issue price: Unknown

22-R55-1.7

1916 Christmas During War
Artist: Jul V. Guldbrandson
Issue price: Unknown

22-R55-1.8

1917 Angel of Peace
Artist: Moere
Issue price: Unknown

22-R55-1.12

1921 Christmas in the Mountains
Artist: Jupp Wiertz
Issue price: Unknown

22-R55-1.13

1922 Advent Branch
Artist: F. Nicolai
Issue price: Unknown

22-R55-1.14

1923 Children in the Winter Wood
Artist: Ernst Hofer
Issue price: Unknown

22-R55-1.18

1927 Station on the Way
Artist: Theo Schmutz-Baudiss
Issue price: Unknown

22-R55-1.19

1928 Chalet Christmas
Artist: Heinrich Fink
Issue price: Unknown

22-R55-1.20

1929 Christmas in the Alps
Artist: Heinrich Fink
Issue price: Unknown

22-R55-1.9

1918 Peace on Earth
Artist: Pfeifer
Issue price: Unknown

22-R55-1.10

1919 St. Christopher with the Christ Child
Artist: Dr. W. Schertel
Issue price: Unknown

22-R55-1.11

1920 The Manger in Bethlehem
Artist: Dr. W. Schertel
Issue price: Unknown

22-R55-1.15

1924 Deer in the Woods
Artist: Theo Karner
Issue price: Unknown

22-R55-1.16

1925 The Three Wise Men
Artist: Tauschek
Issue price: Unknown

22-R55-1.17

1926 Christmas in the Mountains
Artist: Theo Schmutz-Baudiss
Issue price: Unknown

22-R55-1.21

1930 Group of Deer under the Pines
Artist: Theo Karner
Issue price: Unknown

22-R55-1.22

1931 Path of the Magi
Artist: Heinrich Fink
Issue price: Unknown

22-R55-1.23

1932 Christ Child
Artist: Otto Koch
Issue price: Unknown

22-R55-1.24

1933 Through the Night to Light
Artist: Hans Schiffner
Issue price: Unknown

22-R55-1.25

1934 Christmas Peace
Artist: Heinrich Fink
Issue price: Unknown

22-R55-1.26

1935 Christmas by the Sea
Artist: Heinrich Fink
Issue price: Unknown

22-R55-1.30

1939 Schneekoppe Mountain
Artist: Heinrich Fink
Issue price: Unknown

22-R55-1.31

1940 Marien Church in Danzig
Artist: Walter Mutze
Issue price: Unknown

22-R55-1.32

1941 Strassburg Cathedral
Artist: Walter Mutze
Issue price: Unknown

22-R55-1.36

1945 Christmas Peace
Artist: Alfred Mundel
Issue price: Unknown

22-R55-1.37

1946 Christmas in an Alpine Valley
Artist: Willi Hein
Issue price: Unknown

22-R55-1.38

1947 The Dillingen Madonna
Artist: Louis Hagen
Issue price: $6.00

22-R55-1.27

1936 Nurnberg Angel
Artist: Heinrich Fink
Issue price: Unknown

22-R55-1.28

1937 Berchtesgaden
Artist: Heinrich Fink
Issue price: Unknown

22-R55-1.29

1938 Christmas in the Alps
Artist: Heinrich Fink
Issue price: Unknown

22-R55-1.33

1942 Marianburg Castle
Artist: Walter Mutze
Issue price: Unknown

22-R55-1.34

1943 Winter Idyll
Artist: Amadeus Dier
Issue price: Unknown

22-R55-1.35

1944 Wood Scape
Artist: Willi Hein
Issue price: Unknown

22-R55-1.39

1948 Message to the Shepherds
Artist: Richard Hoffman
Issue price: $6.00

22-R55-1.40

1949 The Holy Family
Artist: Prof. Karl
Issue price: $6.00

22-R55-1.41

1950 Christmas in the Forest
Artist: Willi Hein
Issue price: $5.25

22-R55-1.42

1951 Star of Bethlehem
Artist: Anne V. Groote
Issue price: $5.75

22-R55-1.43

1952 Christmas in the Alps
Artist: Willi Hein
Issue price: $5.75

22-R55-1.44

1953 The Holy Light
Artist: Willi Hein
Issue price: $5.75

22-R55-1.48

1957 Christmas by the Sea
Artist: Willi Hein
Issue price: $6.25

22-R55-1.49

1958 Christmas Eve
Artist: Willi Hein
Issue price: $6.50

22-R55-1.50

1959 Midnight Mass
Artist: Willi Hein
Issue price: $6.75

22-R55-1.54

1963 Silent Night
Artist: Willi Hein
Issue price: $8.75

22-R55-1.55

1964 Christmas Market in Nurnberg
Artist: Georg Küspert
Issue price: $8.75

22-R55-1.56

1965 Christmas in Munich
Artist: Georg Küspert
Issue price: $11.00

22-R55-1.45

1954 Christmas Eve
Artist: Willi Hein
Issue price: $6.25

22-R55-1.46

1955 Christmas in a Village
Artist: Willi Hein
Issue price: $6.25

22-R55-1.47

1956 Christmas in the Alps
Artist: Willi Hein
Issue price: $6.25

22-R55-1.51

1960 Christmas in Small Village
Artist: Willi Hein
Issue price: $7.25

22-R55-1.52

1961 Solitary Christmas
Artist: Willi Hein
Issue price: $7.75

22-R55-1.53

1962 Christmas Eve
Artist: Willi Hein
Issue price: $8.75

22-R55-1.57

1966 Christmas in Ulm
Artist: Georg Küspert
Issue price: $11.00

22-R55-1.58

1967 Christmas in Regensburg
Artist: Georg Küspert
Issue price: $11.00

22-R55-1.59

1968 Christmas in Bremen
Artist: Georg Küspert
Issue price: $11.00

22-R55-1.60

1969 Christmas in Rothenburg
Artist: Georg Küspert
Issue price: $15.75

22-R55-1.61

1970 Christmas in Cologne
Artist: Georg Küspert
Issue price: $16.00

22-R55-1.62

1971 Christmas in Garmisch
Artist: Georg Küspert
Prices: Issue $66.00; 1981 High $110.00;
Low $90.00; Close $110.00; Up $20.00

Wiinblad Christmas Series

Artist: Bjørn Wiinblad. Artist's signature
 appears on front
Overglaze-decorated porcelain partially
 hand-painted in 18 colors with 18k
 gold design on border
Diameter: 29.2 centimeters
 (11½ inches)
Attached back hanger
Edition size: Undisclosed
Not numbered, without certificate

22-R55-2.1

1971 Maria and Child
Artist: Bjørn Wiinblad
Prices: Issue $100.00; 1981 High $1620.00;
Low $1590.00; Close $1620.00; Up $20.00

22-R55-2.5

1975 The Annunciation
Artist: Bjørn Wiinblad
Prices: Issue $195.00; 1981 High $230.00;
Low $225.00; Close $230.00; Up $5.00

22-R55-1.63
1972 Christmas Celebration in Franconia
Artist: Georg Küspert
Prices: Issue $66.00; 1981 High $97.00;
Low $91.00; Close $97.00; Up $6.00

22-R55-1.64
1973 Christmas in Lübeck-Holstein
Artist: Georg Küspert
Prices: Issue $84.00; 1981 High $108.00;
Low $101.00; Close $108.00; Up $7.00

22-R55-1.65
1974 Christmas in Wurzburg
Artist: Georg Küspert
Prices: Issue $85.00; 1981 High $100.00;
Low $100.00; Close $100.00; No Change

22-R55-2.2
1972 Caspar
Artist: Bjørn Wiinblad
Prices: Issue $100.00; 1981 High $825.00;
Low $790.00; Close $790.00; Down $35.00

22-R55-2.3
1973 Melchior
Artist: Bjørn Wiinblad
Prices: Issue $125.00; 1981 High $595.00;
Low $595.00; Close $595.00; No Change

22-R55-2.4
1974 Balthazar
Artist: Bjørn Wiinblad
Prices: Issue $125.00; 1981 High $530.00;
Low $510.00; Close $530.00; Up $20.00

22-R55-2.6
1976 Angel with Trumpet
Artist: Bjørn Wiinblad
Prices: Issue $195.00; 1981 High $245.00;
Low $245.00; Close $245.00; No Change

22-R55-2.7
1977 Adoration of the Shepherds
Artist: Bjørn Wiinblad
Prices: Issue $225.00; 1981 High $274.00;
Low $260.00; Close $274.00; Up $14.00

22-R55-2.8
1978 Angel with Harp
Artist: Bjørn Wiinblad
Prices: Issue $275.00; 1981 High $278.00;
Low $278.00; Close $278.00; No Change

22-R55-2.9
1979 Exodus from Egypt
Artist: Bjørn Wiinblad
Prices: Issue $310.00; 1981 High $325.00;
Low $310.00; Close $325.00; Up $15.00

22-R55-2.10
1980 Angel with a Glockenspiel
Artist: Bjørn Wiinblad
Prices: Issue $360.00; 1981 High $360.00;
Low $360.00; Close $360.00; No Change

22-R55-2.11
1981 Christ Child Visits Temple
Artist: Bjørn Wiinblad
Prices: Issue $375.00; 1981 High $375.00;
Low $375.00; Close $375.00; No Change

The Nobility of Children Series

Artist: Edna Hibel. Artist's signature
    appears on front
Overglaze-decorated porcelain banded
    in gold
Diameter: 25.4 centimeters (10 inches)
Attached back hanger
Edition size limited to 12,750
Numbered with certificate

22-R55-6.1
1976 La Contessa Isabella
Artist: Edna Hibel
Prices: Issue $120.00; 1981 High $200.00;
Low $180.00; Close $200.00; Up $20.00

Oriental Gold Series

Artist: Edna Hibel. Artist's signature
    appears on front
Overglaze-decorated porcelain high-
    lighted in gold
Diameter: 25.4 centimeters (10 inches)
Attached back hanger
Edition size limited to 2,000
Numbered with certificate

22-R55-8.1
1976 Yasuko
Artist: Edna Hibel
Prices: Issue $275.00; 1981 High $1100.00;
Low $1050.00; Close $1100.00; Up $50.00

22-R55-2.12
No information available at press time

22-R55-6.2
1977 Le Marquis Maurice-Pierre
Artist: Edna Hibel
Prices: Issue $120.00; 1981 High $130.00;
Low $120.00; Close $120.00; Down $10.00

22-R55-6.3
1978 Baronesse Johanna-Maryke
Van Vollendam Tot Marken
Artist: Edna Hibel
Prices: Issue $130.00; 1981 High $135.00;
Low $135.00; Close $135.00; No Change

22-R55-6.4
1979 Chief Red Feather
Artist: Edna Hibel
Prices: Issue $140.00; 1981 High $140.00;
Low $140.00; Close $140.00; No Change

22-R55-8.2
1977 Mr. Obata
Artist: Edna Hibel
Prices: Issue $275.00; 1981 High $600.00;
Low $550.00; Close $600.00; Up $50.00

22-R55-8.3
1978 Sakura
Artist: Edna Hibel
Prices: Issue $295.00; 1981 High $476.00;
Low $464.00; Close $476.00; Up $12.00

22-R55-8.4
1979 Michio
Artist: Edna Hibel
Prices: Issue $325.00; 1981 High $475.00;
Low $390.00; Close $475.00; Up $85.00

Classic Rose Christmas Series

Artist: Helmut Drexler. Artist's name
  appears on back
Overglaze-decorated porcelain with
  gold inner rim and lettering
Diameter: 21.6 centimeters (8½ inches)
Attached back hanger
Edition size: Undisclosed
Not numbered, without certificate

22-R55-11.1

1974 Memorial Church in Berlin
Artist: Helmut Drexler
Prices: Issue $84.00; 1981 High $170.00;
Low $143.00; Close $170.00; Up $27.00

22-R55-11.2

1975 Freiburg Cathedral
Artist: Helmut Drexler
Prices: Issue $75.00; 1981 High $86.00;
Low $82.00; Close $86.00; Up $4.00

22-R55-11.6

1979 Cathedral in Luxemburg
Artist: Helmut Drexler
Prices: Issue $165.00; 1981 High $150.00;
Low $140.00; Close $140.00; Down $10.00

22-R55-11.7

1980 Christmas in Brussels
Artist: Helmut Drexler
Prices: Issue $190.00; 1981 High $190.00;
Low $182.00; Close $182.00; Down $8.00

22-R55-11.3

1976 The Castle of Cochem
Artist: Helmut Drexler
Prices: Issue $95.00; 1981 High $85.00;
Low $80.00; Close $85.00; Up $5.00

22-R55-11.4

1977 Hannover Town Hall
Artist: Helmut Drexler
Prices: Issue $125.00; 1981 High $110.00;
Low $110.00; Close $110.00; No Change

22-R55-11.5

1978 Cathedral at Aachen
Artist: Helmut Drexler
Prices: Issue $150.00; 1981 High $120.00;
Low $112.00; Close $120.00; Up $8.00

22-R55-11.8

1981 Christmas in Trier
Artist: Helmut Drexler
Prices: Issue $190.00; 1981 High $190.00;
Low $190.00; Close $190.00; No Change

Maker had
no photo at
press time

22-R55-11.9

1982 Milan Cathedral
Artist: Helmut Drexler
Issue price: Undetermined at press time

ROYAL BAYREUTH

The pottery now known as Royal Bayreuth began in 1794 in the mountain village of Tettau as the Koniglich Privilegierter Porzellanfabrik Tettau, the first porcelain manufacturer in Bavaria. Now a subsidiary of Royal Tettau, Royal Bayreuth began its *Mother's Day* series in 1973 with art by contemporary artists.

Brazilian Ozz Franca, a specialist in the art of children's portraiture, began the *Mother's Day* series in 1973. In 1974 Leo Jansen succeeded him as the series artist. Born in The Hague, The Netherlands, Jansen spent his youth in Indonesia, where he developed his skills as a portrait-painter by sketching the bronze-skinned Malay children. He returned to the Netherlands to study at the Academy of Fine Arts, and later refined his work in the famous "Pigalle" section of Paris. His "Young Americans VI" was 1979 Plate of the Year on the Canadian plate market.

Mother's Day Series

Artist: As indicated. Artist's signature appears on back until 1975, on front thereafter
Overglaze-decorated porcelain
Diameter: 19.7 centimeters (7¾ inches)
Attached back hanger
Edition size: As indicated
Numbered without certificate

22-R58-2.4

1976 Young Americans III
Artist: Leo Jansen/Edition: 5,000
Prices: Issue $30.00; 1981 High $60.00;
Low $60.00; Close $60.00; No Change

22-R58-2.1

1973 Consolation
Artist: Ozz Franca/Edition: 4,000
Prices: Issue $16.50; 1981 High $45.00;
Low $40.00; Close $40.00; Down $5.00

22-R58-2.2

1974 Young Americans
Artist: Leo Jansen/Edition: 4,000
Prices: Issue $25.00; 1981 High $110.00;
Low $92.00; Close $110.00; Up $18.00

22-R58-2.3

1975 Young Americans II
Artist: Leo Jansen/Edition: 5,000
Prices: Issue $25.00; 1981 High $115.00;
Low $95.00; Close $115.00; Up $20.00

22-R58-2.5

1977 Young Americans IV
Artist: Leo Jansen/Edition: 5,000
Prices: Issue $40.00; 1981 High $57.00;
Low $50.00; Close $50.00; Down $7.00

22-R58-2.6

1978 Young Americans V
Artist: Leo Jansen/Edition: 5,000
Prices: Issue $45.00; 1981 High $45.00;
Low $40.00; Close $40.00; Down $5.00

22-R58-2.7

1979 Young Americans VI
Artist: Leo Jansen/Edition: 5,000
Prices: Issue $60.00; 1981 High $75.00;
Low $58.00; Close $75.00; Up $17.00

22-R58-2.8

22-R58-2.9

22-R58-2.10

1980 Young Americans VII
Artist: Leo Jansen/Edition: 5,000
Prices: Issue $65.00; 1981 High $65.00;
Low $60.00; Close $60.00; Down $5.00

1981 Young Americans VIII
Artist: Leo Jansen/Edition: 5,000
Prices: Issue $65.00; 1981 High $70.00;
Low $65.00; Close $70.00; Up $5.00

1982 Young Americans IX
Artist: Leo Jansen/Edition: 5,000
Issue price: $65.00

Mr. Obata **22-R55-8.2**
1977 Rosenthal *Oriental Gold*
Detail showing artist Edna Hibel's lavish
use of gold, a technique she mastered in
ten years of study.

Schmid

Schmid was established in Boston in the 1930s. Since then the firm has been a specialized importer of porcelain bells and mugs as well as plates. Schmid limited-edition plates are produced by the Hutschenreuther factory in Germany, a noted manufacturer of porcelain figurines and tableware.

Both the *Christmas* series, which began in 1971, and the *Mother's Day* series, which started the following year, feature art created by the late Berta Hummel. The Hummel plates bear her signature depending on whether Berta Hummel had signed the original artwork. The *Ferrandiz Mother and Child* series began in 1977.

Both Hummel series feature art created by Berta Hummel before she entered the Franciscan order at Siessen in 1934 and took the name Sister Maria Innocentia Hummel (See Germany, Goebel). Prior to taking her vows, she had received extensive training at art academies in Simbach and Munich, where she evolved the distinctive style that instantly identifies her work to collectors worldwide.

Christmas Series

Artist: Berta Hummel. Artist's signature or initials appear on front except 1975, 1977, 1981, and 1982
Overglaze-decorated porcelain
Diameter: 19.7 centimeters (7¾ inches)
Attached back hanger
Edition size undisclosed, limited by year of issue
Not numbered, without certificate

22-S12-1.4

1974 The Guardian Angel
Artist: Berta Hummel
Prices: Issue $18.50; 1981 High $34.00;
Low $31.00; Close $34.00; Up $3.00

22-S12-1.1

1971 Angel in a Christmas Setting
Artist: Berta Hummel
Prices: Issue $15.00; 1981 High $78.00;
Low $65.00; Close $73.00; Up $8.00

22-S12-1.2

1972 Angel with Flute
Artist: Berta Hummel
Prices: Issue $15.00; 1981 High $30.00;
Low $28.00; Close $28.00; Down $2.00

22-S12-1.3

1973 The Nativity
Artist: Berta Hummel
Prices: Issue $15.00; 1981 High $240.00;
Low $225.00; Close $230.00; Up $5.00

22-S12-1.5

1975 Christmas Child
Artist: Berta Hummel
Prices: Issue $25.00; 1981 High $28.00;
Low $28.00; Close $28.00; No Change

22-S12-1.6

1976 Sacred Journey
Artist: Berta Hummel
Prices: Issue $27.50; 1981 High $55.00;
Low $49.00; Close $53.00; Up $4.00

22-S12-1.7

1977 Herald Angel
Artist: Berta Hummel
Prices: Issue $27.50; 1981 High $38.00;
Low $37.00; Close $37.00; Down $1.00

1978 Heavenly Trio   22-S12-1.8
Artist: Berta Hummel
Prices: Issue $32.50; 1981 High $34.00;
Low $30.00; Close $30.00; Down $4.00

1979 Starlight Angel   22-S12-1.9
Artist: Berta Hummel
Prices: Issue $38.00; 1981 High $48.00;
Low $43.00; Close $45.00; Up $2.00

1980 Parade into Toyland   22-S12-1.10
Artist: Berta Hummel
Prices: Issue $45.00; 1981 High $90.00;
Low $45.00; Close $90.00; Up $45.00

Mother's Day Series

Artist: Berta Hummel. Artist's signature
 or initials appear on front from
 1972 thru 1975, and 1977
Overglaze-decorated porcelain
Diameter: 19.7 centimeters (7¾ inches)
Attached back hanger
Edition size undisclosed, limited by
 year of issue
Not numbered, without certificate

1972 Playing Hooky   22-S12-2.1
Artist: Berta Hummel
Prices: Issue $15.00; 1981 High $35.00;
Low $27.00; Close $35.00; Up $8.00

1973 The Little Fisherman   22-S12-2.2
Artist: Berta Hummel
Prices: Issue $15.00; 1981 High $85.00;
Low $74.00; Close $85.00; Up $11.00

1977 Moonlight Return   22-S12-2.6
Artist: Berta Hummel
Prices: Issue $27.50; 1981 High $40.00;
Low $36.00; Close $40.00; Up $4.00

1978 Afternoon Stroll   22-S12-2.7
Artist: Berta Hummel
Prices: Issue $32.50; 1981 High $32.00;
Low $32.00; Close $32.00; No Change

1979 Cherub's Gift   22-S12-2.8
Artist: Berta Hummel
Prices: Issue $38.00; 1981 High $38.00;
Low $35.00; Close $35.00; Down $3.00

22-S12-1.11

1981 A Time to Remember
Artist: Berta Hummel
Prices: Issue $45.00; 1981 High $45.00;
Low $45.00; Close $45.00; No Change

22-S12-1.12

1982 Angelic Procession
Artist: Berta Hummel
Issue price: $45.00

22-S12-2.3

1974 The Bumblebee
Artist: Berta Hummel
Prices: Issue $18.50; 1981 High $38.00;
Low $33.00; Close $38.00; Up $5.00

22-S12-2.4

1975 Message of Love
Artist: Berta Hummel
Prices: Issue $25.00; 1981 High $40.00;
Low $33.00; Close $38.00; Up $5.00

22-S12-2.5

1976 Devotion for Mother
Artist: Berta Hummel
Prices: Issue $27.50; 1981 High $43.00;
Low $35.00; Close $35.00; Down $8.00

22-S12-2.9

1980 Mother's Little Helpers
Artist: Berta Hummel
Prices: Issue $45.00; 1981 High $49.00;
Low $45.00; Close $49.00; Up $4.00

22-S12-2.10

1981 Playtime
Artist: Berta Hummel
Prices: Issue $45.00; 1981 High $45.00;
Low $45.00; Close $45.00; No Change

22-S12-2.11

1982 The Flower Basket
Artist: Berta Hummel
Issue price: $45.00

Ferrandiz Mother and Child Series

Artist: Juan Ferrandiz. Artist's signature appears on front
Overglaze-decorated porcelain banded in gold
Diameter: 25.4 centimeters (10 inches)
Pierced foot rim
Edition size limited to 10,000
Numbered without certificate

22-S12-3.1
1977 Orchard Mother and Child
Artist: Juan Ferrandiz
Prices: Issue $65.00; 1981 High $125.00;
Low $110.00; Close $110.00; Down $15.00

22-S12-3.2
1978 Pastoral Mother and Child
Artist: Juan Ferrandiz
Prices: Issue $75.00; 1981 High $105.00;
Low $95.00; Close $95.00; No Change

22-S12-3.3
1979 Floral Mother
Artist: Juan Ferrandiz
Prices: Issue $95.00; 1981 High $90.00;
Low $86.00; Close $90.00; Up $4.00

22-S12-3.4
1980 Avian Mother
Artist: Juan Ferrandiz
Prices: Issue $100.00; 1981 High $100.00;
Low $92.00; Close $92.00; Down $8.00

22-S12-1.11

1981 A Time to Remember
Artist: Berta Hummel
Prices: Issue $45.00; 1981 High $45.00;
Low $45.00; Close $45.00; No Change

22-S12-1.12

1982 Angelic Procession
Artist: Berta Hummel
Issue price: $45.00

22-S12-2.3

1974 The Bumblebee
Artist: Berta Hummel
Prices: Issue $18.50; 1981 High $38.00;
Low $33.00; Close $38.00; Up $5.00

22-S12-2.4

1975 Message of Love
Artist: Berta Hummel
Prices: Issue $25.00; 1981 High $40.00;
Low $33.00; Close $38.00; Up $5.00

22-S12-2.5

1976 Devotion for Mother
Artist: Berta Hummel
Prices: Issue $27.50; 1981 High $43.00;
Low $35.00; Close $35.00; Down $8.00

22-S12-2.9

1980 Mother's Little Helpers
Artist: Berta Hummel
Prices: Issue $45.00; 1981 High $49.00;
Low $45.00; Close $49.00; Up $4.00

22-S12-2.10

1981 Playtime
Artist: Berta Hummel
Prices: Issue $45.00; 1981 High $45.00;
Low $45.00; Close $45.00; No Change

22-S12-2.11

1982 The Flower Basket
Artist: Berta Hummel
Issue price: $45.00

Ferrandiz Mother and Child Series

Artist: Juan Ferrandiz. Artist's signature
appears on front
Overglaze-decorated porcelain banded
in gold
Diameter: 25.4 centimeters (10 inches)
Pierced foot rim
Edition size limited to 10,000
Numbered without certificate

22-S12-3.1

1977 Orchard Mother and Child
Artist: Juan Ferrandiz
Prices: Issue $65.00; 1981 High $125.00;
Low $110.00; Close $110.00; Down $15.00

22-S12-3.2

1978 Pastoral Mother and Child
Artist: Juan Ferrandiz
Prices: Issue $75.00; 1981 High $105.00;
Low $95.00; Close $95.00; No Change

22-S12-3.3

1979 Floral Mother
Artist: Juan Ferrandiz
Prices: Issue $95.00; 1981 High $90.00;
Low $86.00; Close $90.00; Up $4.00

22-S12-3.4

1980 Avian Mother
Artist: Juan Ferrandiz
Prices: Issue $100.00; 1981 High $100.00;
Low $92.00; Close $92.00; Down $8.00

Kiss of the Child **72-L41-2.1**
1971 Lladro *Mother's Day*
Lladro's unique bas-relief plates
feature bisque-fired centers and highly
glazed borders

MADRE EL BESO DEL NIÑO

Belleek Pottery Ltd., maker of thin, translucent parian china, was established in 1857 by David McBirney and Robert W. Armstrong on the banks of the River Erne near the small village of Belleek in County Fermanagh, Northern Ireland. The site is near deposits of clay discovered when the owner of Castle Caldwell in Fermanagh became interested in the brilliant whitewash used on local cottages and found that his entire estate lay on a bed of feldspar clay.

When combined with metallic washes, this clay produces the unique iridescent effect for which Belleek is known — a mother-of-pearl luster that is used on tea sets, figurines, and tableware. Queen Victoria and her son, the Prince of Wales, are among those who commissioned elaborate table services from the firm. Belleek ware is still made today much as it was a century ago.

Belleek's *Christmas* series, based on Irish subjects, began in 1970 and ended in 1977. The *Irish Wildlife Christmas* series began in 1978.

Artists for Belleek plates are not disclosed.

Christmas Series

Artist: Undisclosed
Parian china
Diameter: 19 centimeters (7½ inches)
No hanger
Edition size limited to announced
   quantity of 7,500
Not numbered, without certificate

26-B18-1.1

1970 Castle Caldwell
Artist: Undisclosed
Prices: Issue $25.00; 1981 High $120.00;
Low $116.00; Close $120.00; Up $4.00

26-B18-1.2

1971 Celtic Cross
Artist: Undisclosed
Prices: Issue $25.00; 1981 High $48.00;
Low $43.00; Close $48.00; Up $5.00

26-B18-1.3

1972 Flight of the Earls
Artist: Undisclosed
Prices: Issue $30.00; 1981 High $51.00;
Low $51.00; Close $51.00; No Change

26-B18-1.4

1973 Tribute to W. B. Yeats
Artist: Undisclosed
Prices: Issue $38.50; 1981 High $65.00;
Low $55.00; Close $65.00; Up $10.00

26-B18-1.5

1974 Devenish Island
Artist: Undisclosed
Prices: Issue $45.00; 1981 High $220.00;
Low $190.00; Close $210.00; Up $20.00

26-B18-1.6

1975 The Celtic Cross
Artist: Undisclosed
Prices: Issue $48.00; 1981 High $60.00;
Low $50.00; Close $60.00; Up $10.00

26-B18-1.7

1976 Dove of Peace
Artist: Undisclosed
Prices: Issue $55.00; 1981 High $78.00;
Low $68.00; Close $78.00; Up $10.00

26-B18-1.8

1977 Wren
Artist: Undisclosed
Prices: Issue $55.00; 1981 High $57.00;
Low $52.00; Close $57.00; Up $5.00

Irish Wildlife Christmas Series

Artist: Undisclosed
Parian china
Diameter: 22.9 centimeters (9 inches)
No hanger
Edition size undisclosed
Not numbered, without certificate

26-B18-2.1

1978 A Leaping Salmon
Artist: Undisclosed
Prices: Issue $55.00; 1981 High $78.00;
Low $72.00; Close $78.00; Up $6.00

26-B18-2.2

1979 Hare at Rest
Artist: Undisclosed
Prices: Issue $58.50; 1981 High $72.00;
Low $68.00; Close $72.00; Up $4.00

Maker had
no photo at
press time

26-B18-2.3

1980 The Hedgehog
Artist: Undisclosed
Prices: Issue $66.50; 1981 High $66.50;
Low $66.50; Close $66.50; No Change

Maker had
no photo at
press time

26-B18-2.4

1981 Red Squirrel
Artist: Undisclosed
Issue price: $78.00

Alba Madonna **84-P29-2.1**
1976 Pickard *Christmas*
Detail showing Pickard's character-
istically lavish use of hand-burnished
23k gold borders

Longton Crown Pottery maintains a long tradition of quality English bone china manufacture. Josiah Spode perfected the process by which animal bone ash is added to china clay to produce bone china, which is creamy white and translucent. His formula came to be known as English bone china and remains the standard today.

Longton Crown Pottery began its first Baronet bone china collector's plate series in 1981 with *The Canterbury Tales* collection, interpreting Geoffrey Chaucer's literary classic of the same name, and with the sponsorship of the Centre for Medieval & Renaissance Studies of Oxford, England.

The artist for the series, G. A. Hoover, carries on a family tradition of artists which began with his grandfather. He earned a Master of Fine Arts degree and is considered a master of the style known as Romantic Realism. His paintings are in permanent collections of the Museums of Art in Medellín, Colombia, and St. Paul, Minnesota, and are also in the Tulane University Museum.

The Canterbury Tales Collection

Artist: G. A. Hoover. Artist's signature appears on front
Baronet bone china
Diameter: 21.6 centimeters (8½ inches)
No hanger
Edition size undisclosed, limited by period of issue
Numbered with certificate

26-L46-1.1

26-L46-1.2

26-L46-1.3

1981 The Man of Law's Tale
Artist: G. A. Hoover
Prices: Issue $29.80; 1981 High $29.80;
Low $29.80; Close $29.80; No Change

1982 The Franklin's Tale
Artist: G. A. Hoover
Issue price: $29.80

1982 The Knight's Tale
Artist: G.A. Hoover
Issue price: $31.80

Royal Doulton dates to 1815, when a potter named John Doulton invested his life savings of £100 in a one-kiln pottery in the Lambeth section of London on the river Thames.

John Doulton's second son, Henry, expanded production from stoneware products to terra cotta for architectural purposes. At the International Exhibition of 1871, Doulton exhibited many of his experimental art pieces. Their favorable reception encouraged him to become committed to the development of decorative ceramics. Further experimentation resulted in the perfection of an extensive range of colors and decorative techniques which established Doulton Lambethware as an art form.

In 1877, Henry Doulton turned his attention to the development of tableware. At a small earthenware factory in Burslem, Staffordshire, table services for everyday use were produced along with more costly services with raised gold and acid-etched decorations, often combined with the finest of hand painting. Queen Victoria conferred knighthood upon Henry Doulton in 1887 for his accomplishments in the area of ceramic techniques, thus making him the first potter in England to receive such an honor. In 1901 the company received the Royal warrant, giving it authority to use *Royal* with its name.

The *Beswick Christmas* series, sponsored by Royal Doulton's Beswick Potteries from 1972 to 1978, depicted Christmas traditions from around the world. The Collector's International Gallery of "Fine Art on Fine China" began with the *Mother and Child* series in 1973. These plates show mothers and children of various countries. Other series in the Collector's International group are by contemporary artists and include the *Commedia Dell' Arte* series begun in 1974 and ended in 1978, and *The Log of the "Dashing Wave"* series which began in 1976. The *Valentine's Day* series also began in 1976 with artwork from Victorian period prints. In 1980 Royal Doulton began the *Portraits of Innocence* series.

Royal Doulton has recruited several important artists to design its collector's plates. John Stobart grew up in the English shipping town of Liverpool. He attended Derby College of Arts and won a scholarship to the Royal Academy of Art in London. He has traveled extensively by sea and some of the most exotic ports in the world have served as settings for his paintings. His works hang in such prestigious collections as the Marine Museum of Upper Canada in Toronto, the National Maritime Museum in Greenwich, England, and the Royal Naval College. His paintings have been featured as cover art for *American Heritage, American Artist, Reader's Digest, Oceans,* and *International Yachtsman.* The maker was the first to commission Edna Hibel to work in the limited-edition plate medium. She has since become one of the most successful plate artists (see Germany, Hibel Studio; Rosenthal). Another famous Royal Doulton artist is LeRoy Neiman, recipient of the gold medal of the *Salon d'Art Moderne* in Paris. His work has appeared on the covers of *Time* and *Newsweek* magazines and is in the permanent collection of Oxford University. Francisco J. J. C. Masseria won his first gold medal at the age of fourteen in the *Salon Annuale de Entre Rios* in his native Argentina. He studied the works of the Italian and Spanish Renaissance masters while in Europe, and there developed his own distinctive style of porcelain-like, mysterious faces set against almost abstract backgrounds.

Beswick Christmas Series

Artist: As indicated
Earthenware in hand-cast bas-relief hand-painted in 15 colors
Diameter: 20.5 centimeters (8 inches square)
Pierced foot rim
Edition size limited to 15,000
Numbered without certificate

26-R62-1.4

1975 Christmas in Norway
Artist: Alton Toby
Prices: Issue $45.00; 1981 High $54.00; Low $48.00; Close $54.00; Up $6.00

26-R62-1.1

1972 Christmas in England
Artist: Harry Sales
Prices: Issue $35.00; 1981 High $48.00;
Low $48.00; Close $48.00; No Change

26-R62-1.2

1973 Christmas in Mexico
Artist: Chavela Castrejon
Prices: Issue $37.50; 1981 High $34.00;
Low $34.00; Close $34.00; No Change

26-R62-1.3

1974 Christmas in Bulgaria
Artist: Dimitri Yordanov
Prices: Issue $37.50; 1981 High $48.00;
Low $44.00; Close $48.00; Up $4.00

26-R62-1.5

1976 Christmas in Holland
Artist: Alton Toby
Prices: Issue $50.00; 1981 High $37.00;
Low $32.00; Close $37.00; Up $2.00

26-R62-1.6

1977 Christmas in Poland
Artist: Alton Toby
Prices: Issue $50.00; 1981 High $74.00;
Low $64.00; Close $74.00; Up $10.00

26-R62-1.7

1978 Christmas in America
Artist: Alton Toby
Prices: Issue $55.00; 1981 High $55.00;
Low $45.00; Close $45.00; Down $7.00

Mother and Child Series

Artist: Edna Hibel. Artist's signature
  appears on front
Bone china banded in gold
Diameter: 21 centimeters (8¼ inches)
No hanger
Edition size limited to 15,000
Numbered since 1974, without
  certificate

26-R62-2.1

1973 Colette and Child
Artist: Edna Hibel
Prices: Issue $40.00; 1981 High $520.00;
Low $500.00; Close $512.00; Up $12.00

26-R62-2.2

1974 Sayuri and Child
Artist: Edna Hibel
Prices: Issue $40.00; 1981 High $228.00;
Low $190.00; Close $228.00; Up $38.00

26-R62-2.4

1976 Marilyn and Child
Artist: Edna Hibel
Prices: Issue $55.00; 1981 High $110.00;
Low $105.00; Close $110.00; Up $5.00

26-R62-2.5

1977 Lucia and Child
Artist: Edna Hibel
Prices: Issue $60.00; 1981 High $94.00;
Low $89.00; Close $94.00; Up $5.00

Commedia Dell' Arte Series

Artist: LeRoy Neiman. Artist's signature
  appears on front
Bone china banded in gold
Diameter: 25.4 centimeters (10 inches)
No hanger
Edition size limited to 15,000
Numbered without certificate

26-R62-3.1

1974 Harlequin
Artist: LeRoy Neiman
Prices: Issue $50.00; 1981 High $96.00;
Low $92.00; Close $96.00; Up $4.00

26-R62-2.3

1975 Kristina and Child
Artist: Edna Hibel
Prices: Issue $50.00; 1981 High $142.00;
Low $132.00; Close $137.00; Up $5.00

26-R62-2.6

1978 Kathleen and Child
Artist: Edna Hibel
Prices: Issue $85.00; 1981 High $120.00;
Low $90.00; Close $120.00; Up $30.00

26-R62-3.2

1975 Pierrot
Artist: LeRoy Neiman
Prices: Issue $60.00; 1981 High $73.00;
Low $63.00; Close $73.00; Up $10.00

26-R62-3.3

1977 Columbine
Artist: LeRoy Neiman
Prices: Issue $70.00; 1981 High $60.00;
Low $60.00; Close $60.00; No Change

26-R62-3.4

1978 Punchinello
Artist: LeRoy Neiman
Prices: Issue $70.00; 1981 High $62.00;
Low $60.00; Close $60.00; Down 2.00

The Log of the "Dashing Wave" Series

Artist: John Stobart. Artist's signature appears on front
Bone china banded in gold
Diameter: 26.7 centimeters (10½ inches)
No hanger
Edition size limited to 15,000
Numbered without certificate

26-R62-6.1

1976 Sailing with the Tide
Artist: John Stobart
Prices: Issue $65.00; 1981 High $120.00; Low $100.00; Close $120.00; Up $20.00

26-R62-6.2

1977 Running Free
Artist: John Stobart
Prices: Issue $70.00; 1981 High $128.00; Low $85.00; Close $128.00; Up $43.00

Valentine's Day Series

Artist: Unknown. Reproduced from nineteenth-century Victorian prints
Bone china banded in gold
Diameter: 21 centimeters (8¼ inches)
No hanger
Edition size undisclosed, limited by period of issue
Not numbered, without certificate

26-R62-7.1

1976 Victorian Boy and Girl
Artist: Unknown
Prices: Issue $25.00; 1981 High $60.00; Low $55.00; Close $55.00; Down $5.00

26-R62-7.4

1979 My Valentine
Artist: Unknown
Prices: Issue $29.95; 1981 High $38.00; Low $38.00; Close $38.00; No Change

26-R62-7.5

1980 On a Swing
Artist: Unknown
Prices: Issue $32.95; 1981 High $32.95; Low $32.95; Close $32.95; No Change

26-R62-6.3

1978 Rounding the Horn
Artist: John Stobart
Prices: Issue $70.00; 1981 High $94.00;
Low $85.00; Close $94.00; Up $9.00

26-R62-6.4

1979 Hong Kong
Artist: John Stobart
Prices: Issue $75.00; 1981 High $96.00;
Low $85.00; Close $96.00; Up $11.00

26-R62-6.5

1981 Bora Bora
Artist: John Stobart
Prices: Issue $95.00; 1981 High $95.00;
Low $95.00; Close $95.00; No Change

26-R62-7.2

1977 My Sweetest Friend
Artist: Unknown
Prices: Issue $25.00; 1981 High $28.00;
Low $25.00; Close $25.00; Down $3.00

26-R62-7.3

1978 If I Loved You
Artist: Unknown
Prices: Issue $25.00; 1981 High $48.00;
Low $44.00; Close $46.00; Up $2.00

26-R62-7.6

1981 Sweet Music
Artist: Unknown
Prices: Issue $35.00; 1981 High $35.00;
Low $35.00; Close $35.00; No Change

26-R62-7.7

1982 From My Heart
Artist: Unknown
Issue price: $35.00

Portraits of Innocence Series

Artist: Francisco Masseria
    Artist's signature appears on front
Bone china banded in gold
Diameter: 20.3 centimeters (8 inches)
No hanger
Edition size limited to 15,000
Numbered without certificate

26-R62-11.1

1980 Panchito
Artist: Francisco Masseria
Prices: Issue $75.00; 1981 High $230.00;
Low $110.00; Close $230.00; Up $120.00

26-R62-11.2

1981 Adrien
Artist: Francisco Masseria
Prices: Issue $85.00; 1981 High $142.00;
Low $85.00; Close $142.00; Up $57.00

26-R62-11.3

1982 Angelica
Artist: Francisco Masseria
Issue price: $95.00

Panchito 26-R62-11.1
1980 Royal Doulton
Portraits of Innocence
Detail showing the distinctive style
of Francisco Masseria, known for his
mysterious faces set against abstract
backgrounds

Royal Worcester

The Worcester Porcelain Company, the oldest porcelain manufactory in England today, was established at Worcester, England, in 1751. Two of its original stockholders – Dr. John Wall, a physician and amateur artist, and William Davis, an apothecary – are credited with perfecting a formula for making soft-paste porelain from soapstone (steatite). Their formula was used until the introduction of bone china in the nineteenth century.

In 1788, King George III gave the company permission to call itself "Manufacturers to Their Majesties." After undergoing a number of changes in ownership, the firm was reorganized in 1862 as the Royal Worcester Porcelain Company in recognition of its long history of royal patronage. More recently, in 1976, Royal Worcester merged with Spode; however, each company has retained its own trademark.

Royal Worcester makes two types of collector's plates: bone china, made at Worcester, England; and pewter, made in the United States (see United States, Royal Worcester).

In 1972, Royal Worcester introduced a series of twelve annual plates, the *Doughty Bird* series, based on the porcelain sculptures of American birds by Dorothy Doughty.

Dorothy Doughty, who died in 1962, was a prominent English sculptor of wildlife. Her series of British and American birds, produced by Royal Worcester, began as early as 1935.

Doughty Bird Series

Artist: Dorothy Doughty. Artist's signature appears on back
Bone china with hand-painted bas-relief and gold scalloped rim
Diameter: 20.3 centimeters (8 inches)
No hanger
Edition size: As indicated
Not numbered, without certificate

26-R76-1.4
1975 Blackburnian Warbler
Artist: Dorothy Doughty/Edition: 3,000
Prices: Issue $195.00; 1981 High $210.00; Low $210.00; Close $210.00; No Change

26-R76-1.1
1972 Redstarts and Beech
Artist: Dorothy Doughty/Edition: 2,750
Prices: Issue $125.00; 1981 High $220.00;
Low $212.00; Close $220.00; Up $8.00

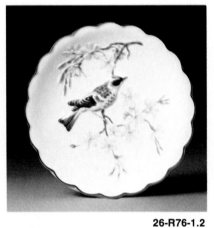

26-R76-1.2
1973 Myrtle Warbler and Cherry
Artist: Dorothy Doughty/Edition: 3,000
Prices: Issue $175.00; 1981 High $212.00;
Low $200.00; Close $212.00; Up $12.00

26-R76-1.3
1974 Blue-Grey Gnatcatchers
Artist: Dorothy Doughty/Edition: 3,000
Prices: Issue $195.00; 1981 High $215.00;
Low $215.00; Close $215.00; No Change

26-R76-1.5
1976 Blue-Winged Sivas and Bamboo
Artist: Dorothy Doughty/Edition: 3,000
Prices: Issue $195.00; 1981 High $210.00;
Low $205.00; Close $210.00; Up $5.00

26-R76-1.6
1977 Paradise Wydah
Artist: Dorothy Doughty/Edition: 3,000
Prices: Issue $195.00; 1981 High $210.00;
Low $200.00; Close $210.00; Up $10.00

26-R76-1.7
1978 Bluetits and Witch Hazel
Artist: Dorothy Doughty/Edition: 3,000
Prices: Issue $195.00; 1981 High $200.00;
Low $200.00; Close $200.00; No Change

26-R76-1.8
1979 Mountain Bluebird and Pine
Artist: Dorothy Doughty/Edition: 3,000
Prices: Issue $195.00; 1981 High $205.00;
Low $195.00; Close $205.00; Up $10.00

26-R76-1.9
1980 Cerulean Warblers and Beech
Artist: Dorothy Doughty/Edition: 3,000
Prices: Issue $315.00; 1981 High $315.00;
Low $315.00; Close $315.00; No Change

Maker had
no photo at
press time

Maker had
no photo at
press time

26-R76-1.10
1981 Willow Warbler and Cranes Bill
Artist: Dorothy Doughty/Edition: 3,000
Issue price: $330.00

26-R76-1.11
1982 Ruby-Crowned Kinglets and Abutilon
Artist: Dorothy Doughty/Edition: 3,000
Issue price: Undetermined at press time

Pink Carnation 38-K32-2.1
1973 King's *Flowers of America*
Detail showing the high-relief modeling of this hand-painted porcelain plate.

Spode

Josiah Spode I established the Spode Works at Stoke-on-Trent, England, in 1776 after spending nearly thirty years learning every facet of the pottery business. From the beginning, the Spode name was highly respected, and the firm has been awarded the Royal warrant by each English monarch since George III.

Josiah Spode perfected the process by which animal bone ash is added to china clay to produce bone china, which is creamy white and translucent. His formula came to be known as English bone china and remains the standard to this day.

Upon Spode's death in 1797, his son, Josiah Spode II, continued the trade, with William Copeland in charge of sales. Josiah Spode III in turn headed the business, but upon his death, Copeland became sole owner, and from 1827 his descendants operated the firm. Under their direction it was called W. T. Copeland & Sons, Ltd., but retained the Spode trademark. Between 1967 and 1976, the firm was owned by Carborundum Company, but in 1976 Spode merged with Royal Worcester of England. The Spode trademark has been retained, and the present factory is located on the site of the original pottery.

Spode's bone china *Christmas* series, which began in 1970 and ended in 1981, is based on old English carols. The plate body itself reproduces an original eighteenth-century Spode model; the designs are based on work by Gillian West, a prominent nineteenth-century British ceramics artist. The 1970 and 1971 plates are decorated in gold; thereafter, decorations are in gold plus a second color which is changed every two years.

Christmas Series

Artist: As indicated
Bone china decorated in gold
Diameter: 20.3 centimeters (8 inches)
No hanger
Edition size undisclosed, limited by
  year of issue
Not numbered, without certificate

26-S63-1.4
1973 We Three Kings of Orient Are
Artist: Gillian West
Prices: Issue $35.00; 1981 High $68.00;
Low $57.00; Close $68.00; Up $11.00

26-S63-1.1
1970 Partridge in a Pear Tree
Artist: Gillian West
Prices: Issue $35.00; 1981 High $72.00;
Low $63.00; Close $70.00; Up $7.00

26-S63-1.2
1971 In Heaven the Angels Singing
Artist: Gillian West
Prices: Issue $35.00; 1981 High $51.00;
Low $47.00; Close $50.00; Up $3.00

26-S63-1.3
1972 We Saw Three Ships A'Sailing
Artist: Gillian West
Prices: Issue $35.00; 1981 High $53.00;
Low $42.00; Close $53.00; Up $9.00

26-S63-1.5
1974 Deck the Halls
Artist: Gillian West
Prices: Issue $35.00; 1981 High $50.00;
Low $50.00; Close $50.00; No Change

26-S63-1.6
1975 Christbaum
Artist: Gillian West
Prices: Issue $45.00; 1981 High $45.00;
Low $42.00; Close $45.00; Up $3.00

26-S63-1.7
1976 Good King Wenceslas
Artist: Gillian West
Prices: Issue $45.00; 1981 High $40.00;
Low $40.00; Close $40.00; No Change

26-S63-1.8

1977 The Holly and the Ivy
Artist: Gillian West
Prices: Issue $45.00; 1981 High $44.00;
Low $41.00; Close $44.00; Up $3.00

26-S63-1.9

1978 While Shepherds Watched
Artist: Gillian West
Prices: Issue $45.00; 1981 High $50.00;
Low $47.00; Close $50.00; Up $3.00

26-S63-1.10

1979 Away in a Manger
Artist: Gillian West
Prices: Issue $50.00; 1981 High $50.00;
Low $50.00; Close $50.00; No Change

26-S63-1.11

1980 Bringing in the Boar's Head
Artist: Paul Wood
Prices: Issue $60.00; 1981 High $65.00;
Low $60.00; Close $65.00; Up $5.00

26-S63-1.12

1981 Make We Merry
Artist: Paul Wood
Prices: Issue $65.00; 1981 High $68.00;
Low $65.00; Close $68.00; Up $3.00

Windsor Castle 26-W90-1.1
1969 Wedgwood *Christmas*
Detail from the first English collector's plate,
showing the famous Wedgwood blue
Jasper ware ground with white Jasper bas-
relief ornamentation

Josiah Wedgwood I, Fellow of the Royal Society, is known as the "father of English potters." He founded the firm that bears his name in 1759 and built a new factory which he called "Etruria" ten years later.

Wedgwood himself developed many of the processes and materials used by the firm to this day. He is perhaps best known for his "Jasper ware" which he perfected in 1774. A vitreous, unglazed stoneware, Jasper is pure white in its original form but can be stained to produce a wide variety of colored backgrounds — green, lilac, yellow, maroon, black, and most popular of all, classic "Wedgwood blue" — onto which white or colored bas-relief decorations are applied by hand.

Although potters in England and abroad tried to duplicate Jasper ware, none was successful, and the Wedgwood name is so firmly linked with Jasper to this day that many people mistakenly think it is the only ware Wedgwood produces, and that it is made only in blue.

In 1940, having outgrown the pottery at Etruria, the firm moved to what has been described as the most up-to-date pottery in the world, near the village of Barlaston, Stoke-on-Trent, Staffordshire, England. There, in 1969, the firm celebrated the two-hundredth anniversary of the Etruria pottery by introducing a *Christmas* series of classic Wedgwood blue-and-white Jasper collector's plates commemorating famous English monuments. In 1972 Wedgwood began a series of *Mothers* plates, issued annually, made in black basalt ware and Jasper wares, and bearing designs created for Wedgwood in the late eighteenth century. The *Bicentennial of American Independence* series, also in blue-and-white Jasper, is a six-plate series which began in 1972 and closed in 1976. It commemorates events which led to American Independence. *The Blossoming of Suzanne* series on Wedgwood bone china, with designs by Mary Vickers, started in 1977. The *Mary Vickers My Memories* series began in 1981.

Artists for Wedgwood over the past two centuries have included some of the most distinguished names in plate design. William Hackwood was a modeler for Wedgwood from 1769 to 1832, and his eighteenth-century designs have been used on Wedgwood Jasper ware for generations. Lady Elizabeth Templetown was a designer for Wedgwood from 1783 to 1787. Most of her designs were modeled by William Hackwood. Among the staff artists of the Wedgwood Design Studio over the past thirty years are Rex Whistler, Eric Ravilious, Edward Bawden, Arnold Machin, Richard Guyatt, and Eduardo Paolozzi. Mary Vickers is one of the leading contemporary Romantic painters, and is also accomplished in lithographs and etchings. She studied at England's St. Martin's School of Art, the New York Art Students League, and the Pratt Institute. Her works are exhibited in major galleries on both sides of the Atlantic, and in private collections such as that of the Duke and Duchess of Marlborough.

Christmas Series

Artist: As indicated
Jasper stoneware
Diameter: 20.3 centimeters (8 inches)
No hanger
Edition size undisclosed, limited by
   year of issue
Not numbered, with certificate

26-W90-1.1
1969 Windsor Castle
Artist: Tom Harper
Prices: Issue $25.00; 1981 High $295.00;
Low $275.00; Close $275.00; No Change

26-W90-1.2
1970 Christmas in Trafalgar Square
Artist: Tom Harper
Prices: Issue $30.00; 1981 High $26.00;
Low $26.00; Close $26.00; No Change

26-W90-1.3
1971 Piccadilly Circus, London
Artist: Tom Harper
Prices: Issue $30.00; 1981 High $35.00;
Low $32.00; Close $35.00; No Change

26-W90-1.4
1972 St. Paul's Cathedral
Artist: Tom Harper
Prices: Issue $35.00; 1981 High $41.00;
Low $36.00; Close $41.00; Up $5.00

26-W90-1.5

1973 The Tower of London
Artist: Tom Harper
Prices: Issue $40.00; 1981 High $50.00;
Low $45.00; Close $45.00; Down $5.00

26-W90-1.6

1974 The Houses of Parliament
Artist: Tom Harper
Prices: Issue $40.00; 1981 High $38.00;
Low $35.00; Close $35.00; Down $3.00

26-W90-1.7

1975 Tower Bridge
Artist: Tom Harper
Prices: Issue $45.00; 1981 High $41.00;
Low $30.00; Close $30.00; Down 11.00

26-W90-1.10

1978 The Horse Guards
Artist: Tom Harper
Prices: Issue $60.00; 1981 High $50.00;
Low $38.00; Close $38.00; Down $12.00

26-W90-1.11

1979 Buckingham Palace
Artist: Undisclosed
Prices: Issue $65.00; 1981 High $63.00;
Low $54.00; Close $54.00; Down $9.00

26-W90-1.12

1980 St. James Palace
Artist: Undisclosed
Prices: Issue $70.00; 1981 High $70.00;
Low $65.00; Close $65.00; Down $5.00

Mothers Series

Artist: As indicated
Jasper stoneware in varying colors
Diameter: 16.5 centimeters (6½ inches)
No hanger
Edition size undisclosed, limited by
    year of issue
Not numbered, without certificate

26-W90-1.8

1976 Hampton Court
Artist: Tom Harper
Prices: Issue $55.00; 1981 High $55.00;
Low $45.00; Close $50.00; Up $5.00

26-W90-1.9

1977 Westminster Abbey
Artist: Tom Harper
Prices: Issue $55.00; 1981 High $42.00;
Low $34.00; Close $34.00; Down $8.00

26-W90-1.13

1981 Marble Arch
Artist: Undisclosed
Prices: Issue $75.00; 1981 High $75.00;
Low $75.00; Close $75.00; No Change

Maker had
no photo at
press time

26-W90-1.14

1982 Lambeth Palace
Artist: Undisclosed
Issue price: $80.00

26-W90-2.1

1971 Sportive Love
Artist: Lady Elizabeth Templetown
Prices: Issue $20.00; 1981 High $24.00;
Low $22.00; Close $24.00; Up $2.00

26-W90-2.2

1972 The Sewing Lesson
Artist: Emma Crewe
Prices: Issue $20.00; 1981 High $30.00;
Low $30.00; Close $30.00; No Change

26-W90-2.3

1973 The Baptism of Achilles
Artist: Lady Elizabeth Templetown
Prices: Issue $25.00; 1981 High $15.00;
Low $13.00; Close $15.00; Up $2.00

26-W90-2.4

1974 Domestic Employment
Artist: Lady Elizabeth Templetown
Prices: Issue $30.00; 1981 High $28.00;
Low $26.00; Close $26.00; Down $2.00

26-W90-2.5

1975 Mother and Child
Artist: Lady Elizabeth Templetown
Prices: Issue $35.00; 1981 High $36.00;
Low $34.00; Close $36.00; Up $2.00

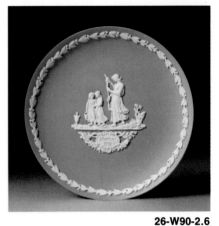

26-W90-2.6

1976 The Spinner
Artist: William Hackwood
Prices: Issue $35.00; 1981 High $33.00;
Low $30.00; Close $30.00; Down $3.00

26-W90-2.9

1979 Deer and Fawn
Artist: Undisclosed
Prices: Issue $45.00; 1981 High $37.00;
Low $35.00; Close $35.00; Down $2.00

26-W90-2.10

1980 Birds
Artist: Undisclosed
Prices: Issue $47.50; 1981 High $51.00;
Low $47.50; Close $51.00; Up $3.50

26-W90-2.11

1981 Mare and Foal
Artist: Undisclosed
Prices: Issue $50.00; 1981 High $50.00;
Low $50.00; Close $50.00; No Change

Bicentennial of American Independence Series

Artist: Undisclosed
Jasper stoneware
Diameter: 20.3 centimeters (8 inches)
No hanger
Edition size undisclosed, limited by
  year of issue
Not numbered, without certificate

26-W90-3.1

1972 Boston Tea Party
Artist: Undisclosed
Prices: Issue $30.00; 1981 High $38.00;
Low $35.00; Close $38.00; Up $3.00

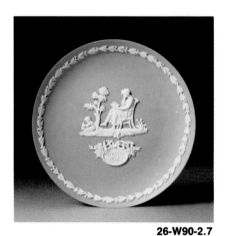

26-W90-2.7

1977 Leisure Time
Artist: William Hackwood
Prices: Issue $35.00; 1981 High $35.00;
Low $30.00; Close $35.00; Up $5.00

26-W90-2.8

1978 Swan and Cygnets
Artist: Undisclosed
Prices: Issue $40.00; 1981 High $40.00;
Low $35.00; Close $35.00; No Change

Maker had
no photo at
press time

26-W90-2.12

1982 Cherubs with Swing
Artist: Undisclosed
Issue price: $55.00

26-W90-3.2

1973 Paul Revere's Ride
Artist: Undisclosed
Prices: Issue $35.00; 1981 High $126.00;
Low $114.00; Close $126.00; Up $12.00

26-W90-3.3

1974 Battle of Concord
Artist: Undisclosed
Prices: Issue $40.00; 1981 High $75.00;
Low $58.00; Close $70.00; Up $12.00

26-W90-3.4

1975 Across the Delaware
Artist: Undisclosed
Prices: Issue $45.00; 1981 High $74.00;
Low $70.00; Close $74.00; Up $4.00

26-W90-3.5

1975 Victory at Yorktown
Artist: Undisclosed
Prices: Issue $45.00; 1981 High $60.00;
Low $56.00; Close $60.00; Up $4.00

26-W90-3.6

1976 Declaration Signed
Artist: Undisclosed
Prices: Issue $45.00; 1981 High $43.00;
Low $43.00; Close $43.00; No Change

Blossoming of Suzanne Series

Artist: Mary Vickers. Artist's signature
   appears on front
Bone china banded in gold
Diameter: 23.5 centimeters (9¼ inches)
No hanger
Edition size: As indicated
Numbered with certificate

26-W90-4.1

1977 Innocence
Artist: Mary Vickers/Edition: 17,000
Prices: Issue $60.00; 1981 High $125.00;
Low $110.00; Close $110.00; Down $15.00

26-W90-4.2

1978 Cherish
Artist: Mary Vickers/Edition: 24,000
Prices: Issue $60.00; 1981 High $62.00;
Low $60.00; Close $62.00; Up $2.00

26-W90-4.3

1979 Daydream
Artist: Mary Vickers/Edition: 24,000
Prices: Issue $65.00; 1981 High $65.00;
Low $65.00; Close $65.00; No Change

26-W90-4.4

1980 Wistful
Artist: Mary Vickers/Edition: 24,000
Prices: Issue $70.00; 1981 High $70.00;
Low $70.00; Close $70.00; No Change

Mary Vickers My Memories Series

Artist: Mary Vickers. Artist's signature
  appears on front
Queensware banded in gold
Diameter: 20.3 centimeters (8 inches)
No hanger
Edition size undisclosed, limited by
  period of issue
Numbered with certificate

26-W90-5.1

1981 Be My Friend
Artist: Mary Vickers
Prices: Issue $27.00; 1981 High $27.00;
Low $27.00; Close $27.00; No Change

26-W90-5.2

1982 Playtime
Artist: Mary Vickers
Issue price: $27.00

The House of Anri, which claims to be the world's largest wood-carving manufactory, is a family firm established in 1916 by Anton Riffeser, Sr. and is headed by his grandson, Ernst Riffeser. The factory is located in the Tyrolean Alps, an area with a long tradition of wood carving.

Anri's *Christmas* series began in 1971. Using a process known as "toriart," the plates are molded and carved in wood material and hand-painted to produce a three-dimensional effect. Each plate is mounted in a circular European maple frame.

A master woodcarver from Saint Ulrich, Italy, Joseph Malfertheiner studied at the Ortesi Academy of Art and became Master Carver for Anri in 1966. Best known for his portrayals of Tyrolean history and three-dimensional replication of Renoir, Van Eyck, and Rembrandt, he has works in private collections in Italy, Austria, Germany, and Australia.

Christmas Series

Artist: As indicated
Hand-painted molded wood material
Diameter: 30.5 centimeters (12 inches)
Attached back hanger
Edition size: As indicated
Numbered since 1972, without
  certificate

38-A54-1.4

1974 Young Man and Girl
Artist: Joseph Malfertheiner
Edition: 10,000
Prices: Issue $50.00; 1981 High $86.00;
Low $80.00; Close $86.00; Up $6.00

38-A54-1.1

1971 St. Jakob in Groden
Artist: Joseph Malfertheiner
Edition: 10,000
Prices: Issue $37.50; 1981 High $90.00;
Low $80.00; Close $90.00; Up $10.00

38-A54-1.2

1972 Pipers at Alberobello
Artist: Joseph Malfertheiner
Edition: 10,000
Prices: Issue $45.00; 1981 High $105.00;
Low $100.00; Close $105.00; Up $5.00

38-A54-1.3

1973 Alpine Horn
Artist: Joseph Malfertheiner
Edition: 10,000
Prices: Issue $45.00; 1981 High $470.00;
Low $350.00; Close $450.00; Up $100.00

38-A54-1.5

1975 Christmas in Ireland
Artist: Joseph Malfertheiner
Edition: 10,000
Prices: Issue $60.00; 1981 High $98.00;
Low $92.00; Close $92.00; Down $1.00

38-A54-1.6

1976 Alpine Christmas
Artist: Joseph Malfertheiner
Edition: 10,000
Prices: Issue $65.00; 1981 High $200.00;
Low $200.00; Close $200.00; No Change

38-A54-1.7

1977 Legend of Heiligenblut
Artist: Joseph Malfertheiner
Edition: 6,000
Prices: Issue $65.00; 1981 High $148.00;
Low $138.00; Close $138.00; Down $10.00

38-A54-1.8

1978 The Klöckler Singers
Artist: Joseph Malfertheiner
Edition: 6,000
Prices: Issue $80.00; 1981 High $110.00;
Low $101.00; Close $110.00; Up $9.00

38-A54-1.9

1979 The Moss Gatherers of Villnoess
Artist: Undisclosed/Edition: 6,000
Prices: Issue $135.00; 1981 High $102.00;
Low $100.00; Close $102.00; Up $2.00

38-A54-1.10

1980 Wintry Church-going in Santa Christina
Artist: Undisclosed/Edition: 6,000
Prices: Issue $165.00; 1981 High $165.00;
Low $165.00; Close $165.00; No Change

38-A54-1.11

1981 Santa Claus in Tyrol
Artist: Undisclosed/Edition: 6,000
Prices: Issue $165.00; 1981 High $165.00;
Low $165.00; Close $165.00; No Change

38-A54-1.12

1982 Star Singers
Artist: Undisclosed/Edition: 6,000
Issue price: $165.00

St. Jakob in Groden 38-A54-1.1
1971 Anri *Christmas*
Detail showing the "toriart" process by
which plates are molded and carved in
wood, then hand painted

King's Porcelain was established in the original Giuseppe Cappe factory in the 1960s. The factory had been known for its Cappe figurines of which King's has retained the original molds.

King's *Flowers of America* series began in 1973 and ended in 1977.

Chief sculptor for King's Porcelain is the Italian artist Aldo Falchi, who studied sculpture in Milan and later collaborated with Bjørn Wiinblad on works for Rosenthal of Germany. Some of his pieces in terra cotta can be found in Verona, Mantova, and Bozzolo, Italy.

Flowers of America Series

Artist: Aldo Falchi. Artist's signature
  appears on back since 1975
High relief, hand-painted porcelain
  banded in gold
Diameter: 22.3 centimeters
  (8¾ inches)
Attached back hanger
Edition size limited to 1,000
Numbered without certificate

38-K32-2.1

1973 Pink Carnation
Artist: Aldo Falchi
Prices: Issue $85.00; 1981 High $130.00;
Low $110.00; Close $130.00; Up $20.00

38-K32-2.2

1974 Red Roses
Artist: Aldo Falchi
Prices: Issue $100.00; 1981 High $145.00;
Low $125.00; Close $145.00; Up $20.00

38-K32-2.3

1975 Yellow Dahlia
Artist: Aldo Falchi
Prices: Issue $110.00; 1981 High $167.00;
Low $136.00; Close $167.00; Up $31.00

38-K32-2.4

1976 Bluebells
Artist: Aldo Falchi
Prices: Issue $130.00; 1981 High $165.00;
Low $148.00; Close $165.00; Up $17.00

38-K32-2.5

1977 Anemones
Artist: Aldo Falchi
Prices: Issue $130.00; 1981 High $170.00;
Low $145.00; Close $170.00; Up $25.00

Veneto Flair

Veneto Flair was established in 1946 by a consortium of potters and painters. Creative World of White Plains, New York, acts as importer and distributor of the Veneto Flair collector's plates.

A centuries-old technique is used to create the Veneto Flair plates. The resulting decorated and glazed earthenware is known as majolica or faience pottery. In this ancient process, terra cotta is hand-thrown on a potter's wheel and the design is incised with a scalpel on the baked clay. Colors are then hand-applied and the plates undergo a series of paintings and firings before a final firing with a secret-formula glaze which produces Veneto Flair's unique mosaic-effect finish.

In 1971, Veneto Flair entered the limited-edition plate market with a single issue, the Bellini "Madonna" plate. The *Last Supper* series, based on da Vinci's painting, and a *Dog* series both began in 1972 and ended in 1976.

Born in Torgiano, Italy, Vincente Tiziano is credited with reviving ancient Etruscan techniques of ceramic production, and his classical style was greatly influenced by the ceramic traditions of the sixteenth century. He is a recipient of the Amerigo Longhi Award from the International Ceramic Show of Deruta in the Italian province of Perugia. Many of his works are on display at the Deruta Ceramic Museum.

Bellini Plate

Artist: Vincente Tiziano
  (after Bellini's *Madonna*)
Terra cotta banded in gold
Diameter: 21.6 centimeters
  (8½ inches)
Pierced foot rim
Edition size limited to 500
Numbered with certificate

38-V22-1.1
1971 Madonna
Artist: Vincente Tiziano
Prices: Issue $45.00; 1981 High $450.00;
Low $420.00; Close $420.00; Down $30.00

Dog Series

Artist: Vincente Tiziano. Artist's
  signature appears on front
Terra cotta banded in gold
Diameter: 21.6 centimeters
  (8½ inches)
Pierced foot rim
Edition size limited to 2,000
Numbered with certificate

38-V22-5.1
1972 German Shepherd
Artist: Vincente Tiziano
Prices: Issue $37.50; 1981 High $65.00;
Low $65.00; Close $65.00; No Change

38-V22-5.2
1973 Poodle
Artist: Vincente Tiziano
Prices: Issue $37.50; 1981 High $44.00;
Low $44.00; Close $44.00; No Change

38-V22-5.3

1974 Doberman
Artist: Vincente Tiziano
Prices: Issue $37.50; 1981 High $28.00;
Low $26.00; Close $26.00; Down $2.00

38-V22-5.4

1975 Collie
Artist: Vincente Tiziano
Prices: Issue $40.00; 1981 High $40.00;
Low $40.00; Close $40.00; No Change

38-V22-5.5

1976 Dachshund
Artist: Vincente Tiziano
Prices: Issue $45.00; 1981 High $40.00;
Low $38.00; Close $40.00; Up $2.00

Last Supper Series

Artist: Vincente Tiziano (after Leonardo
da Vinci's *Last Supper)*. Artist's
signature appears on front
Terra cotta banded in gold
Diameter: 21.6 centimeters
   (8½ inches)
Pierced foot rim
Edition size limited to 2,000
Numbered with certificate

38-V22-6.1

1973 Last Supper—Scene I
Artist: Vincente Tiziano
Prices: Issue $100.00; 1981 High $75.00;
Low $70.00; Close $75.00; Up $5.00

38-V22-6.2

1973 Last Supper—Scene II
Artist: Vincente Tiziano
Prices: Issue $70.00; 1981 High $85.00;
Low $78.00; Close $85.00; Up $7.00

38-V22-6.3

1974 Last Supper—Scene III
Artist: Vincente Tiziano
Prices: Issue $70.00; 1981 High $85.00;
Low $70.00; Close $85.00; Up $15.00

38-V22-6.4

1975 Last Supper—Scene IV
Artist: Vincente Tiziano
Prices: Issue $70.00; 1981 High $80.00
Low $68.00; Close $80.00; Up $12.00

38-V22-6.5

1976 Last Supper—Scene V
Artist: Vincente Tiziano
Prices: Issue $70.00; 1981 High $90.00;
Low $85.00; Close $90.00; Up $5.00

Madonna 38-V22-1.1
1971 Veneto Flair *Bellini Plate*
The unique mosaic effect is a result of
Veneto Flair's secret-formula glaze

Studio Dante di Volteradici

Located in Tuscany, world center for the mining and carving of alabaster, the Studio Dante di Volteradici continues the Italian tradition of alabaster sculpturing.

Di Volteradici's *Grand Opera* series, commissioned by the Museo Teatrale alla Scala to commemorate the two-hundredth anniversary of La Scala Opera House, began in 1976. *Madonne Viventi (Living Madonnas)*, its first proprietary series, began in 1978.

Gino Ruggeri, a sculptor in the neo-classic tradition, is best known for his work "The Crucifix," sculpted for the Casa Serena Institute of Cecina Mare, and his two sculptures, "Memorials to the Fallen," which pay tribute to World War I victims. Now in his late 70s, Ruggeri's last completed work was the "Aida" plate. His successor as designer of the *Grand Opera* series is Franco Ingargiola, whom Ruggeri personally tutored and who works in onyx and ceramics as well as alabaster. Alberto Santangela, current sculptor of the *Madonne Viventi* series, sculpts in the style of the Italian High Renaissance.

Grand Opera Series

Artist: As indicated. Artist's signature appears on front
Ivory alabaster
Diameter: 21.6 centimeters (8½ inches)
Attached back hanger
Edition size undisclosed, limited by period of issue
Numbered with certificate

38-V90-1.4

1979 Aida
Artist: Gino Ruggeri
Prices: Issue $40.00; 1981 High $45.00; Low $45.00; Close $45.00; No Change

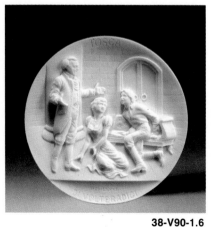

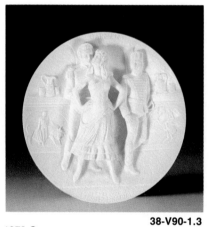

38-V90-1.1

1976 Rigoletto
Artist: Gino Ruggeri
Prices: Issue $35.00; 1981 High $180.00;
Low $150.00; Close $180.00; Up $30.00

38-V90-1.2

1977 Madama Butterfly
Artist: Gino Ruggeri
Prices: Issue $35.00; 1981 High $56.00;
Low $56.00; Close $56.00; No Change

38-V90-1.3

1978 Carmen
Artist: Gino Ruggeri
Prices: Issue $40.00; 1981 High $45.00;
Low $45.00; Close $45.00; No Change

Maker had
no photo at
press time

38-V90-1.5

1980 The Barber of Seville
Artist: Franco Ingargiola
Prices: Issue $40.00; 1981 High $60.00;
Low $40.00; Close $60.00; Up $20.00

38-V90-1.6

1981 Tosca
Artist: Franco Ingargiola
Prices: Issue $40.00; 1981 High $40.00;
Low $40.00; Close $40.00; No Change

38-V90-1.7

1982 Pagliacci
Artist: Franco Ingargiola
Issue price: $40.00

Madonne Viventi Series
(Living Madonnas Series)

Artist: As indicated. Artist's signature
  appears on front
Ivory alabaster
Diameter: 21.6 centimeters
  (8½ inches)
Attached back hanger
Edition size undisclosed, limited by
  period of issue
Numbered with certificate

38-V90-2.1

1978 Madonna Pensosa
(The Pensive Madonna)
Artist: Ado Santini
Prices: Issue $45.00; 1981 High $52.00;
Low $52.00; Close $52.00; No Change

38-V90-2.2

1979 Madonna Serena
(The Serene Madonna)
Artist: Alberto Santangela
Prices: Issue $45.00; 1981 High $45.00;
Low $45.00; Close $45.00; No Change

38-V90-2.3

1980 Madonna Beata
(The Beatific Madonna)
Artist: Alberto Santangela
Prices: Issue $45.00; 1981 High $45.00;
Low $45.00; Close $45.00; No Change

38-V90-2.4

1981 Madonna Profetica
(The Prophetic Madonna)
Artist: Alberto Santangela
Prices: Issue $45.00; 1981 High $45.00;
Low $45.00; Close $45.00; No Change

38-V90-2.5

1982 Madonna Modesta
(The Demure Madonna)
Artist: Alberto Santangela
Issue price: $45.00

Rigoletto **38-V90-1.1**
1976 Studio Dante di Volteradici
Grand Opera
Detail of the first fully undercut ivory
alabaster collector's plate

Fukagawa

Although the present Fukagawa Porcelain factory was organized in the 1880s in Arita by the Fukagawa family, the heritage of its Izumistone porcelain goes back some four centuries to the discovery of kaolin deposits on the island of Kyushu, Japan. It was there, on the slopes of Mount Izumi, that the Korean master potter Yi Samp'yöng ended his twenty-year search for a pure white clay base to be used in the manufacture of fine porcelain. As the direct result of his discovery, a number of small porcelain workshops — the first in all Japan — sprang up in the nearby town of Arita, and delicate plates and saucers were being shipped to the West from the harbor city of Imari decades before porcelain manufacture began in Europe.

The establishment of Fukagawa Porcelain was actually a merger of a number of small workshops whose standards and techniques dated to the time of Yi Samp'yöng. In 1913, Fukagawa was granted the title "Purveyor to the Imperial Household," which indicates patronage from the royal family of Japan. In recognition of this honor, all Fukagawa ceramics bear the imprint "Imperial." The factory, which is still in the hands of the Fukagawa family, continues to employ the original Izumiyama clay from Mount Izumi to give its porcelain a uniquely white body.

In 1977, Fukagawa began its first series of collector's plates — the *Warabe No Haiku (Haiku about Children)* series. The series ended in 1980.

Master of the traditional "Sea of Whiteness" style, Suetomi is the principal artist for Fukagawa and is the recipient of the Gold Prize from Japan's Ministry of International Trade and Industry.

Warabe No Haiku Series
(Haiku about Children)

Artist: Suetomi. Artist's signature and
  seal appear on front
Overglaze-decorated porcelain
Diameter: 26 centimeters (10¼ inches)
No hanger
Edition size undisclosed, limited by
  period of issue
Numbered with certificate
Original Haiku poem appears on front

42-F78-1.1

1977 Beneath the Plum Branch
Artist: Suetomi
Prices: Issue $38.00; 1981 High $47.00;
Low $45.00; Close $45.00; Down $2.00

42-F78-1.2

1978 Child of Straw
Artist: Suetomi
Prices: Issue $42.00; 1981 High $42.00;
Low $42.00; Close $42.00; No Change

42-F78-1.3

1979 Dragon Dance
Artist: Suetomi
Prices: Issue $42.00; 1981 High $42.00;
Low $42.00; Close $42.00; No Change

42-F78-1.4

1980 Mask Dancing
Artist: Suetomi
Prices: Issue $42.00; 1981 High $105.00;
Low $42.00; Close $105.00; Up $63.00

Dave Grossman Designs

Dave Grossman Designs, Inc., headquartered in St. Louis, Missouri, was formed in 1969 to market metal sculptures created by Dave Grossman. The firm entered the collectibles market in 1973 with a series of handcrafted porcelain figurines based on the *Saturday Evening Post* covers painted by Norman Rockwell. Subsequent creations have included porcelain mugs, Christmas ornaments, and limited-edition lithographs — all based on Rockwell works.

In 1979, the first issue in the Dave Grossman Designs *Annual* series was introduced, with the bas-relief design inspired by a famous Rockwell *Post* cover. Plates in the series are produced for the firm by Goto, of Seto City, Japan.

Dave Grossman, a noted sculptor who has been commissioned to create works for Presidents Johnson and Nixon, sculpts the master for each plate in the series.

Dave Grossman Designs Annual Series

Artist: Dave Grossman
Porcelain with hand-painted bas-relief
Diameter: 19 centimeters (7½ inches)
Pierced foot rim
Edition size undisclosed, limited by
  year of issue
Not numbered, without certificate

42-G74-1.1

1979 Leapfrog
Artist: Dave Grossman
Prices: Issue $50.00; 1981 High $65.00;
Low $47.00; Close $47.00; Down $18.00

42-G74-1.2

1980 The Lovers
Artist: Dave Grossman
Prices: Issue $60.00; 1981 High $60.00;
Low $50.00; Close $50.00; Down $10.00

42-G74-1.3

1981 Dreams of Long Ago
Artist: Dave Grossman
Prices: Issue $60.00; 1981 High $60.00;
Low $60.00; Close $60.00; No Change

Schmid

A Japanese subsidiary of Schmid (see Germany, Schmid) produces several series of plates based on contemporary cartoon characters.

The *Peanuts Christmas* series and the *Peanuts Mother's Day* series began in 1972. The *Peanuts Valentine's Day* series began in 1977. The *Disney Christmas* series was introduced in 1973 and the *Disney Mother's Day* series in 1974. The *Raggedy Ann Annual* series started in 1980.

Cartoonist Charles Schulz, creator of the widely-syndicated cartoon strip "Peanuts," designs or approves all plates in the three *Peanuts* series. Walt Disney Productions staff artists design both *Disney* series. Artists for the *Raggedy Ann* series are not disclosed.

Peanuts Christmas Series

Artist: Charles Schulz. Artist's signature appears on front
Overglaze-decorated porcelain
Diameter: 19 centimeters (7½ inches)
Attached back hanger
Edition size undisclosed, limited by year of issue, except as indicated
Not numbered except as indicated, without certificate

42-S12-1.4
1975 Woodstock, Santa Claus
Artist: Charles Schulz
Prices: Issue $12.50; 1981 High $19.00; Low $15.00; Close $19.00; Up $4.00

42-S12-1.1
1972 Snoopy Guides the Sleigh
Artist: Charles Schulz
Prices: Issue $10.00; 1981 High $70.00;
Low $60.00; Close $70.00; Up $10.00

42-S12-1.2
1973 Christmas Eve at the Doghouse
Artist: Charles Schulz
Prices: Issue $10.00; 1981 High $120.00;
Low $90.00; Close $120.00; Up $30.00

42-S12-1.3
1974 Christmas Eve at the Fireplace
Artist: Charles Schulz
Prices: Issue $10.00; 1981 High $60.00;
Low $45.00; Close $60.00; Up $15.00

42-S12-1.5
1976 Woodstock's Christmas
Artist: Charles Schulz
Prices: Issue $13.00; 1981 High $24.00;
Low $15.00; Close $24.00; Up $9.00

42-S12-1.6
1977 Deck the Doghouse
Artist: Charles Schulz
Prices: Issue $13.00; 1981 High $18.00;
Low $18.00; Close $18.00; No Change

42-S12-1.7
1978 Filling the Stocking
Artist: Charles Schulz
Prices: Issue $15.00; 1981 High $20.00;
Low $16.00; Close $20.00; Up $4.00

42-S12-1.8

1979 Christmas at Hand
Artist: Charles Schulz/Edition 15,000
Prices: Issue $17.50; 1981 High $25.00;
Low $22.00; Close $25.00; Up $3.00

42-S12-1.9

1980 Waiting for Santa
Artist: Charles Schulz/Edition 15,000
Prices: Issue $17.50; 1981 High $45.00;
Low $17.50; Close $45.00; Up $27.50

42-S12-1.10

1981 A Christmas Wish
Artist: Charles Schulz/Edition 15,000
Prices: Issue $17.50; 1981 High $17.50;
Low $17.50; Close $17.50; No Change

Peanuts Mother's Day Series

Artist: Charles Schulz. Artist's signature
    appears on front except 1975
Overglaze-decorated porcelain
Diameter: 19 centimeters (7½ inches)
Attached back hanger
Edition size undisclosed, limited by
    year of issue, except as indicated
Not numbered except as indicated,
    without certificate

42-S12-2.1

1972 Linus
Artist: Charles Schulz
Prices: Issue $10.00; 1981 High $11.00;
Low $11.00; Close $11.00; No Change

42-S12-2.2

1973 Mom?
Artist: Charles Schulz
Prices: Issue $10.00; 1981 High $16.00;
Low $14.00; Close $16.00; Up $2.00

42-S12-2.6

1977 Dear Mom
Artist: Charles Schulz
Prices: Issue $13.00; 1981 High $13.00;
Low $13.00; Close $13.00; No Change

42-S12-2.7

1978 Thoughts that Count
Artist: Charles Schulz
Prices: Issue $15.00; 1981 High $12.00;
Low $12.00; Close $12.00; No Change

42-S12-2.8

1979 A Special Letter
Artist: Charles Schulz/Edition: 10,000
Prices: Issue $17.50; 1981 High $13.00;
Low $13.00; Close $13.00; No Change

42-S12-1.11
1982 Perfect Performance
Artist: Charles Schulz/Edition: 15,000
Issue price: $18.50

42-S12-2.3
1974 Snoopy and Woodstock on Parade
Artist: Charles Schulz
Prices: Issue $10.00; 1981 High $18.00;
Low $18.00; Close $18.00; No Change

42-S12-2.4
1975 A Kiss for Lucy
Artist: Charles Schulz
Prices: Issue $12.50; 1981 High $16.00;
Low $16.00; Close $16.00; No Change

42-S12-2.5
1976 Linus and Snoopy
Artist: Charles Schulz
Prices: Issue $13.00; 1981 High $16.00;
Low $16.00; Close $16.00; No Change

42-S12-2.9
1980 A Tribute to Mom
Artist: Charles Schulz/Edition: 10,000
Prices: Issue $17.50; 1981 High $21.00;
Low $17.50; Close $21.00; Up $3.50

42-S12-2.10
1981 Mission for Mom
Artist: Charles Schulz/Edition: 10,000
Prices: Issue $17.50; 1981 High $17.50;
Low $17.50; Close $17.50; No Change

42-S12-2.11
1982 Which Way to Mother?
Artist: Charles Schulz/Edition: 10,000
Issue price: $18.50

Disney Christmas Series

Artist: Undisclosed
Overglaze-decorated porcelain
Diameter: 19 centimeters (7½ inches)
Attached back hanger
Edition size undisclosed, limited by
   year of issue, except as indicated
Not numbered except as indicated,
   without certificate

42-S12-3.1
1973 Sleigh Ride
Artist: Undisclosed
Prices: Issue $10.00; 1981 High $325.00;
Low $290.00; Close $325.00; Up $35.00

42-S12-3.2
1974 Decorating the Tree
Artist: Undisclosed
Prices: Issue $10.00; 1981 High $45.00;
Low $43.00; Close $45.00; Up $2.00

42-S12-3.6
1978 Night Before Christmas
Artist: Undisclosed
Prices: Issue $15.00; 1981 High $21.00;
Low $17.00; Close $21.00; Up $3.00

42-S12-3.7
1979 Santa's Surprise
Artist: Undisclosed/Edition 15,000
Prices: Issue $17.50; 1981 High $18.00;
Low $18.00; Close $18.00; No Change

Disney Mother's Day Series

Artist: Undisclosed
Overglaze-decorated porcelain
Diameter: 19 centimeters (7½ inches)
Attached back hanger
Edition size undisclosed, limited by
   year of issue, except as indicated
Not numbered except as indicated,
   without certificate

42-S12-4.1
1974 Flowers for Mother
Artist: Undisclosed
Prices: Issue $10.00; 1981 High $60.00;
Low $48.00; Close $60.00; Up $12.00

42-S12-4.2
1975 Snow White and the Seven Dwarfs
Artist: Undisclosed
Prices: Issue $12.50; 1981 High $23.00;
Low $23.00; Close $23.00; No Change

42-S12-3.3

1975 Caroling
Artist: Undisclosed
Prices: Issue $12.50; 1981 High $20.00;
Low $18.00; Close $18.00; Down $2.00

42-S12-3.4

1976 Building a Snowman
Artist: Undisclosed
Prices: Issue $13.00; 1981 High $15.00;
Low $15.00; Close $15.00; No Change

42-S12-3.5

1977 Down the Chimney
Artist: Undisclosed
Prices: Issue $13.00; 1981 High $15.00;
Low $15.00; Close $15.00; No Change

42-S12-3.8

1980 Sleigh Ride
Artist: Undisclosed/Edition: 15,000
Prices: Issue $17.50; 1981 High $35.00;
Low $17.50; Close $35.00; Up $17.50

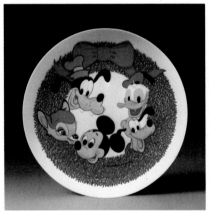

42-S12-3.9

1981 Happy Holidays
Artist: Undisclosed/Edition: 15,000
Prices: Issue $17.50; 1981 High $17.50;
Low $17.50; Close $17.50; No Change

42-S12-3.10

1982 Winter Games
Artist: Undisclosed/Edition: 15,000
Issue price: $18.50

42-S12-4.3

1976 Minnie Mouse and Friends
Artist: Undisclosed
Prices: Issue $13.00; 1981 High $25.00;
Low $22.00; Close $25.00; Up $3.00

42-S12-4.4

1977 Pluto's Pals
Artist: Undisclosed
Prices: Issue $13.00; 1981 High $13.00;
Low $13.00; Close $13.00; No Change

42-S12-4.5

1978 Flowers for Bambi
Artist: Undisclosed
Prices: Issue $15.00; 1981 High $18.00;
Low $18.00; Close $18.00; No Change

42-S12-4.6

1979 Happy Feet
Artist: Undisclosed/Edition: 10,000
Prices: Issue $17.50; 1981 High $13.00;
Low $13.00; Close $13.00; No Change

42-S12-4.7

1980 Minnie's Surprise
Artist: Undisclosed/Edition: 10,000
Prices: Issue $17.50; 1981 High $17.50;
Low $17.50; Close $17.50; No Change

42-S12-4.8

1981 Playmates
Artist: Undisclosed/Edition: 10,000
Prices: Issue $17.50; 1981 High $17.50;
Low $17.50; Close $17.50; No Change

Peanuts Valentine's Day Series

Artist: Charles Schulz. Artist's signature
appears on front
Overglaze-decorated porcelain
Diameter: 19 centimeters (7½ inches)
Attached back hanger
Edition size undisclosed, limited by
year of issue
Not numbered, without certificate

42-S12-7.1

1977 Home Is Where the Heart Is
Artist: Charles Schulz
Prices: Issue $13.00; 1981 High $18.00;
Low $15.00; Close $18.00; Up $3.00

42-S12-7.4

1980 From Snoopy, with Love
Artist: Charles Schulz
Prices: Issue $17.50; 1981 High $17.50;
Low $17.50; Close $17.50; No Change

49-S12-4.9

1982 A Dream Come True
Artist: Undisclosed/Edition: 10,000
Issue price: $18.50

42-S12-7.2

1978 Heavenly Bliss
Artist: Charles Schulz
Prices: Issue $13.00; 1981 High $15.00;
Low $15.00; Close $15.00; No Change

42-S12-7.3

1979 Love Match
Artist: Charles Schulz
Prices: Issue $17.50; 1981 High $18.00;
Low $18.00; Close $18.00; No Change

42-S12-7.5

1981 Hearts-a-Flutter
Artist: Charles Schulz
Prices: Issue $17.50; 1981 High $37.00;
Low $17.50; Close $37.00; Up $19.50

42-S12-7.6

1982 Love Patch
Artist: Charles Schulz
Issue price: $17.50

Raggedy Ann Annual Series

Artist: Undisclosed
Overglaze-decorated porcelain
Diameter: 19 centimeters (7½ inches)
Attached back hanger
Edition size limited to 10,000
Numbered without certificate

42-S12-9.1

1980 The Sunshine Wagon
Artist: Undisclosed/Edition: 10,000
Prices: Issue $17.50; 1981 High $68.00;
Low $23.00; Close $68.00; Up $45.00

42-S12-9.2

1981 The Raggedy Shuffle
Artist: Undisclosed/Edition: 10,000
Prices: Issue $17.50; 1981 High $20.00;
Low $17.50; Close $20.00; Up $2.50

42-S12-9.3

1982 Flying High
Artist: Undisclosed/Edition: 10,000
Issue price: $18.50

Freddie in the Bathtub 84-C72-1.1
1979 Crown Parian
Freddie the Freeloader
Detail showing the signature of well-known
comedian and plate artist Red Skelton

Porsgrund

Johan Jeremiason established Porsgrund, Norway's only porcelain factory, in 1885. Jeremiason began his business by importing English clay which was modeled by ceramist Carl Bauer. Porcelain tableware and decorative wares have been produced since then. Porsgrund's first collector's plate was a 1909 Christmas issue entitled "Christmas Flowers." The series was abandoned after a single issue.

A *Christmas* series based on religious themes was introduced in 1968 and ended with the 1977 issue. In 1978 Porsgrund began a nostalgic Christmas series entitled the *Traditional Norwegian Christmas* series. The *Mother's Day* series began in 1970.

Born in Fredrikstad, Norway, Gunnar Bratlie is a master of the traditional Norwegian folk art known as "rosemaling" and he has worked in such diverse styles as oil, tempera, aquarelle, and etching. Among his many awards are the Scandinavian book prize for illustration, a contest-winning city design for Fredrikstad's 400-year jubilee, and a special stipend from the Norwegian Design Organization. His work is represented in many museums around the world, most notably in the Commune of Oslo, the Art Society of Fredrikstad, the Museo del Arte in Pisoia, Italy, and at Oregon University in the United States. In 1967 Bratlie was commissioned as the sole artist for the Porsgrund Pottery. His works primarily depict Norwegian country scenes.

Christmas Series

Artist: Gunnar Bratlie
Porcelain decorated in cobalt blue
  underglaze
Diameter: 17.8 centimeters (7 inches)
Pierced foot rim
Edition size undisclosed, limited by
  year of issue
Not numbered, without certificate

54-P62-1.4
1971 A Child Is Born in Bethlehem
Artist: Gunnar Bratlie
Prices: Issue $12.00; 1981 High $20.00;
Low $17.00; Close $20.00; Up $3.00

54-P62-1.1

1968 Church Scene
Artist: Gunnar Bratlie
Prices: Issue $12.00; 1981 High $210.00;
Low $200.00; Close $210.00; Up $10.00

54-P62-1.2

1969 Three Kings
Artist: Gunnar Bratlie
Prices: Issue $12.00; 1981 High $30.00;
Low $20.00; Close $30.00; Up $10.00

54-P62-1.3

1970 Road to Bethlehem
Artist: Gunnar Bratlie
Prices: Issue $12.00; 1981 High $10.00;
Low $10.00; Close $10.00; No Change

54-P62-1.5

1972 Hark, the Herald Angels Sing
Artist: Gunnar Bratlie
Prices: Issue $12.00; 1981 High $24.00;
Low $24.00; Close $24.00; No Change

54-P62-1.6

1973 Promise of the Savior
Artist: Gunnar Bratlie
Prices: Issue $15.00; 1981 High $25.00;
Low $25.00; Close $25.00; No Change

54-P62-1.7

1974 The Shepherds
Artist: Gunnar Bratlie
Prices: Issue $15.00; 1981 High $45.00;
Low $33.00; Close $45.00; Up $12.00

54-P62-1.8

1975 Jesus on the Road to the Temple
Artist: Gunnar Bratlie
Prices: Issue $19.50; 1981 High $23.00;
Low $20.00; Close $23.00; Up $3.00

54-P62-1.9

1976 Jesus and the Elders
Artist: Gunnar Bratlie
Prices: Issue $22.00; 1981 High $17.00;
Low $17.00; Close $17.00; No Change

54-P62-1.10

1977 The Draught of Fish
Artist: Gunnar Bratlie
Prices: Issue $24.00; 1981 High $18.00;
Low $17.00; Close $17.00; Down $1.00

Mother's Day Series

Artist: Gunnar Bratlie
Porcelain decorated in cobalt blue
  underglaze
Diameter: 12.7 centimeters (5 inches)
Pierced foot rim
Edition size undisclosed, limited by
  year of issue
Not numbered, without certificate

54-P62-2.1

1970 Mare and Foal
Artist: Gunnar Bratlie
Prices: Issue $7.50; 1981 High $13.00;
Low $13.00; Close $13.00; No Change

54-P62-2.2

1971 Boy and Geese
Artist: Gunnar Bratlie
Prices: Issue $7.50; 1981 High $14.00;
Low $14.00; Close $14.00; No Change

54-P62-2.6

1975 Dog and Puppies
Artist: Gunnar Bratlie
Prices: Issue $12.50; 1981 High $22.00;
Low $20.00; Close $22.00; Up $2.00

54-P62-2.7

1976 Girl and Calf
Artist: Gunnar Bratlie
Prices: Issue $15.00; 1981 High $25.00;
Low $22.00; Close $25.00; Up $3.00

54-P62-2.3

1972 Doe and Fawn
Artist: Gunnar Bratlie
Prices: Issue $10.00; 1981 High $8.00;
Low $8.00; Close $8.00; No Change

54-P62-2.4

1973 Cat and Kittens
Artist: Gunnar Bratlie
Prices: Issue $10.00; 1981 High $11.00;
Low $10.00; Close $10.00; Down $1.00

54-P62-2.5

1974 Boy and Goats
Artist: Gunnar Bratlie
Prices: Issue $10.00; 1981 High $14.00;
Low $14.00; Close $14.00; No Change

54-P62-2.8

1977 Boy and Chickens
Artist: Gunnar Bratlie
Prices: Issue $16.50; 1981 High $21.00;
Low $20.00; Close $21.00; Up $1.00

54-P62-2.9

1978 Girl and Pigs
Artist: Gunnar Bratlie
Prices: Issue $17.50; 1981 High $25.00;
Low $22.00; Close $25.00; Up $3.00

54-P62-2.10

1979 Boy and Reindeer
Artist: Gunnar Bratlie
Prices: Issue $19.50; 1981 High $25.00;
Low $20.00; Close $25.00; Up $5.00

54-P62-2.11

1980 Girl and Lambs
Artist: Gunnar Bratlie
Prices: Issue $21.50; 1981 High $27.00;
Low $21.50; Close $27.00; Up $5.50

54-P62-2.12

1981 Boy and Birds
Artist: Gunnar Bratlie
Prices: Issue $24.00; 1981 High $24.00;
Low $24.00; Close $24.00; No Change

54-P62-2.13

1982 Girl and Rabbits
Artist: Gunnar Bratlie
Issue price: $26.00

Traditional Norwegian Christmas Series

Artist: Gunnar Bratlie. Artist's initials
 appear on back
Porcelain decorated in cobalt blue
 underglaze
Diameter: 17.8 centimeters (7 inches)
Pierced foot rim
Edition size undisclosed, limited by
 year of issue
Not numbered, without certificate

54-P62-5.1

**1978 Guests Are Coming for Christmas
 Eve**
Artist: Gunnar Bratlie
Prices: Issue $27.00; 1981 High $30.00;
Low $26.00; Close $30.00; Up $3.00

54-P62-5.2

1979 Home for Christmas
Artist: Gunnar Bratlie
Prices: Issue $30.00; 1981 High $30.00;
Low $30.00; Close $30.00; No Change

54-P62-5.3

1980 Preparing for Christmas
Artist: Gunnar Bratlie
Prices: Issue $34.00; 1981 High $48.00;
Low $34.00; Close $48.00; Up $14.00

54-P62-5.4

1981 Christmas Skating
Artist: Gunnar Bratlie
Prices: Issue $38.00; 1981 High $38.00;
Low $38.00; Close $38.00; No Change

54-P62-5.5

1982 White Christmas
Artist: Gunnar Bratlie
Issue price: Undetermined at press time

Adoration of the Kings 84-R18-2.4
1973 Reed & Barton *Christmas*
Detail showing artist Roger Johnson's pioneering work in the Damascene silver medium — an electroplating process that combines silver, gold, copper, and bronze.

LLADRÓ

The Lladró Porcelain factory was established in the 1950s by three Lladró brothers — Juan, Jose, and Vicente, sons of a peasant. At night, they studied porcelain designing, modeling, and firing and built their first kiln while in their teens. By 1970 their factory was one of the best-equipped in Europe and had become known for its vases and figurines.

Lladró initiated its limited-edition *Christmas* series and *Mother's Day* series in 1971; both ended in 1979.

Artists for Lladró plates are not disclosed.

Christmas Series

Artist: Undisclosed
White bisque center in bas-relief with underglaze-decorated porcelain border and banded in 14k gold rim
Diameter: 20.3 centimeters (8 inches)
No hanger
Edition size undisclosed, limited by year of issue
Not numbered, without certificate

72-L41-1.1

1971 Caroling
Artist: Undisclosed
Prices: Issue $27.50; 1981 High $20.00;
Low $14.00; Close $20.00; Up $6.00

72-L41-1.2

1972 Carolers
Artist: Undisclosed
Prices: Issue $35.00; 1981 High $42.00;
Low $38.00; Close $42.00; Up $4.00

72-L41-1.3

1973 Boy and Girl
Artist: Undisclosed
Prices: Issue $45.00; 1981 High $48.00;
Low $48.00; Close $48.00; No Change

72-L41-1.4

1974 Carolers
Artist: Undisclosed
Prices: Issue $55.00; 1981 High $82.00;
Low $82.00; Close $82.00; No Change

72-L41-1.5

1975 Cherubs
Artist: Undisclosed
Prices: Issue $60.00; 1981 High $60.00;
Low $56.00; Close $60.00; Up $4.00

72-L41-1.6

1976 Christ Child
Artist: Undisclosed
Prices: Issue $60.00; 1981 High $44.00;
Low $42.00; Close $42.00; Down $2.00

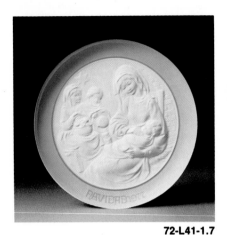

72-L41-1.7

1977 Nativity Scene
Artist: Undisclosed
Prices: Issue $80.00; 1981 High $58.00;
Low $58.00; Close $58.00; No Change

72-L41-1.8

1978 Caroling Child
Artist: Undisclosed
Prices: Issue $80.00; 1981 High $60.00;
Low $58.00; Close $58.00; Down $2.00

72-L41-1.9

1979 Snow Dance
Artist: Undisclosed
Prices: Issue $90.00; 1981 High $80.00;
Low $70.00; Close $70.00; Down $10.00

Mother's Day Series

Artist: Undisclosed
White bisque center in bas-relief with
  underglaze-decorated porcelain
  border and banded in gold
Diameter: 20.3 centimeters (8 inches)
No hanger
Edition size undisclosed, limited by
  year of issue
Not numbered, without certificate

72-L41-2.1

1971 Kiss of the Child
Artist: Undisclosed
Prices: Issue $27.50; 1981 High $77.00;
Low $77.00; Close $77.00; No Change

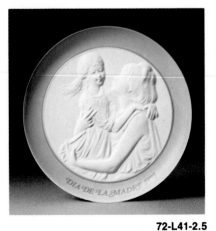

72-L41-2.5

1975 Mother and Child
Artist: Undisclosed
Prices: Issue $60.00; 1981 High $52.00;
Low $52.00; Close $52.00; No Change

72-L41-2.6

1976 Tender Vigil
Artist: Undisclosed
Prices: Issue $60.00; 1981 High $44.00;
Low $40.00; Close $40.00; Down $4.00

72-L41-2.2

1972 Bird and Chicks
Artist: Undisclosed
Prices: Issue $27.50; 1981 High $18.00;
Low $18.00; Close $18.00; No Change

72-L41-2.3

1973 Mother and Children
Artist: Undisclosed
Prices: Issue $35.00; 1981 High $26.00;
Low $26.00; Close $26.00; No Change

72-L41-2.4

1974 Mother Nursing
Artist: Undisclosed
Prices: Issue $45.00; 1981 High $120.00;
Low $120.00; Close $120.00; No Change

72-L41-2.7

1977 Mother and Daughter
Artist: Undisclosed
Prices: Issue $67.50; 1981 High $52.00;
Low $50.00; Close $50.00; Down $2.00

72-L41-2.8

1978 The New Arrival
Artist: Undisclosed
Prices: Issue $80.00; 1981 High $57.00;
Low $55.00; Close $55.00; Down $2.00

72-L41-2.9

1979 Off to School
Artist: Undisclosed
Prices: Issue $90.00; 1981 High $80.00;
Low $75.00; Close $75.00; Down $5.00

Orrefors was originally established in 1726 as an ironworks. In 1898 they began manufacturing glass ink bottles and window glass. Although the ironworks was no longer profitable, Johan Ekman purchased the property in 1913. He was interested in improving the facilities for glassmaking and recognized the importance of the valuable forest land of the area as fuel for glass furnaces. He eventually built an entire community around the glassworks.

Orrefors crystal is made from a mixture of seashore sand and potash, plus a heavy lead content. The ornamentation is created by master blowers who apply liquid molten glass in desired shapes.

In 1970 Orrefors began its *Annual Cathedral* series, made in untinted crystal, depicting famous places of worship. This series ended in 1978. These plates are handmade with the designs engraved in the crystal and filled with 24k gold.

John Selbing is regarded as one of the world's leading photographers of glass. He is credited with developing the technique which enabled production of inlaid-gold crystal plates. At the age of nineteen he joined Orrefors and for forty-six years handled their design, photography and advertising projects. For the last several years he has been working independently in fine art.

Annual Cathedral Series

Artist: John Selbing
Leaded crystal with engraved designs inlaid in 24k gold
Diameter: 25.4 centimeters (10 inches)
No hanger
Edition size: As indicated
Numbered since 1975, without certificate

76-O74-1.1

1970 Notre Dame Cathedral
Artist: John Selbing/Edition: 5,000
Prices: Issue $50.00; 1981 High $70.00;
Low $57.00; Close $70.00; Up $13.00

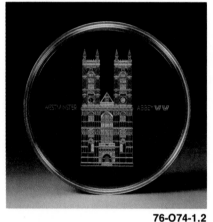

76-O74-1.2

1971 Westminster Abbey
Artist: John Selbing/Edition: 5,000
Prices: Issue $50.00; 1981 High $42.00;
Low $35.00; Close $42.00; Up $7.00

76-O74-1.3

1972 Basilica di San Marco
Artist: John Selbing/Edition: 5,000
Prices: Issue $50.00; 1981 High $60.00;
Low $58.00; Close $60.00; Up $2.00

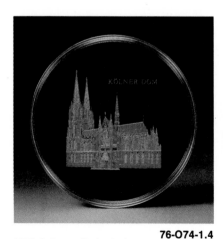

76-O74-1.4

1973 Cologne Cathedral
Artist: John Selbing/Edition: 5,000
Prices: Issue $50.00; 1981 High $65.00;
Low $60.00; Close $65.00; Up $5.00

76-O74-1.5

1974 Temple Rue de la Victoire, Paris
Artist: John Selbing/Edition: 5,000
Prices: Issue $60.00; 1981 High $70.00;
Low $69.00; Close $70.00; Up $1.00

76-O74-1.6

1975 Basilica di San Pietro, Rome
Artist: John Selbing/Edition: 5,000
Prices: Issue $85.00; 1981 High $130.00;
Low $115.00; Close $130.00; Up $15.00

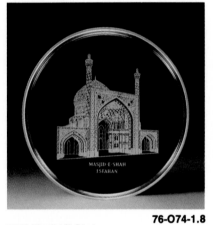

76-O74-1.7

1976 Christ Church, Philadelphia
Artist: John Selbing/Edition: 3,000
Prices: Issue $85.00; 1981 High $85.00;
Low $85.00; Close $85.00; No Change

76-O74-1.8

1977 Masjid-E-Shah
Artist: John Selbing/Edition: 3,000
Prices: Issue $90.00; 1981 High $103.00;
Low $90.00; Close $103.00; Up $8.00

76-O74-1.9

1978 Santiago de Compostela
Artist: John Selbing/Edition: 3,000
Prices: Issue $95.00; 1981 High $105.00;
Low $100.00; Close $105.00; Up $5.00

Angelica 84-M58-1.1
1981 Morgantown Crystal
Michael Yates' Country Ladies
Detail of double intaglio carving in full
lead crystal

The Rörstrand Porcelain Factory is Sweden's oldest pottery and the second oldest in Europe. Originally founded in Stockholm in 1726 under government patronage, the plant was later moved inland to Lidkoping for safety during World War II.

Rörstrand is one of the few factories in the world that produces all three ceramic bodies — porcelain, stoneware, and high-fired earthenware. The output of the factory includes both dinnerware and decorative art, including collector's plates. Rörstrand's first collector's plate series was a *Christmas* series (OTC), started in 1904 and ended in 1926. In 1968 Rörstrand began its series of square *Christmas* plates with designs derived from Swedish folk tales and traditions.

Rörstrand artist Gunnar Nylund has exhibited at the Swedish National Museum and is widely known for his monumental ceramic reliefs.

Christmas Series

Artist: Gunnar Nylund
Porcelain decorated in Scandia blue
  underglaze
Diameter: 19 centimeters (7½ inches
  square)
Pierced foot rim
Edition size undisclosed, limited by
  year of issue
Not numbered, without certificate

76-R54-1.4

1971 Nils in Lapland
Artist: Gunnar Nylund
Prices: Issue $15.00; 1981 High $27.00;
Low $27.00; Close $27.00; No Change

76-R54-1.1

1968 Bringing Home the Tree
Artist: Gunnar Nylund
Prices: Issue $12.00; 1981 High $590.00;
Low $565.00; Close $590.00; Up $25.00

76-R54-1.2

1969 Fisherman Sailing Home
Artist: Gunnar Nylund
Prices: Issue $13.50; 1981 High $103.00;
Low $103.00; Close $103.00; No Change

76-R54-1.3

1970 Nils with His Geese
Artist: Gunnar Nylund
Prices: Issue $13.50; 1981 High $29.00;
Low $29.00; Close $29.00; No Change

76-R54-1.5

1972 Dalecarlian Fiddler
Artist: Gunnar Nylund
Prices: Issue $15.00; 1981 High $34.00;
Low $32.00; Close $32.00; Down $2.00

76-R54-1.6

1973 Farm in Smaland
Artist: Gunnar Nylund
Prices: Issue $16.00; 1981 High $98.00;
Low $98.00; Close $98.00; No Change

76-R54-1.7

1974 Vadstena
Artist: Gunnar Nylund
Prices: Issue $19.00; 1981 High $60.00;
Low $60.00; Close $60.00; No Change

76-R54-1.8

1975 Nils in Vastmanland
Artist: Gunnar Nylund
Prices: Issue $20.00; 1981 High $36.00;
Low $36.00; Close $36.00; No Change

76-R54-1.9

1976 Nils in Uppland
Artist: Gunnar Nylund
Prices: Issue $20.00; 1981 High $30.00;
Low $30.00; Close $30.00; No Change

76-R54-1.10

1977 Nils in Värmland
Artist: Gunnar Nylund
Prices: Issue $29.50; 1981 High $30.00;
Low $30.00; Close $30.00; No Change

76-R54-1.11

1978 Nils in Fjallbacka
Artist: Gunnar Nylund
Prices: Issue $32.50; 1981 High $32.50;
Low $32.50; Close $32.50; No Change

76-R54-1.12

1979 Nils in Vaestergoetland
Artist: Gunnar Nylund
Prices: Issue $38.50; 1981 High $38.50;
Low $34.00; Close $34.00; Down $4.50

76-R54-1.13

1980 Nils in Halland
Artist: Gunnar Nylund
Prices: Issue $55.00; 1981 High $54.00;
Low $47.50; Close $54.00; Up $6.50

76-R54-1.14

1981 Nils in Gotland
Artist: Gunnar Nylund
Prices: Issue $55.00; 1981 High $55.00;
Low $55.00; Close $55.00; No Change

76-R54-1.15

1982 Nils at Skansen in Stockholm
Artist: Gunnar Nylund
Issue price: $47.50

L'Arc de Triomphe **18-D15-6.1**
1980 D'Arceau-Limoges *Les Douzes*
Sites Parisiens de Louis Dali
Detail showing Impressionistic brushwork of
artist Louis Dali

Artists of the World

Initially organized as DeGrazia of Scottsdale, the company was founded by James LaFond to represent Arizona artist Ted DeGrazia. The present name, Artists of the World, was adopted in 1977 when the company's scope was enlarged to include additional artists.

Children of Aberdeen, a proprietary series with artwork by Kee Fung Ng, began in 1979 and depicts the children who live on boats anchored at the fishing village of Aberdeen near Hong Kong.

Artist Kee Fung Ng was born in Canton, China, and educated at its Fu San Art School. His works have received critical acclaim for their subtle balancing of both Eastern and Western artistic concepts.

Children of Aberdeen Series

Artist: Kee Fung Ng. Artist's signature
  appears on front
China banded in gold
Diameter: 25.4 centimeters (10 inches)
No hanger
Edition size unannounced
Numbered with certificate

84-A72-1.1

1979 Girl with Little Brother
Artist: Kee Fung Ng
Prices: Issue $50.00; 1981 High $55.00;
Low $50.00; Close $55.00; Up $5.00

84-A72-1.2

1980 Sampan Girl
Artist: Kee Fung Ng
Prices: Issue $50.00; 1981 High $58.00;
Low $50.00; Close $58.00; Up $8.00

84-A72-1.3

1981 Girl with Little Sister
Artist: Kee Fung Ng
Prices: Issue $55.00; 1981 High $58.00;
Low $55.00; Close $58.00; Up $3.00

84-A72-1.4

1982 Girl with Seashells
Artist: Kee Fung Ng
Issue price: $60.00

perfection in porcelain

Crown Parian, Ltd. was incorporated in South El Monte, California in 1978 for the purpose of producing fine porcelain limited-edition plates and related products.

Crown Parian began the *Freddie the Freeloader* series in 1979.

Red Skelton, a comedian widely known for his film, stage, and television characterizations, has also earned a devoted following for his artwork.

Freddie the Freeloader Series

Artist: Red Skelton. Artist's signature
  appears on front
Overglaze-decorated porcelain banded
  in gold
Diameter: 21.6 centimeters (8½ inches)
No hanger
Edition size limited to 10,000
Numbered without certificate

84-C72-1.1

1979 Freddie in the Bathtub
Artist: Red Skelton
Prices: Issue $55.00; 1981 High $300.00;
Low $105.00; Close $300.00; Up $195.00

84-C72-1.2

1980 Freddie's Shack
Artist: Red Skelton
Prices: Issue $55.00; 1981 High $130.00;
Low $55.00; Close $130.00; Up $75.00

84-C72-1.3

1981 Freddie on the Green
Artist: Red Skelton
Prices: Issue $60.00; 1981 High $92.00;
Low $60.00; Close $92.00; Up $32.00

84-C72-1.4

1982 Love That Freddie
Artist: Red Skelton
Issue price: $60.00

Fairmont

Fairmont China was established in 1976 to produce limited-edition plates. Two series began that year: the *Holiday* series with artwork by Ted DeGrazia, and the *Famous Clowns* series by comedian Red Skelton. In 1977, Fairmont issued the third plate in the *Irene Spencer Annual* series and in 1978 the third plate in the *DeGrazia Children* series, both originally started by Gorham (see United States, Gorham). In 1979 Fairmont started their *Classical American Beauties* series and, in 1981, began their *Playful Memories* series with artwork by Su Etém.

Ted DeGrazia, one-time apprentice to the great Mexican muralist Diego Rivera, first came to international attention in 1970 when his work was featured on a UNICEF card. Since then, his stylized re-creations of Southwestern subjects and themes have made him one of the most instantly recognizable of American artists. Irene Spencer received her training at Chicago's Academy of Art and the Chicago Art Institute, where she developed her distinctive style, reminiscent of the Old Masters. In addition to her accomplishments as a fine artist, she has written and illustrated children's books and worked as a newspaper cartoonist and a commercial artist. Red Skelton, a comedian widely known for his film, stage, and television characterizations, has also earned a devoted following for his artwork. Su Etém is a self-taught painter, and has held numerous shows in California, including such cities as Costa Mesa, Westminister, and Huntington Beach.

DeGrazia Holiday Series

Artist: Ted DeGrazia. Artist's signature appears on front; first 500 autographed on back
China banded in gold
Diameter: 26 centimeters (10¼ inches)
No hanger
Edition size limited to 10,000
Numbered since 1977, without certificate

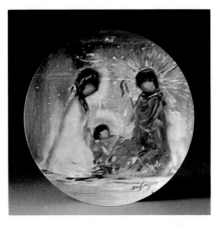

84-F4-1.4

1979 The Nativity
Artist: Ted DeGrazia
Prices: Issue $50.00; 1981 High $68.00; Low $48.00; Close $68.00; Up $20.00

84-F4-1.1

1976 The Festival of Lights
Artist: Ted DeGrazia
Prices: Issue $45.00; 1981 High $185.00;
Low $125.00; Close $185.00; Up $60.00

84-F4-1.2

1977 The Bell of Hope
Artist: Ted DeGrazia
Prices: Issue $45.00; 1981 High $130.00;
Low $50.00; Close $130.00; Up $80.00

84-F4-1.3

1978 Little Madonna
Artist: Ted DeGrazia
Prices: Issue $45.00; 1981 High $165.00;
Low $90.00; Close $165.00; Up $75.00

84-F4-1.5

1980 Little Pima Indian Drummer Boy
Artist: Ted DeGrazia
Prices: Issue $50.00; 1981 High $70.00;
Low $50.00; Close $70.00; Up $20.00

84-F4-1.6

1981 Little Prayer—The Christmas Angel
Artist: Ted DeGrazia
Prices: Issue $55.00; 1981 High $60.00;
Low $55.00; Close $60.00; Up $5.00

84-F4-1.7

1982 The Blue Boy
Artist: Ted DeGrazia
Issue price: $60.00

Famous Clowns Series

Artist: Red Skelton. Artist's signature
  appears on front
China banded in gold
Diameter: 21.6 centimeters (8½ inches)
No hanger
Edition size limited to 10,000
Numbered without certificate

84-F4-2.1

1976 Freddie the Freeloader
Artist: Red Skelton
Prices: Issue $55.00; 1981 High $450.00;
Low $360.00; Close $450.00; Up $90.00

84-F4-2.2

1977 W. C. Fields
Artist: Red Skelton
Prices: Issue $55.00; 1981 High $123.00;
Low $80.00; Close $123.00; Up $43.00

DeGrazia Children Series

Artist: Ted DeGrazia. Artist's signature
  appears on front; first 500
  autographed on back
China banded in gold
Diameter: 26 centimeters (10¼ inches)
No hanger
Edition size limited to 10,000
Numbered without certificate

84-F4-4.1

1978 Flower Girl
Artist: Ted DeGrazia
Prices: Issue $45.00; 1981 High $160.00;
Low $88.00; Close $157.00; Up $69.00

84-F4-4.2

1979 Flower Boy
Artist: Ted DeGrazia
Prices: Issue $45.00; 1981 High $110.00;
Low $63.00; Close $110.00; Up $47.00

Irene Spencer's Special Requests

Artist: Irene Spencer. Artist's signature
  appears on front
China with gold design on border
Diameter: 26 centimeters (10¼ inches)
No hanger
Edition size limited to 10,000
Numbered without certificate

84-F4-7.1

1978 Hug Me
Artist: Irene Spencer
Prices: Issue $55.00; 1981 High $92.00;
Low $90.00; Close $90.00; No Change

84-F4-7.2

1978 Sleep Little Baby
Artist: Irene Spencer
Prices: Issue $65.00; 1981 High $75.00;
Low $67.00; Close $67.00; Down $2.00

84-F4-2.3

1978 Happy
Artist: Red Skelton
Prices: Issue $55.00; 1981 High $110.00;
Low $75.00; Close $110.00; Up $35.00

84-F4-2.4

1979 The Pledge
Artist: Red Skelton
Prices: Issue $55.00; 1981 High $110.00;
Low $77.00; Close $110.00; Up $33.00

84-F4-4.3

1980 Little Cocopah Indian Girl
Artist: Ted DeGrazia
Prices: Issue $50.00; 1981 High $62.00;
Low $50.00; Close $62.00; Up $12.00

84-F4-4.4

1981 Beautiful Burden
Artist: Ted DeGrazia
Prices: Issue $50.00; 1981 High $50.00;
Low $50.00; Close $50.00; No Change

84-F4-4.5

1982 Merry Little Indian
Artist: Ted DeGrazia
Issue price: $55.00

Classical American Beauties

Artist: Vincent. Artist's signature
   appears on front
China banded in gold
Diameter: 26 centimeters (10¼ inches)
No hanger
Edition size limited to 7,500
Numbered without certificate

84-F4-8.1

1979 Colleen
Artist: Vincent
Prices: Issue $60.00; 1981 High $96.00;
Low $74.00; Close $96.00; Up $22.00

84-F4-8.2

1979 Heather
Artist: Vincent
Prices: Issue $60.00; 1981 High $72.00;
Low $55.00; Close $68.00; Up $13.00

84-F4-8.3

1980 Dawn
Artist: Vincent
Prices: Issue $60.00; 1981 High $62.00;
Low $60.00; Close $62.00; Up $2.00

84-F4-8.4

1981 Eve
Artist: Vincent
Issue price: $60.00

Playful Memories Series

Artist: Su Etém. Artist's signature
   appears on front
China banded in gold
Diameter: 22.3 centimeters
   (8¾ inches)
No hanger
Edition size limited to 10,000
Numbered without certificate

84-F4-10.1

1981 Renee
Artist: Su Etém
Issue price: $39.50

84-F4-10.2

1982 Jeremy
Artist: Su Etém
Issue price: $42.50

Bringing Home the Tree 84-F64-1.1
1970 Franklin Mint *Rockwell Christmas*
Detail from the first sterling silver collector's
plate, which is also the first plate by
Norman Rockwell

The Franklin Mint, the world's largest private mint, was established in the Philadelphia vicinity in 1965 by Joseph Segel. The firm specializes in porcelain collectibles, sculptures, fine art prints, jewelry, and has several international subsidiaries and branches.

The Franklin Mint entered the limited-edition plate field in 1970 with the six-plate *Rockwell Christmas* series, crafted in sterling silver.

The *Rockwell Christmas* series is the only one to be designed especially for the collector's plate market by the artist, Norman Rockwell. One of the most widely-known artists in the twentieth century, Norman Rockwell created well over 3,000 works including 323 *Saturday Evening Post* covers as well as numerous illustrations for *Life, Look, Boys Life,* and annual Boy Scout calendars. His works hang in a number of museums: from the Smithsonian Institution and the Metropolitan Museum of Art in New York, to the Corner House in the artist's adopted home of Stockbridge, Massachusetts.

Rockwell Christmas Series

Artist: Norman Rockwell. Artist's
   signature appears on front
Etched sterling silver
Diameter: 20.3 centimeters (8 inches)
No hanger
Edition size: As indicated
Numbered, with certificate since 1972

84-F64-1.1

1970 Bringing Home the Tree
Artist: Norman Rockwell/Edition: 18,321
Prices: Issue $100.00; 1981 High $390.00;
Low $380.00; Close $390.00; Up $10.00

84-F64-1.2

1971 Under the Mistletoe
Artist: Norman Rockwell/Edition: 24,792
Prices: Issue $100.00; 1981 High $165.00;
Low $160.00; Close $160.00; Down $5.00

84-F64-1.3

1972 The Carolers
Artist: Norman Rockwell/Edition: 29,074
Prices: Issue $125.00; 1981 High $165.00;
Low $162.00; Close $162.00; Down $3.00

84-F64-1.4

1973 Trimming the Tree
Artist: Norman Rockwell/Edition: 18,010
Prices: Issue $125.00; 1981 High $173.00;
Low $170.00; Close $173.00; Up $3.00

84-F64-1.5

1974 Hanging the Wreath
Artist: Norman Rockwell/Edition: 12,822
Prices: Issue $175.00; 1981 High $173.00;
Low $170.00; Close $173.00; Up $3.00

84-F64-1.6

1975 Home for Christmas
Artist: Norman Rockwell/Edition: 11,059
Prices: Issue $180.00; 1981 High $200.00;
Low $175.00; Close $200.00; Up $25.00

In 1831 Jabez Gorham, a silversmith, established the Gorham Corporation. Today a division of Textron, the firm is one of the world's largest producers of sterling and hollowware, figurines, and ornaments.

Gorham Corporation acquired crystal and china manufacturing companies in 1970, enabling it to produce limited-edition plates in china as well as silver.

Gorham's *Rockwell Four Seasons* series, which began in 1971 and ended in 1980, was comprised of four plates each year (spring, summer, fall, and winter). A *Christmas* series, also with artwork by Norman Rockwell, was started in 1974. The *Irene Spencer Annual* series began in 1974. The *DeGrazia Children* series and the *Sugar and Spice* series began in 1976 with the latter ending in 1979. The *Prince Tatters* series was started in 1977 and ended in 1980.

Since 1978, Fairmont China has made the *DeGrazia Children* plates (see United States, Fairmont). The *Sugar and Spice* and *Prince Tatters* series are produced for Kern Collectibles by Gorham (see United States, Kern Collectibles).

One of the most widely-known artists in the twentieth century, Norman Rockwell created well over 3,000 works including 323 *Saturday Evening Post* covers as well as numerous illustrations for *Life, Look, Boys Life,* and annual Boy Scout calendars. His works hang in a number of museums: from the Smithsonian Institution and the Metropolitan Museum of Art in New York, to the Corner House in the artist's adopted home of Stockbridge, Massachusetts. Irene Spencer received her training at Chicago's Academy of Art and the Chicago Art Institute, where she developed her distinctive style, reminiscent of the Old Masters. In addition to her accomplishments as a fine artist, she has written and illustrated children's books and worked as a newspaper cartoonist. Ted DeGrazia, one-time apprentice to the great Mexican muralist Diego Rivera, first came to international attention in 1960 when his work was featured on a UNICEF card. Since then, his stylized re-creations of Southwestern subjects and themes have made him one of the most instantly recognizable of American artists. Born in The Hague, The Netherlands, Leo Jansen spent his youth in Indonesia, where he developed his skills as a portrait painter by sketching the bronze-skinned Malay children. He returned to The Netherlands to study at the Academy of Fine Arts and later refined his work in the famous "Pigalle" section of Paris.

GORHAM

EST. 1831

Rockwell Four Seasons Series

Artist: Norman Rockwell. Artist's
  signature appears on front
China banded in 24k gold
Diameter: 26.7 centimeters (10½ inches)
No hanger
Edition size undisclosed, limited by
  year of issue
Not numbered, without certificate
Issued in sets of four

84-G58-1.1-1
1971 A Boy and His Dog;
        A Boy Meets His Dog
Artist: Norman Rockwell
Prices: Issue $50.00; 1981 High $480.00;
Low $470.00; Close $470.00; Down $10.00

84-G58-1.1-2
1971 Adventurers Between Adventures

84-G58-1.1-3
1971 A Mysterious Malady

84-G58-1.1-4
1971 Price of Parenthood

1972 Young Love; Flying Colors
Artist: Norman Rockwell
Prices: Issue $60.00; 1981 High $210.00;
Low $200.00; Close $210.00; Up $5.00

1972 Beguiling Buttercup

1972 A Scholarly Pace

**1973 The Ages of Love;
Sweet Song So Young**
Artist: Norman Rockwell
Prices: Issue $60.00; 1981 High $380.00;
Low $340.00; Close $380.00; Up $40.00

1974 Grandpa and Me; Day Dreamers
Artist: Norman Rockwell
Prices: Issue $60.00; 1981 High $165.00;
Low $160.00; Close $160.00; Down $5.00

1974 Goin' Fishin'

1974 Pensive Pals

84-G58-1.2-4

1972 Downhill Daring

84-G58-1.3-2

1973 Flowers in Tender Bloom

84-G58-1.3-3

1973 Fondly Do We Remember

84-G58-1.3-4

1973 Gaily Sharing Vintage

84-G58-1.4-4

1974 Gay Blades

84-G58-1.5-1

1975 Me and My Pal;
    Young Man's Fancy
Artist: Norman Rockwell
Prices: Issue $70.00; 1981 High $250.00;
Low $220.00; Close $240.00; Up $20.00

84-G58-1.6-1
1976 Grand Pals; Soaring Spirits
Artist: Norman Rockwell
Prices: Issue $70.00; 1981 High $300.00;
Low $278.00; Close $278.00; Down $7.00

84-G58-1.6-2
1976 Fish Finders

84-G58-1.6-3
1976 Ghostly Gourds

84-G58-1.7-1
1977 Going on Sixteen; Sweet Serenade
Artist: Norman Rockwell
Prices: Issue $75.00; 1981 High $275.00;
Low $240.00; Close $275.00; Up $35.00

1975 Fisherman's Paradise   **84-G58-1.5-2**

84-G58-1.5-3   1975 Disastrous Daring

1975 A Lickin' Good Bath   **84-G58-1.5-4**

84-G58-1.6-4

1976 Snow Sculpture

1977 Sheer Agony   **84-G58-1.7-2**

84-G58-1.7-3   1977 Pilgrimage

1977 Chilling Chore   **84-G58-1.7-4**

84-G58-1.8-1

1978 The Tender Years; Spring Tonic
Artist: Norman Rockwell
Prices: Issue $100.00; 1981 High $110.00;
Low $105.00; Close $105.00; Down $5.00

84-G58-1.8-2

1978 Cool Aid

84-G58-1.8-3

1978 Chilly Reception

84-G58-1.9-1

1979 A Helping Hand;
Closed for Business
Artist: Norman Rockwell
Prices: Issue $100.00; 1981 High $115.00;
Low $100.00; Close $110.00; Down $5.00

84-G58-1.10-1

1980 Dad's Boy; In His Spirit
Artist: Norman Rockwell
Prices: Issue $135.00; 1981 High $135.00;
Low $135.00; Close $135.00; No Change

84-G58-1.10-2

1980 Trout Dinner

84-G58-1.10-3

1980 Careful Aim

84-G58-1.8-4

1978 New Year Look

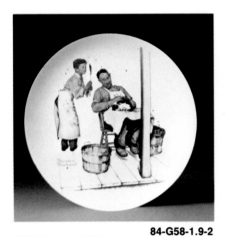

84-G58-1.9-2

1979 Swatters Rights

84-G58-1.9-3

1979 The Coal Season's Coming

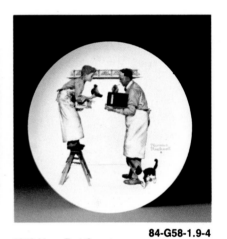

84-G58-1.9-4

1979 Year End Count

84-G58-1.10-4

1980 Ski Skills

Rockwell Christmas Series

Artist: Norman Rockwell. Artist's
   signature appears on front
China banded in 24k gold
Diameter: 21.6 centimeters
   (8½ inches)
No hanger
Edition size undisclosed, limited by year
   of issue
Not numbered, without certificate

1974 Tiny Tim
Artist: Norman Rockwell
Prices: Issue $12.50; 1981 High $61.00;
Low $53.00; Close $61.00; Up $8.00

84-G58-3.1

1975 Good Deeds
Artist: Norman Rockwell
Prices: Issue $17.50; 1981 High $52.00;
Low $43.00; Close $52.00; Up $9.00

84-G58-3.2

1979 Santa's Helpers
Artist: Norman Rockwell
Prices: Issue $24.50; 1981 High $25.00;
Low $24.50; Close $25.00; Up $.50

84-G58-3.6

1980 Letter to Santa
Artist: Norman Rockwell
Prices: Issue $27.50; 1981 High $27.50;
Low $27.50; Close $27.50; No Change

84-G58-3.7

Irene Spencer Annual

Artist: Irene Spencer. Artist's signature
   appears on front
China banded in 24k gold
Diameter: 21.6 centimeters
   (8½ inches)
No hanger
Edition size limited to announced
   quantity of 10,000
Not numbered, without certificate

1974 Dear Child
Artist: Irene Spencer
Prices: Issue $37.50; 1981 High $125.00
Low $114.00; Close $125.00; Up $11.00

84-G58-4.1

1975 Promises to Keep
Artist: Irene Spencer
Prices: Issue $40.00; 1981 High $35.00
Low $35.00; Close $35.00; No Change

84-G58-4.2

84-G58-3.3

1976 Christmas Trio
Artist: Norman Rockwell
Prices: Issue $19.50; 1981 High $38.00;
Low $22.00; Close $38.00; Up $16.00

84-G58-3.4

1977 Yuletide Reckoning
Artist: Norman Rockwell
Prices: Issue $19.50; 1981 High $50.00;
Low $38.00; Close $50.00; Up $12.00

84-G58-3.5

1978 Planning Christmas Visits
Artist: Norman Rockwell
Prices: Issue $24.50; 1981 High $33.00;
Low $30.00; Close $30.00; Down $3.00

84-G58-3.8

1981 Santa Plans His Visit
Artist: Norman Rockwell
Prices: Issue $29.50; 1981 High $29.50;
Low $29.50; Close $29.50; No Change

84-G58-3.9

1982 The Jolly Coachman
Artist: Norman Rockwell
Issue price: $29.50

DeGrazia Children Series

Artist: Ted DeGrazia. Artist's signature
   appears on front
China banded in 24k gold
Diameter: 26.7 centimeters
   (10½ inches)
No hanger
Edition size: As indicated
Not numbered, without certificate

84-G58-5.1

1976 Los Niños
Artist: Ted DeGrazia / Edition: 5,000
Prices: Issue $35.00; 1981 High $805.00;
Low $600.00; Close $805.00; Up $205.00

84-G58-5.2

1977 The White Dove
Artist: Ted DeGrazia / Edition: 10,000
Prices: Issue $40.00; 1981 High $128.00;
Low $64.00; Close $128.00; Up $64.00

Sugar and Spice Series

Artist: Leo Jansen. Artist's signature
   appears on front
China banded in 24k gold
Diameter: 21.6 centimeters
   (8½ inches)
No hanger
Edition size limited to 7,500
Numbered without certificate

84-G58-6.1

1976 Dana and Debbie
Artist: Leo Jansen
Prices: Issue $40.00; 1981 High $110.00;
Low $60.00; Close $110.00; Up $50.00

84-G58-6.2

1977 Becky and Baby
Artist: Leo Jansen
Prices: Issue $42.50; 1981 High $85.00;
Low $37.00; Close $85.00; Up $48.00

Prince Tatters Series

Artist: Leo Jansen. Artist's signature
   appears on front
China banded in 24k gold
Diameter: 21.6 centimeters
   (8½ inches)
No hanger
Edition size limited to 7,500
Numbered without certificate

84-G58-8.1

1977 Johnny and Duke
Artist: Leo Jansen
Prices: Issue $40.00; 1981 High $56.00;
Low $43.00; Close $56.00; Up $13.00

84-G58-6.3

84-G58-6.4

1978 Jeanette and Julie
Artist: Leo Jansen
Prices: Issue $47.50; 1981 High $62.00;
Low $45.00; Close $62.00; Up $17.00

1979 Ramona and Rachel
Artist: Leo Jansen
Prices: Issue $50.00; 1981 High $80.00;
Low $50.00; Close $80.00; Up $30.00

84-G58-8.2

84-G58-8.3

84-G58-8.4

1978 Randy and Rex
Artist: Leo Jansen
Prices: Issue $42.50; 1981 High $70.00;
Low $38.00; Close $70.00; Up $32.00

1979 Furry Friends
Artist: Leo Jansen
Prices: Issue $47.50; 1981 High 50.00
Low $40.00; Close $50.00; Up $10.00

1980 Benji's Burro
Artist: Leo Jansen
Prices: Issue $50.00; 1981 High $97.00;
Low $50.00; Close $97.00; Up $47.00

**Incolay Studios
of California**

Incolay Studios has been creating cameo *objets d'art* in Incolay stone since 1965. The manufacturing process by which Incolay stone is created is a closely guarded secret, but it is acknowledged that the process includes the addition of a range of quartz-based minerals to replicate the coloring and weight of semi-precious stone cameos of the past.

Incolay Studios began its first series of collector's plates, the *Romantic Poets Collection,* in 1977. The series is inspired by the poetry of early nineteenth-century poets. In 1979, a second series of cameo plates, the *Great Romances of History Collection,* began.

Gayle Bright Appleby, designer of the first four issues in the *Romantic Poets Collection,* is widely known for the intricate detail of her sculptures in Incolay stone and in bronze, silver, and gold. Roger Akers, the present sculptor, was schooled at the Cooper School of Art and the Art Institute of Chicago. His work has been selected by the Illinois Arts Council for permanent museum display. Carl Romanelli, sculptor of the *Great Romances of History Collection,* has works on display throughout the world. One of the most famous is his bust of John Henry Cardinal Newman, which is on permanent display at the Vatican.

Romantic Poets Collection

Artist: As indicated. Artist's
    signature appears on front
Incolay stone with high relief cameos
Diameter: 26 centimeters
    (10¼ inches)
Attached back hanger
Edition size undisclosed, limited by
    announced period of issue
Numbered with certificate

84-I31-1.1
1977 She Walks in Beauty
Artist: Gayle Bright Appleby
Prices: Issue $60.00; 1981 High $280.00;
Low $250.00; Close $275.00; Up $25.00

84-I31-1.2
1978 A Thing of Beauty Is a Joy Forever
Artist: Gayle Bright Appleby
Prices: Issue $60.00; 1981 High $80.00;
Low $80.00; Close $80.00; No Change

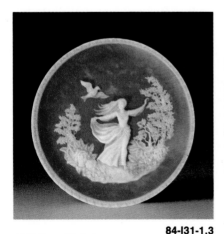

84-I31-1.3
1979 To a Skylark
Artist: Gayle Bright Appleby
Prices: Issue $65.00; 1981 High $65.00;
Los $65.00; Close $65.00; No Change

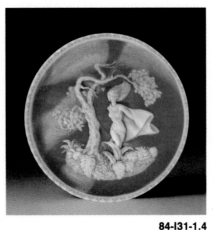

84-I31-1.4
1980 She Was a Phantom of Delight
Artist: Gayle Bright Appleby
Prices: Issue $65.00; 1981 High $70.00;
Low $65.00; Close $70.00; Up $5.00

84-I31-1.5
1981 The Kiss
Artist: Roger Akers
Prices: Issue $65.00; 1981 High $65.00;
Low $65.00; Close $65.00; No Change

Great Romances of History Collection

Artist: Carl Romanelli. Artist's signature
    appears on front
Incolay stone with high relief cameos
Diameter: 26 centimeters
    (10¼ inches)
Attached back hanger
Edition size undisclosed, limited by
    announced period of issue
Numbered with certificate

84-I31-3.1

1979 Antony and Cleopatra
Artist: Carl Romanelli
Prices: Issue $65.00; 1981 High $68.00;
Low $65.00; Close $68.00; Up $3.00

84-I31-3.2

1980 The Taj Mahal Lovers
Artist: Carl Romanelli
Prices: Issue $65.00; 1981 High $73.00;
Low $65.00; Close $73.00; Up $8.00

84-I31-3.3

1981 Lancelot and Guinevere
Artist: Carl Romanelli
Prices: Issue $65.00; 1981 High $65.00;
Low $65.00; Close $65.00; No Change

84-I31-3.4

No information available at press time

She Walks in Beauty 84-I31-1.1
1977 Incolay *Romantic Poets*
Detail from the first cameo-carved
collector's plate

International

International Silver Company, one of the world's largest manufacturers of silver and silver-plated ware, traces its origin to a pewter shop established by Ashbil Griswold in Meriden in 1808. Rogers Brothers, developers of a silver electroplating process, became affiliated with the firm in 1862, and International Silver was incorporated in 1898.

The firm introduced limited-edition pewter plates in 1972 with its six-plate United States Bicentennial *We Are One* series. This series ended in 1975.

Sculptor Manuel de Oliveira, Portuguese-born creator of the *We Are One* series, received widespread recognition for his bicentennial creation. The collection has been acquired by the Smithsonian Institution in Washington, D.C.

We Are One (Bicentennial Series)

Artist: Manuel de Oliveira (after works by Carl Sundberg). Artist's signature appears on back
Pewter with sculpted designs in high relief
Diameter: 22.3 centimeters (8¾ inches)
Attached back hanger
Edition size limited to 7,500
Numbered with certificate

84-I61-1.1
1972 Declaration of Independence
Artist: Manuel de Oliveira
Prices: Issue $40.00; 1981 High $360.00;
Low $320.00; Close $360.00; Up $40.00

84-I61-1.2
1973 The Midnight Ride of Paul Revere
Artist: Manuel de Oliveira
Prices: Issue $40.00; 1981 High $145.00;
Low $145.00; Close $145.00; No Change

84-I61-1.3
1973 Stand at Concord Bridge
Artist: Manuel de Oliveira
Prices: Issue $40.00; 1981 High $140.00;
Low $120.00; Close $140.00; Up $20.00

84-I61-1.4
1974 Crossing the Delaware
Artist: Manuel de Oliveira
Prices: Issue $50.00; 1981 High $83.00;
Low $78.00; Close $83.00; Up $5.00

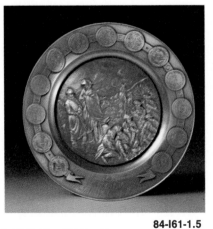

84-I61-1.5
1974 Battle of Valley Forge
Artist: Manuel de Oliveira
Prices: Issue $50.00; 1981 High $70.00;
Low $70.00; Close $70.00; No Change

84-I61-1.6
1975 Surrender at Yorktown
Artist: Manuel de Oliveira
Prices: Issue $50.00; 1981 High $65.00;
Low $55.00; Close $65.00; Up $10.00

The story of Kern Collectibles dates to 1969 when Oscar L. Kern founded Commemorative Imports, a distributor of limited-edition collectibles. Mr. Kern expanded his business one step further in 1972 with the establishment of Kern Collectibles. Kern Collectibles issues limited-edition plates produced especially for the company by several of the world's fine china manufacturers.

The *Runci Mother's Day* series started in 1977 and was completed with the fourth issue in 1980. *Leaders of Tomorrow* began in 1980 and will comprise four issues by Leo Jansen.

Italian-born Edward Runci is a leading contemporary exponent of Impressionism. Born in The Hague, The Netherlands, Leo Jansen spent his youth in Indonesia, where he developed his skills as a portrait painter by sketching the bronze-skinned Malay children. He returned to the Netherlands to study at the Academy of Fine Arts and later refined his work in the famous "Pigalle" section of Paris.

Runci Mother's Day Series

Artist: Edward Runci. Artist's signature
  appears on front
Overglaze-decorated porcelain banded
  in gold
Diameter: 19 centimeters (7½ inches)
Attached back hanger
Edition size limited to 5,000
Numbered without certificate

84-K20-6.1

1977 Darcy
Artist: Edward Runci
Prices: Issue $50.00; 1981 High $66.00;
Low $50.00; Close $66.00; Up $16.00

84-K20-6.2

1978 A Moment to Reflect
Artist: Edward Runci
Prices: Issue $55.00; 1981 High $48.00;
Low $48.00; Close $48.00; No Change

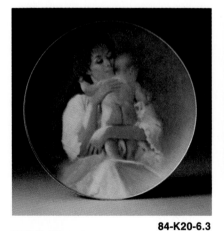

84-K20-6.3

1979 Fulfillment
Artist: Edward Runci
Prices: Issue $45.00; 1981 High $58.00;
Low $48.00; Close $58.00; Up $10.00

84-K20-6.4

1980 A Renewal of Faith
Artist: Edward Runci
Price: Issue $45.00; 1981 High $50.00;
Low $45.00; Close $50.00; Up $5.00

Leaders of Tomorrow Series

Artist: Leo Jansen. Artist's signature
  appears on front
China banded in gold
Diameter: 21.6 centimeters (8½ inches)
No hanger
Edition size limited to 9,800
Numbered with certificate

84-K20-7.1

1980 Future Physician
Artist: Leo Jansen
Issue price: $50.00

84-K20-7.2

1981 Future Farmer
Artist: Leo Jansen
Issue price: $50.00

84-K20-7.3

1982 Future Florist
Artist: Leo Jansen
Issue price: $50.00

Over the Rainbow 84-K41-1.1
1977 Edwin M. Knowles *Wizard of Oz*
Detail from the first collector's plate ever
based on a motion picture

The Edwin M. Knowles heritage of fine china can be traced to the early nineteenth century when Isaac Knowles, father of Edwin, established the family firm — Knowles, Taylor and Knowles — in East Liverpool, Ohio. The site was chosen for its proximity to deposits of high-quality kaolin clay. The firm became well known for its production of Lotus ware.

After apprenticing with Knowles, Taylor and Knowles, Edwin established his own company in Newell, West Virginia, and became a pre-eminent force in American china. He was honored by election to the presidency of the United States Potters Association.

After his death, the company ceased operations for a period of time until entering into an affiliation with the Bradford Exchange in order to preserve its time-honored name.

Since 1975 the Edwin M. Knowles name has appeared on issues certified by the Rockwell Society of America (see United States, Rockwell Society). The *Wizard of Oz,* first proprietary series to bear the name of Knowles, began in 1977 and ended in 1980. The *Americana Holidays* series and the *Gone With the Wind* series, which is endorsed by Metro-Goldwyn-Mayer, began in 1978. Knowles' latest series is the *Csatari Grandparent Plate* series, which began in 1980.

Knowles has commissioned a number of important contemporary artists to create its plates, including: James Auckland, whose stylistic blend of fantasy and realism is uniquely suited to the *Wizard of Oz* series; Raymond Kursár, twice recipient of the Award of Merit from the Society of Illustrators and well-known for his prize-winning Broadway show posters; Don Spaulding, Norman Rockwell protégé and a leading exponent of authentic historical detail in painting; and Joseph Csatari, winner of the Gold Medal from the Society of Illustrators of New York and designer of a commemorative stamp which took his work to an audience of more than one hundred countries.

Wizard of Oz Series

Artist: James Auckland. Artist's
signature appears on front
China
Diameter: 21.6 centimeters
(8½ inches) through 1979; 25.4
centimeters (10 inches) for 1980
plate
No hanger
Edition size undisclosed, limited by
announced period of issue
Numbered with certificate

84-K41-1.1
1977 Over the Rainbow
Artist: James Auckland
Prices: Issue $19.00; 1981 High $220.00;
Low $100.00; Close $220.00; Up $120.00

84-K41-1.2
1978 If I Only Had a Brain
Artist: James Auckland
Prices: Issue $19.00; 1981 High $43.00;
Low $40.00; Close $43.00; Up $3.00

84-K41-1.3
1978 If I Only Had a Heart
Artist: James Auckland
Prices: Issue $19.00; 1981 High $42.00;
Low $35.00; Close $42.00; Up $7.00

84-K41-1.4
1978 If I Were King of the Forest
Artist: James Auckland
Prices: Issue $19.00; 1981 High $32.00;
Low $30.00; Close $32.00; Up $2.00

84-K41-1.5
1979 The Wicked Witch of the West
Artist: James Auckland
Prices: Issue $19.00; 1981 High $29.00;
Low $27.00; Close $29.00; Up $2.00

84-K41-1.6

1979 Follow the Yellow Brick Road
Artist: James Auckland
Prices: Issue $19.00; 1981 High $25.00;
Low $20.00; Close 25.00; Up $5.00

84-K41-1.7

1979 Wonderful Wizard of Oz
Artist: James Auckland
Prices: Issue $19.00; 1981 High $25.00;
Low $20.00; Close $25.00; Up $5.00

84-K41-1.8

1980 The Grand Finale
(We're Off to See the Wizard)
Artist: James Auckland
Prices: Issue $24.00; 1981 High $24.00;
Low $24.00; Close $24.00; No Change

Americana Holidays Series

Artist: Don Spaulding. Artist's signature
  appears on front
China
Diameter: 21.6 centimeters
  (8½ inches)
No hanger
Edition size undisclosed, limited by
  period of issue
Numbered with certificate

84-K41-2.1

1978 Fourth of July
Artist: Don Spaulding
Prices: Issue $26.00; 1981 High $39.00;
Low $34.00; Close $39.00; Up $5.00

84-K41-2.2

1979 Thanksgiving
Artist: Don Spaulding
Prices: Issue $26.00; 1981 High $77.00;
Low $28.00; Close $77.00; Up $49.00

Gone With the Wind Series

Artist: Raymond Kursár. Artist's
  signature appears on front
China
Diameter: 21.6 centimeters
  (8½ inches)
No hanger
Edition size undisclosed, limited by
  period of issue
Numbered with certificate

84-K41-3.1

1978 Scarlett
Artist: Raymond Kursár
Prices: Issue $21.50; 1981 High $290.00;
Low $110.00; Close $290.00; Up $180.00

84-K41-3.2

1979 Ashley
Artist: Raymond Kursár
Prices: Issue $21.50; 1981 High $70.00;
Low $23.00; Close $70.00; Up $47.00

84-K41-2.3

1980 Easter
Artist: Don Spaulding
Prices: Issue $26.00; 1981 High $55.00;
Low $34.00; Close $55.00; Up $21.00

84-K41-2.4

1981 Valentine's Day
Artist: Don Spaulding
Prices: Issue $26.00; 1981 High $26.00;
Low $26.00; Close $26.00; No Change

84-K41-2.5

1982 Father's Day
Artist: Don Spaulding
Issue price: $26.00

84-K41-3.3

1980 Melanie
Artist: Raymond Kursár
Prices: Issue $21.50; 1981 High $21.50;
Low $21.50; Close $21.50; No Change

84-K41-3.4

1981 Rhett
Artist: Raymond Kursár
Prices: Issue $23.50; 1981 High $23.50;
Low $23.50; Close $23.50; No Change

84-K41-3.5

1982 Mammy Lacing Scarlett
Artist: Raymond Kursár
Issue price: $23.50

Csatari Grandparent Plate Series

Artist: Joseph Csatari. Artist's signature
 appears on front
China
Diameter: 21.6 centimeters
 (8½ inches)
No hanger
Edition size undisclosed, limited by
 period of issue
Numbered with certificate

84-K41-4.1
1980 Bedtime Story
Artist: Joseph Csatari
Prices: Issue $18.00; 1981 High $58.00;
Low $18.00; Close $58.00; Up $40.00

84-K41-4.2
1981 The Skating Lesson
Artist: Joseph Csatari
Prices: Issue $20.00; 1981 High $20.00;
Low $20.00; Close $20.00; No Change

84-K41-4.3
No information available at press time

Declaration of Independence 84-I61-1.1
1972 International *We Are One*
Detail showing the high relief designs of
the first pewter collector's plate

LENOX

Walter Scott Lenox and his partner, Jonathan Coxon, Sr., established the Ceramic Art Company in Trenton, New Jersey, in 1889. In 1895 Lenox bought out Coxon and operated the business alone until it was reorganized in 1906 as Lenox, Inc. The plant later moved to Pomona. The firm's early products were bowls, vases, figurines, and later, tableware. All were made in "American Belleek," named for the town in Ireland where this creamy, ivory-tinted ware was first produced.

During World War I, Lenox was commissioned to supply President Wilson with a complete 1,700-piece dinner service, the first wholly American china ever used in the White House. Later, both Presidents Franklin Roosevelt and Harry Truman commissioned Lenox to make sets of dinnerware. In 1981, the Reagan administration commissioned Lenox to create a 4,372-piece dinnerware set for the White House.

In 1970 Lenox introduced its *Boehm Bird* series using paintings by artist Edward Marshall Boehm. The *Boehm Woodland Wildlife* series began in 1973 with artwork adapted from original Boehm sculptures.

From a background as farmer and veterinarian, Edward Marshall Boehm became a full-time sculptor in 1949, and at his death in 1969 was recognized as one of America's greatest wildlife artists. His faithful replication of nature scenes won a substantial following and his work has appeared in the collections of Dwight D. Eisenhower, John F. Kennedy, Lyndon B. Johnson, Queen Elizabeth II, and Pope John XXIII, as well as in many prestigious museums, including the Smithsonian Institution.

Boehm Bird Series

Artist: Edward Marshall Boehm
  Artist's name appears on back
China with 24k gold design on border
Diameter: 26.7 centimeters (10½ inches)
No hanger
Edition size undisclosed
Not numbered, without certificate

84-L18-1.4

1973 Meadowlark
Artist: Edward Marshall Boehm
Prices: Issue $41.00; 1981 High $75.00;
Low $70.00; Close $75.00; Up $5.00

84-L18-1.1

1970 Wood Thrush
Artist: Edward Marshall Boehm
Prices: Issue $35.00; 1981 High $325.00;
Low $295.00; Close $325.00; Up $30.00

84-L18-1.2

1971 Goldfinch
Artist: Edward Marshall Boehm
Prices: Issue $35.00; 1981 High $115.00;
Low $110.00; Close $112.00; Up $2.00

84-L18-1.3

1972 Mountain Bluebird
Artist: Edward Marshall Boehm
Prices: Issue $37.50; 1981 High $85.00;
Low $60.00; Close $80.00; Up $20.00

84-L18-1.5

1974 Rufous Hummingbird
Artist: Edward Marshall Boehm
Prices: Issue $45.00; 1981 High $80.00;
Low $66.00; Close $80.00; Up $14.00

84-L18-1.6

1975 American Redstart
Artist: Edward Marshall Boehm
Prices: Issue $50.00; 1981 High $75.00;
Low $50.00; Close $75.00; Up $25.00

84-L18-1.7

1976 Cardinal
Artist: Edward Marshall Boehm
Prices: Issue $53.00; 1981 High $65.00;
Low $60.00; Close $65.00; Up $5.00

84-L18-1.8

1977 Robins
Artist: Edward Marshall Boehm
Prices: Issue $55.00; 1981 High $56.00;
Low $53.00; Close $56.00; Up $3.00

84-L18-1.9

1978 Mockingbirds
Artist: Edward Marshall Boehm
Prices: Issue $58.00; 1981 High $76.00;
Low $63.00; Close $76.00; Up $13.00

84-L18-1.10

1979 Golden-Crowned Kinglets
Artist: Edward Marshall Boehm
Prices: Issue $65.00; 1981 High $65.00;
Low $65.00; Close $65.00; No Change

Boehm Woodland Wildlife Series

Artist: Edward Marshall Boehm
  Artist's name appears on back
China with 24k gold design on border
Diameter: 26.7 centimeters (10½ inches)
No hanger
Edition size undisclosed
Not numbered, without certificate

84-L18-3.1

1973 Raccoons
Artist: Edward Marshall Boehm
Prices: Issue $50.00; 1981 High $80.00;
Low $76.00; Close $80.00; Up $4.00

84-L18-3.2

1974 Red Foxes
Artist: Edward Marshall Boehm
Prices: Issue $52.50; 1981 High $56.00;
Low $46.00; Close $46.00; Down $7.00

84-L18-3.6

1978 Whitetail Deer
Artist: Edward Marshall Boehm
Prices: Issue $70.00; 1981 High $60.00;
Low $52.00; Close $60.00; Up $8.00

84-L18-3.7

1979 Squirrels
Artist: Edward Marshall Boehm
Prices: Issue $76.00; 1981 High $75.00;
Low $75.00; Close $75.00; No Change

84-L18-1.11
1980 Black-Throated Blue Warblers
Artist: Edward Marshall Boehm
Prices: Issue $80.00; 1981 High $83.00;
Low $80.00; Close $83.00; Up $3.00

84-L18-1.12
1981 Eastern Phoebes
Artist: Edward Marshall Boehm
Prices: Issue $90.00; 1981 High $90.00;
Low $90.00; Close $90.00; No Change

84-L18-3.3
1975 Cottontail Rabbits
Artist: Edward Marshall Boehm
Prices: Issue $58.50; 1981 High $67.00;
Low $62.00; Close $67.00; Up $5.00

84-L18-3.4
1976 Eastern Chipmunks
Artist: Edward Marshall Boehm
Prices: Issue $62.50; 1981 High $65.00;
Low $60.00; Close $65.00; Up $5.00

84-L18-3.5
1977 Beaver
Artist: Edward Marshall Boehm
Prices: Issue $67.50; 1981 High $70.00;
Low $65.00; Close $70.00; Up $5.00

84-L18-3.8
1980 Bobcats
Artist: Edward Marshall Boehm
Prices: Issue $92.50; 1981 High $92.50;
Low $92.50; Close $92.50; No Change

84-L18-3.9
1981 Martens
Artist: Edward Marshall Boehm
Prices: Issue $100.00; 1981 High $100.00;
Low $100.00; Close $100.00; No Change

Maker had
no photo at
press time

84-L18-3.10
1982 Otters
Artist: Edward Marshall Boehm
Issue price: $100.00

Morgantown Crystal

Floyd Jones and his father founded the Monongahela Valley Cut Glass company in 1912 at Morgantown, West Virginia. Their most famous design was an elegant pattern known as "Morgantown Rose." The company flourished under the direction of the Jones family for four generations. In 1977 John Heiner purchased the firm and renamed it Morgantown Crystal, recently expanding operations to include glass etching and engraving as well as cutting.

The first limited-edition collector's plate series to bear the Morgantown Crystal hallmark, *Yates' Country Ladies,* began in 1981.

Designs for issues in the series are by Michael Yates. Born in Pennsylvania, Yates studied at the Art Institute of Pittsburgh. His works appear in numerous public buildings and churches throughout America as well as in many private collections. Prominent figures who have commissioned his work include Gerald Ford, the late Golda Meir, Johnny Cash, and former First Lady Pat Nixon.

Michael Yates' Country Ladies Series

Artist: Michael Yates. Artist's signature appears on front
Full-lead crystal
Diameter: 22.6 centimeters (8⅞ inches)
No hanger
Edition size limited to 30,000
Numbered with certificate

84-M58-1.1

1981 Angelica
Artist: Michael Yates
Prices: Issue $75.00; 1981 High $75.00; Low $75.00; Close $75.00; No Change

84-M58-1.2

1982 Violet
Artist: Michael Yates
Issue price: $75.00

Pickard was established in Edgerton, Wisconsin, in 1894 by Wilder Austin Pickard, then moved to Chicago in 1897. For some forty years the Pickard China Studio, as the firm was then known, was a decorating company employing artists to hand paint white blanks of bowls, pitchers, and other items obtained from factories in Europe.

In 1920 Pickard was incorporated and in 1938 moved to Antioch, Illinois, the site of the present pottery. Here the firm began making its own fine china. Today Pickard, Inc. is headed by Henry A. Pickard, a third generation descendant of the founder, making it the only American china company in the hands of the founding family.

In 1970 Pickard introduced its *Lockhart Wildlife* series. These plates were issued in pairs during the first four years of the series, but from 1974 individual plates were issued. The *Christmas* series began in 1976, and in 1978 Pickard began the *Children of Renoir* series which ended in 1980. Pickard began its *Mother's Love* series in 1980 with artwork by Irene Spencer and in 1981 introduced *Oleg Cassini's Most Beautiful Women of All Time Collection.* The *Children of Mexico* series began in 1981 with artwork by Jorge Sanchez.

James Lockhart, an ardent naturalist and conservationist, is widely-known for his realistic portrayals of wild animals in their natural habitats. The designs for Pickard's *Christmas* and *Children of Renoir* series are reproductions of works by the Masters. Irene Spencer received her training at the Academy of Art and the Chicago Art Institute, where she developed her distinctive style, reminiscent of the Old Masters. In addition to her accomplishments as a fine artist, she has written and illustrated children's books and worked as a newspaper cartoonist. Oleg Cassini, the best known name in contemporary fashion, is also an accomplished artist. Born in Paris in 1913, Cassini is the son of Count and Countess Loiewski Cassini. As an adult, he renounced his right to the title of Count to become an American citizen. He received a law degree from the University of Florence and also graduated from Florence's prestigious Academia delle Belle Artis. During the 1940s he worked as a fashion designer in Hollywood for such celebrities as Gene Tierney and Grace Kelly. Former First Lady Jacqueline Kennedy named Cassini her official couturier. Mexican artist Jorge Sanchez studied at the Art Academy of San Carlos and has held numerous one-man shows throughout Mexico. In 1978 the Museum of Mexico City exhibited his series of twenty-one paintings depicting the life of Sor Juana Ines de la Cruz.

Lockhart Wildlife Series

Artist: James Lockhart. Artist's
   signature appears on front
China banded in 24k gold
Diameter: As indicated
No hanger
Edition size: As indicated
Numbered with certificate

84-P29-1.1-1

1970 Woodcock
Artist: James Lockhart/Edition: 2,000
Diameter:26.7 cm. (10½ in.)
Pair Prices: Issue $150.00; 1981 High $370.00;
Low $315.00; Close $370.00; Up $55.00

84-P29-1.1-2

1970 Ruffed Grouse

84-P29-1.2-1

1971 Green-Winged Teal
Artist: James Lockhart/Edition: 2,000
Diameter: 26.7 cm. (10½ in.)
Pair Prices: Issue $150.00; 1981 High $225.00;
Low $198.00; Close $225.00; Up $27.00

84-P29-1.2-2

1971 Mallard

84-P29-1.3-1

1972 Mockingbird
Artist: James Lockhart/Edition: 2,000
Diameter: 26.7 cm. (10½ in.)
Pair Prices: Issue $162.50; 1981 High $225.00;
Low $198.00; Close $225.00; Up $27.00

84-P29-1.3-2

1972 Cardinal

84-P29-1.5

1974 American Bald Eagle
Artist: James Lockhart/Edition: 2,000
Diameter: 33 cm. (13 in.)
Prices: Issue $150.00; 1981 High $610.00;
Low $590.00; Close $610.00; Up $10.00

84-P29-1.6

1975 White-Tailed Deer
Artist: James Lockhart/Edition: 2,500
Diameter: 27.9 cm. (11 in.)
Prices: Issue $100.00; 1981 High $130.00;
Low $110.00; Close $130.00; Up $20.00

84-P29-1.9

1978 American Panther
Artist: James Lockhart/Edition: 2,000
Diameter: 33 cm. (13 in.)
Prices: Issue $175.00; 1981 High $250.00;
Low $220.00; Close $220.00; Down $5.00

84-P29-1.10

1979 The Red Fox
Artist: James Lockhart/Edition: 2,500
Diameter: 27.9 cm. (11 in.)
Prices: Issue $120.00; 1981 High $110.00;
Low $98.00; Close $110.00; Up $12.00

84-P29-1.4-1

1973 Wild Turkey
Artist: James Lockhart/Edition: 2,000
Diameter: 26.7 cm. (10½ in.)
Pair Prices: Issue $162.50; 1981 High $225.00;
Low $190.00; Close $225.00; Up $35.00

84-P29-1.4-2

1973 Ring-Necked Pheasant

84-P29-1.7

1976 American Buffalo
Artist: James Lockhart/Edition: 2,500
Diameter: 33 cm. (13 in.)
Prices: Issue $165.00; 1981 High $187.00;
Low $180.00; Close $187.00; Up $7.00

84-P29-1.8

1977 Great Horned Owl
Artist: James Lockhart/Edition: 2,500
Diameter: 27.9 cm. (11 in.)
Prices: Issue $100.00; 1981 High $137.00;
Low $135.00; Close $135.00; Down $2.00

84-P29-1.11

1980 Trumpeter Swan
Artist: James Lockhart/Edition: 2,000
Diameter: 33 cm. (13 in.)
Prices: Issue $200.00; 1981 High $200.00;
Low $200.00; Close $200.00; No Change

Christmas Series

Artist: As indicated
China with 24k gold design on border
Diameter: 21 centimeters (8¼ inches)
No hanger
Edition size: As indicated
Numbered without certificate

84-P29-2.1

1976 The Alba Madonna
Artist: Raphael/Edition: 7,500
Prices: Issue $60.00; 1981 High $270.00;
Low $250.00; Close $260.00; Up $10.00

84-P29-2.2

1977 The Nativity
Artist: Lorenzo Lotto/Edition: 7,500
Prices: Issue $65.00; 1981 High $140.00;
Low $130.00; Close $135.00; Up $5.00

84-P29-2.3

1978 The Rest on the Flight into Egypt
Artist: Gerard David/Edition: 10,000
Prices: Issue $65.00; 1981 High $130.00;
Low $110.00; Close $128.00; Up $18.00

84-P29-2.4

1979 Adoration of the Magi
Artist: Botticelli/Edition: 10,000
Prices: Issue $70.00; 1981 High $75.00;
Low $70.00; Close $75.00; Up $5.00

84-P29-2.5

**1980 Madonna and Child with the Infant
Saint John**
Artist: Sodoma/Edition: 10,000
Prices: Issue $80.00; 1981 High $80.00;
Low $80.00; Close $80.00; No Change

84-P29-2.6

1981 Madonna and Child with Angels
Artist: Hans Memling/Edition: 10,000
Prices: Issue $90.00; 1981 High $90.00;
Low $90.00; Close $90.00; No Change

The Children of Renoir Series

Artist: Pierre Auguste Renoir. Artist's
 name appears on back
China banded in 24k gold
Diameter: 21 centimeters (8¼ inches)
No hanger
Edition size limited to 5,000. Two
 annual issues
Numbered without certificate

84-P29-4.1
1978 A Girl with a Watering Can
Artist: Pierre Auguste Renoir
Prices: Issue $50.00; 1981 High $260.00;
Low $240.00; Close $240.00; Down $5.00

84-P29-4.2
1978 Child in White
Artist: Pierre Auguste Renoir
Prices: Issue $50.00; 1981 High $125.00;
Low $118.00; Close $118.00; Down $7.00

84-P29-4.3
1979 Girl with Hoop
Artist: Pierre Auguste Renoir
Prices: Issue $55.00; 1981 High $115.00;
Low $115.00; Close $115.00; No Change

84-P29-4.4
1979 At the Piano
Artist: Pierre Auguste Renoir
Prices: Issue $55.00; 1981 High $126.00;
Low $125.00; Close $126.00; Up $1.00

84-P29-4.5
1980 Two Little Circus Girls
Artist: Pierre Auguste Renoir
Prices: Issue $60.00; 1981 High $95.00;
Low $95.00; Close $95.00; No Change

84-P29-4.6
1980 The Artist's Son Jean
Artist: Pierre Auguste Renoir
Prices: Issue $60.00; 1981 High $105.00;
Low $60.00; Close $99.00; Up $39.00

Oleg Cassini's Most Beautiful Women of All Time Collection

Artist: Oleg Cassini. Artist's signature
    appears on front
China banded in 24k gold
Diameter: 26.7 centimeters (10½ inches)
No hanger
Edition size undisclosed, limited by
    year of issue
Numbered with certificate

84-P29-5.1

1981 Helen of Troy
Artist: Oleg Cassini
Prices: Issue $75.00; 1981 High $75.00;
Low $75.00; Close $75.00: No Change

84-P29-5.2

1982 Marie Antoinette
Artist: Oleg Cassini
Issue price: $75.00

Mother's Love Series

Artist: Irene Spencer. Artist's signature
    appears on front
China banded in 24k gold
Diameter: 23.8 centimeters (9⅜ inches)
No hanger
Edition size limited to 7,500
Numbered without certificate

84-P29-6.1

1980 Miracle
Artist: Irene Spencer
Prices: Issue $95.00; 1981 High $240.00;
Low $160.00; Close $240.00; Up $80.00

Children of Mexico Series

Artist: Jorge Sanchez. Artist's signature
    appears on front
China banded in 24k gold
Diameter: 26.7 centimeters (10½ inches)
No hanger
Edition size limited to 5,000
Numbered without certificate

84-P29-7.1

1981 Maria
Artist: Jorge Sanchez
Issue price $85.00

84-P29-6.2   84-P29-6.3
1981 Story Time   No information available at press time
Artist: Irene Spencer
Prices: Issue $110.00; 1981 High $110.00;
Low $110.00; Close $110.00: No Change

84-P29-7.2   84-P29-7.3
1981 Miguel   **1982 Regina**
Artist: Jorge Sanchez   Artist: Jorge Sanchez
Issue price $85.00   Issue price: $90.00

Reco International was founded in 1967 by Heio W. Reich who continues as its president. From the beginning the firm has been an importer and maker of limited-edition plates.

World of Children, Reco International's first U.S. proprietary series, was introduced in 1977, with designs by John McClelland. The series ended in 1980. A second series with designs by the same artist, *McClelland's Mother Goose* series, was introduced in 1979. In 1981, Reco International began a third series, the *McClelland Children's Circus Collection.*

John McClelland is an author of books on flower and portrait painting and is particularly noted for his portraiture of personages in politics and the arts.

The World of Children Series

Artist: John McClelland. Artist's
  signature appears on front
China banded in 24k gold
Diameter: 26.7 centimeters (10½ inches)
No hanger
Edition size: As indicated
Numbered with certificate since 1978

84-R60-1.1
1977 Rainy Day Fun
Artist: John McClelland/Edition: 10,000
Prices: Issue $50.00; 1981 High $240.00;
Low $160.00; Close $230.00; Up $70.00

84-R60-1.2
1978 When I Grow Up
Artist: John McClelland/Edition: 15,000
Prices: Issue $50.00; 1981 High $120.00;
Low $75.00; Close $120.00; Up $45.00

84-R60-1.3
1979 You're Invited
Artist: John McClelland/Edition: 15,000
Prices: Issue $50.00; 1981 High $80.00;
Low $60.00; Close $80.00; Up $20.00

84-R60-1.4
1980 Kittens for Sale
Artist: John McClelland/Edition: 15,000
Prices: Issue $50.00; 1981 High $65.00;
Low $50.00; Close $65.00; Up $15.00

McClelland's Mother Goose Series

Artist: John McClelland. Artist's
  signature appears on front
China
Diameter: 21.6 centimeters (8½ inches)
No hanger
Edition size undisclosed, limited by
  year of issue
Numbered with certificate

84-R60-2.1

1979 Mary, Mary
Artist: John McClelland
Prices: Issue $22.50; 1981 High $318.00;
Low $128.00; Close $318.00; Up $190.00

84-R60-2.2

1980 Little Boy Blue
Artist: John McClelland
Prices: Issue $22.50; 1981 High $108.00;
Low $22.50; Close $108.00; Up $85.50

84-R60-2.3

1981 Little Miss Muffet
Artist: John McClelland
Prices: Issue $24.50; 1981 High $24.50;
Low $24.50; Close $24.50; No Change

84-R60-2.4

1982 Little Jack Horner
Artist: John McClelland
Issue price: $24.50

McClelland Children's Circus Series

Artist: John McClelland. Artist's
  signature appears on front
China
Diameter: 24.1 centimeters (9½ inches)
No hanger
Edition size undisclosed, limited by
  year of issue
Numbered with certificate

84-R60-3.1

1981 Tommy the Clown
Artist: John McClelland
Prices: Issue $29.50; 1981 High $29.50;
Low $29.50; Close $29.50; No Change

84-R60-3.2

1982 Katie the Tightrope Walker
Artist: John McClelland
Issue price: $29.50

Mary, Mary **84-R60-2.1**
1979 Reco International
McClelland's Mother Goose
Detail showing the rich interplay of colors
that is artist John McClelland's hallmark

Reed & Barton

Reed & Barton Silversmiths traces its origin to a factory established by Isaac Babbitt in the early nineteenth century. In 1824 Babbitt developed an alloy, harder and more lustrous than pewter, which he named Britannia metal. Henry G. Reed and Charles E. Barton, artists working for Babbitt, acquired the firm in the 1830s and continued to manufacture Britannia ware. In the late 1840s, the factory began to produce plated silverware. Reed & Barton was incorporated in 1888 and started producing solid silver services. Sterling flatware and hollowware soon replaced plated ware as their largest line. In 1903 the firm began reproducing colonial pewter ware.

In 1970 Reed & Barton began their *Christmas* series which changes theme every three years. The first three plates are based on Christmas carols; the second three are based on fifteenth-century altar art; the next are based on American Christmas scenes; and the next depict nineteenth-century American illustrations.

Artist Robert Johnson, whose works are in private collections throughout the United States, Europe, and the Far East, developed the patented electroplating process used in the creation of the Reed & Barton *Christmas* series. The medium, known as Damascene silver, combines silver, gold, copper, and bronze, and the electroplating process is derived from a hand-craft method perfected at Damascus in the middle ages. Maxwell Mays specializes in Americana, and his art has appeared in such magazines as *Collier's*, *Yankee*, *Cosmopolitan*, and *New England*.

Christmas Series

Artist: As indicated
Damascene silver
Diameter: 27.9 centimeters (11 inches) through 1978; thereafter, 20.3 centimeters (8 inches)
No hanger
Edition size: As indicated
Numbered without certificate through 1978; thereafter not numbered; accompanied with numbered certificate

84-R18-2.4

1973 Adoration of the Kings
Artist: Rogier van der Weyden/Edition: 7,500
Prices: Issue $60.00; 1981 High $75.00; Low $70.00; Close $75.00; Up $5.00

84-R18-2.1
1970 A Partridge in a Pear Tree
Artist: Robert Johnson/Edition: 2,500
Prices: Issue $55.00; 1981 High $218.00;
Low $215.00; Close $218.00; Up $3.00

84-R18-2.2
1971 We Three Kings of Orient Are
Artist: Robert Johnson/Edition: 7,500
Prices: Issue $60.00; 1981 High $75.00;
Low $70.00; Close $75.00; Up $5.00

84-R18-2.3
1972 Hark! The Herald Angels Sing
Artist: Robert Johnson/Edition: 7,500
Prices: Issue $60.00; 1981 High $60.00;
Low $60.00; Close $60.00; No Change

84-R18-2.5
1974 The Adoration of the Magi
Artist: Fra Angelico and Fra Lippi/Edition: 7,500
Prices: Issue $65.00; 1981 High $72.00;
Low $65.00; Close $72.00; Up $7.00

84-R18-2.6
1975 Adoration of the Kings
Artist: Steven Lochner/Edition: 7,500
Prices: Issue $65.00; 1981 High $65.00;
Low $65.00; Close $65.00; No Change

84-R18-2.7
1976 Morning Train
Artist: Maxwell Mays/Edition: 7,500
Prices: Issue $65.00; 1981 High $58.00;
Low $55.00; Close $55.00; Down $3.00

84-R18-2.8

1977 Decorating the Church
Artist: Maxwell Mays/Edition: 7,500
Prices: Issue $65.00; 1981 High $54.00;
Low $54.00; Close $54.00; No Change

84-R18-2.9

1978 The General Store at Christmas Time
Artist: Maxwell Mays/Edition: 7,500
Prices: Issue $65.00; 1981 High $75.00;
Low $75.00; Close $75.00; No Change

84-R18-2.10

1979 Merry Old Santa Claus
Artist: Thomas Nast/Edition: 2,500
Prices: Issue $55.00; 1981 High $63.00;
Low $55.00; Close $63.00; Up $8.00

84-R18-2.11

1980 Gathering Christmas Greens
Artist: Unknown/Edition: 2,500
Prices: Issue $65.00; 1981 High $65.00;
Low $65.00; Close $65.00; No Change

84-R18-2.12

1981 The Shopkeeper at Christmas
Artist: W. L. Sheppard/Edition: 2,500
Prices: Issue $75.00; 1981 High $75.00;
Low $75.00; Close $75.00; No Change

Brown's Lincoln **84-R69-1.1**
1976 River Shore *Famous Americans*
Detail from the first copper collector's plate

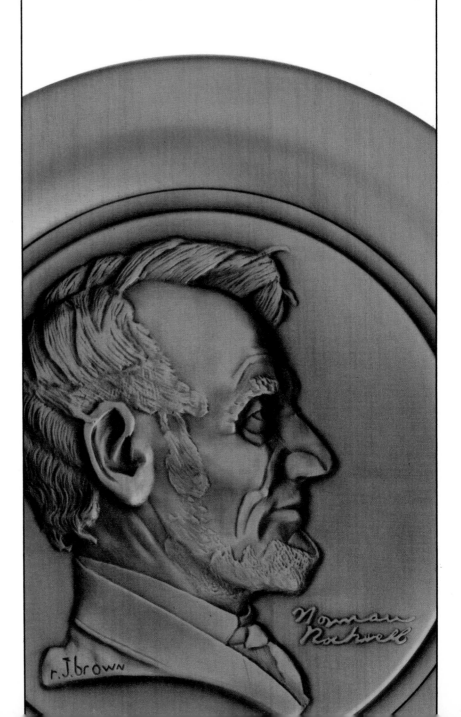

River Shore, Ltd.®

Creators of Museum Quality Limited Editions

River Shore, Ltd. was established in 1975 to market limited-edition collectibles.

In 1976 River Shore began its *Famous Americans* series, the first collector's plates crafted in copper, based on artwork by Norman Rockwell and sculpted by Roger Brown. The series ended in 1979. River Shore introduced its *Signs of Love* series in 1981.

Roger Brown, who sculpted the *Famous Americans* series, studied at the New York Sculpture Center and is a member of the National Sculpture Society. His works appear in museums throughout the United States, including the Lyndon Baines Johnson Memorial Library and the Teterboro Aviation Museum. Yin-Rei Hicks, a native of mainland China, was born during the Maoist takeover. Her family later fled to Taiwan, where her artistic ability first gained recognition. She won two scholarships from the University of Louisville in Kentucky, and graduated with a Master's Degree in Creative Art. Hicks has since become a prominent illustrator and designer of limited-edition collectibles.

Famous Americans Series

Artist: Roger Brown (after works by
   Norman Rockwell). Artist's signature
   appears on front along with name of
   Norman Rockwell
Copper
Diameter: 20.3 centimeters (8 inches)
No hanger
Edition size limited to 9,500
Numbered with certificate

84-R69-1.1
1976 Lincoln
Artist: Roger Brown
Prices: Issue $40.00; 1981 High $440.00;
Low $420.00; Close $420.00; Down $5.00

84-R69-1.2
1977 Rockwell
Artist: Roger Brown
Prices: Issue $45.00; 1981 High $179.00;
Low $162.00; Close $162.00; Down $17.00

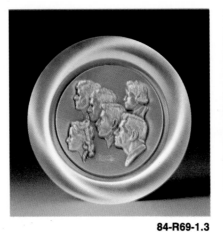

84-R69-1.3
1978 Peace Corps
Artist: Roger Brown
Prices: Issue $45.00; 1981 High $120.00;
Low $105.00; Close $120.00; Up $15.00

84-R69-1.4
1979 Spirit of Lindbergh
Artist: Roger Brown
Prices: Issue $50.00; 1981 High $58.00;
Low $58.00; Close $58.00; No Change

Signs of Love Series

Artist: Yin Rei Hicks. Artist's signature
appears on front
China
Diameter: 21.6 centimeters (8½ inches)
No hanger
Edition size undisclosed, limited by
announced period of issue
Numbered with certificate

84-R69-2.1

1981 A Kiss for Mother
Artist: Yin Rei Hicks
Prices: Issue $18.50; 1981 High $18.50;
Low $18.50; Close $18.50; No Change

84-R69-2.2

1981 A Watchful Eye
Artist: Yin Rei Hicks
Prices: Issue $21.50; 1981 High $21.50;
Low $21.50; Close $21.50; No Change

84-R69-2.3

1982 A Gentle Persuasion
Artist: Yin Rei Hicks
Issue price: $21.50

84-R69-2.4

1982 A Protective Embrace
Artist: Yin Rei Hicks
Issue price: $23.50

Los Ninos 84-G58-5.1
1976 Gorham *DeGrazia Children*
Detail from the first plate by Ted DeGrazia,
famous Southwestern artist

Rockwell Society

The Rockwell Society of America is a chartered non-profit organization devoted to the study and appreciation of the works of Norman Rockwell. The Society's *Christmas* series began in 1974, with the first issue manufactured by Ridgewood. Subsequent issues have been made by the Edwin M. Knowles China Company (see United States, Knowles). The *Mother's Day* series started in 1976 and in 1977 the *Rockwell Heritage* series began. The Rockwell Society's latest series is *Rockwell's Rediscovered Women,* which began in 1981.

One of the most widely-known artists in the twentieth century, Norman Rockwell created well over 3,000 works including 323 *Saturday Evening Post* covers as well as numerous illustrations for *Life, Look, Boys Life,* and annual Boy Scout calendars. His works hang in a number of museums: from the Smithsonian Institution and the Metropolitan Museum of Art in New York, to the Corner House in the artist's adopted home of Stockbridge, Massachusetts.

Christmas Series

Artist: Norman Rockwell. Artist's
  signature appears on front
China
Diameter: 21.6 centimeters (8½ inches)
No hanger
Edition size undisclosed, limited by
  announced period of issue
Numbered with certificate

Los Ninos **84-G58-5.1**
1976 Gorham *DeGrazia Children*
Detail from the first plate by Ted DeGrazia,
famous Southwestern artist

Rockwell Society

The Rockwell Society of America is a chartered non-profit organization devoted to the study and appreciation of the works of Norman Rockwell. The Society's *Christmas* series began in 1974, with the first issue manufactured by Ridgewood. Subsequent issues have been made by the Edwin M. Knowles China Company (see United States, Knowles). The *Mother's Day* series started in 1976 and in 1977 the *Rockwell Heritage* series began. The Rockwell Society's latest series is *Rockwell's Rediscovered Women,* which began in 1981.

One of the most widely-known artists in the twentieth century, Norman Rockwell created well over 3,000 works including 323 *Saturday Evening Post* covers as well as numerous illustrations for *Life, Look, Boys Life,* and annual Boy Scout calendars. His works hang in a number of museums: from the Smithsonian Institution and the Metropolitan Museum of Art in New York, to the Corner House in the artist's adopted home of Stockbridge, Massachusetts.

Christmas Series

Artist: Norman Rockwell. Artist's
  signature appears on front
China
Diameter: 21.6 centimeters (8½ inches)
No hanger
Edition size undisclosed, limited by
  announced period of issue
Numbered with certificate

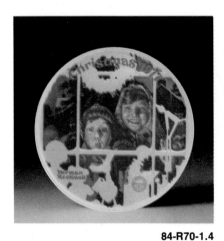

84-R70-1.1
1974 Scotty Gets His Tree
Artist: Norman Rockwell
Prices: Issue $24.50; 1981 High $170.00;
Low $165.00; Close $170.00; Up $5.00

84-R70-1.2
1975 Angel with a Black Eye
Artist: Norman Rockwell
Prices: Issue $24.50; 1981 High $98.00;
Low $95.00; Close $98.00; Up $3.00

84-R70-1.3
1976 Golden Christmas
Artist: Norman Rockwell
Prices: Issue $24.50; 1981 High $60.00;
Low $53.00; Close $60.00; Up $7.00

84-R70-1.4
1977 Toy Shop Window
Artist: Norman Rockwell
Prices: Issue $24.50; 1981 High $52.00;
Low $46.00; Close $52.00; Up $6.00

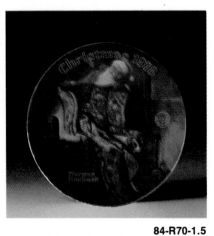

84-R70-1.5
1978 Christmas Dream
Artist: Norman Rockwell
Prices: Issue $24.50; 1981 High $73.00;
Low $50.00; Close $73.00; Up $23.00

84-R70-1.6
1979 Somebody's Up There
Artist: Norman Rockwell
Prices: Issue $24.50; 1981 High $30.00;
Low $27.00; Close $30.00; Up $3.00

84-R70-1.7

1980 Scotty Plays Santa
Artist: Norman Rockwell
Prices: Issue $24.50; 1981 High $42.50;
Low $24.50; Close $42.00; Up $17.50

84-R70-1.8

1981 Wrapped Up in Christmas
Artist: Norman Rockwell
Prices: Issue $25.50; 1981 High $25.50;
Low $25.50; Close $25.50: No Change

84-R70-1.9

No information available at press time

Mother's Day Series

Artist: Norman Rockwell. Artist's
  signature appears on front
China
Diameter: 21.6 centimeters (8½ inches)
No hanger
Edition size undisclosed, limited by
  announced period of issue
Numbered with certificate

84-R70-2.1

1976 A Mother's Love
Artist: Norman Rockwell
Prices: Issue $24.50; 1981 High $123.00;
Low $115.00; Close $123.00; Up $8.00

84-R70-2.4

1979 Reflections
Artist: Norman Rockwell
Prices: Issue $24.50; 1981 High $36.00;
Low $28.00; Close $36.00; Up $8.00

84-R70-2.5

1980 A Mother's Pride
Artist: Norman Rockwell
Prices: Issue $24.50; 1981 High $24.50;
Low $24.50; Close $24.50; No Change

84-R70-2.2

1977 Faith
Artist: Norman Rockwell
Prices: Issue $24.50; 1981 High $72.00;
Low $54.00; Close $72.00; Up $18.00

84-R70-2.3

1978 Bedtime
Artist: Norman Rockwell
Prices: Issue $24.50; 1981 High $104.00;
Low $95.00; Close $104.00; Up $9.00

84-R70-2.6

1981 After the Party
Artist: Norman Rockwell
Prices: Issue $24.50; 1981 High $29.00;
Low $24.50; Close $29.00; Up $4.50

84-R70-2.7

1982 The Cooking Lesson
Artist: Norman Rockwell
Issue price: $25.50

Rockwell Heritage Series

Artist: Norman Rockwell. Artist's
  signature appears on front
China
Diameter: 21.6 centimeters (8½ inches)
No hanger
Edition size undisclosed, limited by
  announced period of issue
Numbered with certificate

84-R70-3.1

1977 The Toy Maker
Artist: Norman Rockwell
Prices: Issue $14.50; 1981 High $300.00;
Low $195.00; Close $300.00; Up $105.00

84-R70-3.4

1980 The Ship Builder
Artist: Norman Rockwell
Prices: Issue $19.50; 1981 High $62.00;
Low $19.50; Close $62.00; Up $42.50

Rockwell's Rediscovered Women Series

Artist: Norman Rockwell. Artist's
  signature appears on front
China
Diameter: 21.6 centimeters (8½ inches)
No hanger
Edition size undisclosed, limited by
  announced period of issue
Numbered with certificate

84-R70-4.1

1981 Dreaming in the Attic
Artist: Norman Rockwell
Prices: Issue $19.50; 1981 High $19.50;
Low $19.50; Close $19.50; No Change

84-R70-3.2

1978 The Cobbler
Artist: Norman Rockwell
Prices: Issue $19.50; 1981 High $167.00;
Low $84.00; Close $167.00; Up $83.00

84-R70-3.3

1979 The Lighthouse Keeper's Daughter
Artist: Norman Rockwell
Prices: Issue $19.50; 1981 High $125.00;
Low $52.00; Close $125.00; Up $73.00

84-R70-3.5

1981 The Music Maker
Artist: Norman Rockwell
Prices: Issue $19.50; 1981 High $25.00;
Low $19.50; Close $25.00; Up $5.50

84-R70-3.6

1982 The Tycoon
Artist: Norman Rockwell
Issue price: $19.50

84-R70-4.2

1982 Waiting on the Shore
Artist: Norman Rockwell
Prices: Issue $22.50; 1981 High $22.50;
Low $22.50; Close $22.50: No Change

84-R61-0.0

Royal Devon plates are manufactured by the Gorham Company (see United States, Gorham). Both the *Christmas* series and *Mother's Day* series, bearing artwork by Norman Rockwell, began in 1975. Both series ended in 1980.

One of the most widely-known artists in the twentieth century, Norman Rockwell created well over 3,000 works including 323 *Saturday Evening Post* covers as well as numerous illustrations for *Life, Look, Boys Life,* and annual Boy Scout calendars. His works hang in a number of museums: from the Smithsonian Institution and the Metropolitan Museum of Art in New York, to the Corner House in the artist's adopted home of Stockbridge, Massachusetts.

Christmas Series

Artist: Norman Rockwell. Artist's signature appears on front
China banded in gold
Diameter: 21.6 centimeters (8½ inches)
No hanger
Edition size undisclosed, limited by year of issue
Not numbered, without certificate

84-R61-1.1
1975 Downhill Daring
Artist: Norman Rockwell
Prices: Issue $24.50; 1981 High $48.00;
Low $40.00; Close $48.00; Up $8.00

84-R61-1.2
1976 The Christmas Gift
Artist: Norman Rockwell
Prices: Issue $24.50; 1981 High $120.00;
Low $85.00; Close $120.00; Up $35.00

84-R61-1.3
1977 The Big Moment
Artist: Norman Rockwell
Prices: Issue $27.50; 1981 High $121.00;
Low $88.00; Close $121.00; Up $33.00

84-R61-1.4
1978 Puppets for Christmas
Artist: Norman Rockwell
Prices: Issue $27.50; 1981 High $54.00;
Low $50.00; Close $54.00; Up $4.00

84-R61-1.5
1979 One Present Too Many
Artist: Norman Rockwell
Prices: Issue $31.50; 1981 High $31.50;
Low $31.50; Close $31.50; No Change

84-R61-1.6
1980 Gramps Meets Gramps
Artist: Norman Rockwell
Prices: Issue $33.00; 1981 High $33.00;
Low $33.00; Close $33.00; No Change

Mother's Day Series

Artist: Norman Rockwell. Artist's
  signature appears on front
China banded in gold
Diameter: 21.6 centimeters (8½ inches)
No hanger
Edition size undisclosed, limited by
  year of issue
Not numbered, without certificate

84-R61-2.1

1975 Doctor and the Doll
Artist: Norman Rockwell
Prices: Issue $23.50; 1981 High $82.00;
Low $65.00; Close $82.00; Up $17.00

84-R61-2.2

1976 Puppy Love
Artist: Norman Rockwell
Prices: Issue $24.50; 1981 High $92.00;
Low $82.00; Close $92.00; Up $10.00

84-R61-2.3

1977 The Family
Artist: Norman Rockwell
Prices: Issue $24.50; 1981 High $133.00;
Low $82.00; Close $133.00; Up $51.00

84-R61-2.4

1978 Mother's Day Off
Artist: Norman Rockwell
Prices: Issue $27.00; 1981 High $72.00;
Low $66.00; Close $66.00; Down $2.00

84-R61-2.5

1979 Mother's Evening Out
Artist: Norman Rockwell
Prices: Issue $30.00; 1981 High $36.00;
Low $32.00; Close $34.00; Up $2.00

84-R61-2.6

1980 Mother's Treat
Artist: Norman Rockwell
Prices: Issue $32.50; 1981 High $32.50;
Low $32.50; Close $32.50; No Change

The Toy Maker 84-R70-3.1
1977 Rockwell Society *Heritage*
Detail from one of the most sought after
Rockwell plates of all time

Royal Worcester

Royal Worcester is the American subsidiary of the English company of the same name (see Great Britain, Royal Worcester). The firm was established in the United States after World War II.

In 1972 Royal Worcester initiated the *Birth of a Nation* series of five annual pewter plates to commemorate the Bicentennial of the United States.

Massachusetts-born sculptor Prescott Baston studied at Boston's Vesper George School of Art, working in an array of materials: paint, clay, plastic, rubber, metal, and wood. Upon graduation he worked as a designer of figurines for various companies before establishing his own firm, Sebastian Studios, in 1938. His miniature sculptures gained him an international reputation. He was subsequently commissioned to design the *Birth of a Nation* series for Royal Worcester.

Birth of a Nation Series

Artist: Prescott Baston
Pewter with designs in bas-relief
Diameter: 26 centimeters (10¼ inches)
No hanger
Edition size limited to 10,000
Numbered without certificate

84-R76-1.1

1972 Boston Tea Party
Artist: Prescott Baston
Prices: Issue $45.00; 1981 High $270.00;
Low $260.00; Close $260.00; Down $10.00

84-R76-1.2

1973 The Ride of Paul Revere
Artist: Prescott Baston
Prices: Issue $45.00; 1981 High $221.00;
Low $221.00; Close $221.00; No Change

84-R76-1.3

1974 Incident at Concord Bridge
Artist: Prescott Baston
Prices: Issue $50.00; 1981 High $74.00;
Low $70.00; Close $70.00; Down $4.00

84-R76-1.4

1975 Signing of the Declaration of Independence
Artist: Prescott Baston
Prices: Issue $65.00; 1981 High $58.00;
Low $58.00; Close $58.00; No Change

84-R76-1.5

1976 Washington Crossing the Delaware
Artist: Prescott Baston
Prices: Issue $65.00; 1981 High $83.00;
Low $74.00; Close $83.00; Up $5.00

FINE CHINA
BY
VILETTA
U.S.A.

Viletta China Company was started in 1959 in Roseberg, Oregon, by Viletta West, who hand-painted china and sold it through stores in the Pacific Northwest. The firm is involved in many areas of the giftware and fine china field, including commemorative china items and limited-edition collector's plates.

In 1979 Viletta China moved from Roseberg to Houston, Texas.

The *Nutcracker Ballet Plate Collection* began in 1978 and ended in 1980. The *Zolan's Children* series began in 1978 and was completed in 1981.

Shell Fisher's work represents some of the finest examples of contemporary realism. Fisher studied at the Art Institute of Chicago and at the American Academy of Art. One of his oil paintings won first prize at the 1977 Artist's Guild Annual Chicago Artist's Show, and Fisher's works are on display at the Art Institute of Chicago and at the Chicago Wildlife Museum. Fisher has also done commissioned work for Queen Elizabeth II and Sammy Davis, Jr. Donald Zolan also studied at the Art Institute of Chicago and won a scholarship to the American Academy of Art. His works, created in the representational style, hang in numerous galleries throughout the United States and in private collections in Mexico, Australia, France, Italy, South Korea, and Colombia.

Zolan's Children Series

Artist: Donald Zolan. Artist's signature
  appears on front
China
Diameter: 21.6 centimeters (8½ inches)
No hanger
Edition size undisclosed, limited by
  period of issue
Numbered with certificate

84-V36-1.1

1978 Erik and Dandelion
Artist: Donald Zolan
Prices: Issue $19.00; 1981 High $245.00;
Low $120.00; Close $245.00; Up $125.00

84-V36-1.2

1979 Sabina in the Grass
Artist: Donald Zolan
Prices: Issue $22.00; 1981 High $220.00;
Low $120.00; Close $220.00; Up $100.00

84-V36-1.3

1980 By Myself
Artist: Donald Zolan
Prices: Issue $24.00; 1981 High $45.00;
Low $24.00; Close $45.00; Up $21.00

84-V36-1.4

1981 For You
Artist: Donald Zolan
Prices: Issue $24.00; 1981 High $24.00;
Low $24.00; Close $24.00; No Change

Nutcracker Ballet Plate Collection

Artist: Shell Fisher. Artist's signature
  appears on front
China
Diameter: 21.6 centimeters (8½ inches)
No hanger
Edition size undisclosed, limited by
  year of issue
Numbered with certificate

84-V36-2.1

1978 Clara and Nutcracker
Artist: Shell Fisher
Prices: Issue $19.50; 1981 High $80.00;
Low $68.00; Close $68.00; Down $2.00

84-V36-2.2

1979 A Gift from Godfather
Artist: Shell Fisher
Prices: Issue $19.50; 1981 High $45.00;
Low $34.00; Close $45.00; Up $11.00

84-V36-2.3

1979 The Sugarplum Fairy
Artist: Shell Fisher
Prices: Issue $19.50; 1981 High $42.00;
Low $34.00; Close $42.00; Up $8.00

84-V36-2.4

1979 The Snow King and Queen
Artist: Shell Fisher
Prices: Issue $19.50; 1981 High $48.00;
Low $27.00; Close $48.00; Up $21.00

84-V36-2.5

1980 The Waltz of the Flowers
Artist: Shell Fisher
Prices: Issue $19.50; 1981 High $21.00;
Low $19.50; Close $21.00; Up $1.50

84-V36-2.6

1980 Clara and the Prince
Artist: Shell Fisher
Prices: Issue $19.50; 1981 High $28.00;
Low $19.50; Close $28.00; Up $8.50

Abbey Press (Viletta), **U.S.A.**
Accent on Art, **U.S.A.**
Addams Family (Schmid), **U.S.A.**
American Archives (International
  Silver), **U.S.A.**
American Arts Services (Viletta), **U.S.A.**
American Commemorative (Gorham),
  U.S.A.
American Express (Gorham), **U.S.A.**
American Express (Lenox), **U.S.A.**
American Heritage Art (Crown Parian),
  U.S.A.
American Historical Plates (Castleton
  China), **U.S.A.**
American Preservation Guild (Gorham),
  U.S.A.
American Rose Society (Gorham),
  U.S.A.
Anna-Perenna, **Ger.**
Anri, **Italy**
Antique Trader, **U.S.A.**
Arabia, **Finland**
Arizona Artisan, **U.S.A.**
Arlington Mint, **U.S.A.**
Armstrong, **U.S.A.**
Arta, **Austria**
Artists of the World, **U.S.A.**
Audubon Crystal, **U.S.A.**
Avondale, **U.S.A.**
  see also: Judaic Heritage Society
Aynsley, **G.B.**

Bareuther, **Ger.**
Barthmann, **Ger.**
Bayel of France, **Fr.**
Christian Bell (Schumann), **Can.**
Bengough, **Can.**
Berlin Design, **Ger.**
Betourne Studios, **Fr.**
Bing & Grøndahl, **Den.**
  see also: Ghent Collection

Blue Delft (Schoonhaven), **Neth.**
Boehm Studios, **G.B.**
  see also: Hamilton Collection
Bohemia, **Czech.**
Bonita Silver, **Mex.**
Brantwood Collection, **U.S.A.**
Braymer Hall, **U.S.A.**
Briarcrest, **U.S.A.**
John Brindle Fine Arts, **U.S.A.**
Brown & Bigelow (Gorham), **U.S.A.**

Caithness Glass, **G.B.**
Calhoun's Collectors Society, **U.S.A.**
Calhoun's Collectors Society
  (Schumann), **U.S.A.**
Calhoun's Collectors Society
  (Woodmere), **U.S.A.**
California Porcelain and Bronze, **U.S.A.**
Capo Di Monte, **Italy**
Carlo Monti, **Italy**
Carson Mint (Viletta), **U.S.A.**
Cartier, **Fr.**
Castleton China, **U.S.A.**
  see also: American Historical Plates
Castleton China, (Shenango), **U.S.A.**
Caverswall, see: Ghent Collection
Certified Rarities, **U.S.A.**
Chilmark, **U.S.A.**
Cleveland Mint, **U.S.A.**
Coalport, **G.B.**
Collector Creations (Reed & Barton),
  U.S.A.
Collector's Heirlooms (Fairmont), **U.S.A.**
Collector's Heirlooms (Viletta), **U.S.A.**
Collectors Weekly, **U.S.A.**
Continental Mint, **U.S.A.**
Count Agazzi, **Italy**
Creative World, **U.S.A.**
Cristal D'Albret, **Fr.**

Crown Delft, **Neth.**
Crown Parian, **U.S.A.**
  see also: American Heritage Art
Curator Collection, **U.S.A.**

Danbury Mint, **U.S.A.**
Daum, **Fr.**
Stuart Devlin Silver, **U.S.A.**
Dresden, **Ger.**

Ebeling & Reuss, **U.S.A.**
R. J. Ernst Enterprises (Viletta), **U.S.A.**

Fairmont, **U.S.A.**
  see also:
    Collector's Heirlooms
    Ghent Collection
    Mistwood Designs
Fenton Glass, **U.S.A.**
Fleetwood Collection (Gorham), **U.S.A.**
Fostoria, **U.S.A.**
Franklin Crystal, **U.S.A.**
Franklin Mint, **U.S.A.**
Franklin Porcelain, **U.S.A.**
Frankoma Pottery, **U.S.A.**
Fürstenberg, **Ger.**

Ghent Collection, **U.S.A.**
Ghent Collection (Bing & Grøndahl),
  U.S.A.
Ghent Collection (Caverswall), **U.S.A.**

Ghent Collection (Fairmont), **U.S.A.**
Ghent Collection (Gorham), **U.S.A.**
Ghent Collection (Kaiser), **U.S.A.**
Ghent Collection (Viletta), **U.S.A.**
Glaskunst/Schott Zwiesel, **Ger.**
Gnomes United, **U.S.A.**
Goebel, **Ger.**
Golf Digest, **U.S.A.**
Gorham, **U.S.A.**
  see also:
    American Commemorative
    American Express
    American Preservation Guild
    American Rose Society
    Brown & Bigelow
    Fleetwood Collection
    Ghent Collection
    Kern Collectibles
    Lincoln Mint
    Volair
Gourinat-Dolan, **Fr.**
Grafburg, **Ger.**
Grande Copenhagen, **Den.**
Grande Danica, **Den.**
Greentree Potteries, **U.S.A.**
Dave Grossman Designs, **U.S.A.**

Hackett American Collectors, **U.S.A.**
Hamilton Collection, **U.S.A.**
Hamilton Collection (Boehm Studios), **U.S.A.**
Hamilton Collection (Porcelaine Ariel), **U.S.A.**
Hamilton Collection (Royal Devon), **U.S.A.**
Hamilton Collection (Viletta), **U.S.A.**
Hamilton Mint, **U.S.A.**
Haviland, **Fr.**
Haviland & Parlon, **Fr.**
  see also: Kern Collectibles
Heinrich, **Ger.**
Hibel Studio (Kaiser), **Ger.**
Hibel Studio (Rosenthal), **Ger.**
Historic Providence Mint, **U.S.A.**
Ralph Homan Studios (Viletta), **U.S.A.**
Home Plates (Mingolla), **U.S.A.**
Hornsea, **G.B.**
Hudson Pewter, **U.S.A.**
Hutschenreuther, **Ger.**

Imperial, **U.S.A.**
Incolay, **U.S.A.**
International Museum, **U.S.A.**
International Silver, **U.S.A.**
  see also: American Archives
Interpace, **U.S.A.**

J M Company, **U.S.A.**
Georg Jensen, **Den.**
Svend Jensen, **Den.**
Josair, **Fr.**
Joys (Viletta), **U.S.A.**
Judaic Heritage Society, **U.S.A.**
Judaic Heritage Society (Avondale), **U.S.A.**
Judaic Heritage Society (Viletta), **U.S.A.**

KPM-Royal Berlin, **Ger.**
Kaiser, **Ger.**
  see also:
    Ghent Collection
    Hibel Studio
Keller & George (Reed & Barton), **U.S.A.**
Kensington, **U.S.A.**
Kera, **Den.**
Kern Collectibles, **U.S.A.**
Kern Collectibles (Gorham), **U.S.A.**
Kern Collectibles (Haviland & Parlon), **U.S.A.**
Kern Collectibles (Pickard), **U.S.A.**
Kern Collectibles (Rosenthal), **U.S.A.**
Kern Collectibles (Royal Bayreuth), **U.S.A.**
Kern Collectibles (Sango), **U.S.A.**
Kilkelly, **U.S.A.**
Kings, **Italy**
Kirk, **U.S.A.**
Koscherak Bros., **Czech.**
Kosta, **Swed.**
Kurz (Shuler International), **Neth.**

Lake Shore Prints, **U.S.A.**
Lapsys, **U.S.A.**
Lenox, **U.S.A.**
  see also: American Express
Lihs-Lindner, **Ger.**
Lincoln Mint, **U.S.A.**
Lincoln Mint (Gorham), **U.S.A**
Litt, **U.S.A.**
Lund & Clausen, **Den.**
Lynell Studios, **U.S.A.**

Mallek Studios, **U.S.A.**
Manjundo, **Japan**
Marmot, **Ger.**
Mason, **G.B.**
Master Engravers of America, **U.S.A.**
McCalla Enterprises (Viletta), **U.S.A.**
Meissen, **Ger.**
Metal Arts, **U.S.A.**
Metawa, **Neth.**

Metlox, see: Vernonware
Metropolitan Museum of Art, **U.S.A.**
Mingolla, see: Home Plates
Mistwood Designs (Fairmont), **U.S.A.**
Modern Masters, **U.S.A.**
Moser, **Czech.**
Moussalli, **U.S.A.**
Mueller, **Ger.**
Museum Editions (Ridgewood), **U.S.A.**
Museum Editions (Viletta), **U.S.A.**

Noritake, **Japan**

Ohio Arts, **U.S.A.**
Orrefors, **Swed.**

Palisander, **Den.**
Paramount Classics (Pickard), **U.S.A.**
Pemberton & Oakes (Viletta), **U.S.A.**
Pickard, **U.S.A.**
  see also:
    Kern Collectibles
    Paramount Classics
Poillerat, **Fr.**
Poole Pottery, **G.B.**
Porcelaine Ariel, see: Hamilton Collection
Porsgrund, **Nor.**
Puiforcat, **Fr.**

Ram, **U.S.A.**
Raynaud-Limoges, **Fr.**
Reco International, **U.S.A.**
Reed & Barton, **U.S.A.**
  see also:
    Collector Creations
    Keller & George
Ridgewood, **U.S.A.**
  see also: Museum Editions
River Shore, **U.S.A.**
Rockwell Collectors Club, **U.S.A.**
Rockwell Museum, **U.S.A.**
Roman Ceramica Excelsis, **Mex.**
Rörstrand, **Swed.**
Rosenthal, **Ger.**
  see also:
    Hibel Studio
    Kern Collectibles
Royal Bayreuth, **Ger.**
  see also: Kern Collectibles
Royal Copenhagen, **Den.**
Royal Cornwall, **China/Taiwan, U.S.A.**

Royal Delft, **Neth.**
Royal Devon, see: Hamilton Collection
Royal Doulton, **G.B.**
Royal Grafton, **G.B.**
Royal Limoges, **Fr.**
Royal Tettau, **Ger.**
Royal Worcester, **G.B., U.S.A.**
Royale, **Ger.**
Royale Germania, **Ger.**
Royalwood, **U.S.A.**
John A. Ruthven, **U.S.A.**

Sabino, **Fr.**
Sango, **Japan**
   see also: Kern Collectibles
Santa Clara, **Spain**
Sarna, **India**
Schmid, **Ger., Japan**
   see also: Addams Family
Schoonhaven, see: Blue Delft
Schumann, **Ger.**
   see also:
    Calhoun's Collectors Society
    Christian Bell
Sebastian, **U.S.A.**
Seeley's Ceramic Services, **U.S.A.**
Seven Seas, **U.S.A.**
Shenango, see: Castleton China
Shuler International, see: Kurz
Silver Creations, **U.S.A.**
Smith Glass, **U.S.A.**
Spode, **G.B.**
Sterling America, **U.S.A.**
Stieff, **U.S.A.**
Stumar, **Ger.**
Syracuse China, **U.S.A.**

Tirschenreuth, **Ger.**
Towle Silversmiths, **U.S.A.**

U.S. Historical Society, **U.S.A.**

Vague Shadows, **U.S.A.**
Val St. Lambert, **Belg.**
Veneto Flair, **Italy**
Vernonware (Metlox Potteries), **U.S.A.**
Viletta, **U.S.A.**
   see also:
   Abbey Press
   American Arts Services
   Carson Mint
   Collector's Heirlooms
   R. J. Ernst Enterprises

   Ghent Collection
   Hamilton Collection
   Ralph Homan Studios
   Joys
   Judaic Heritage Society
   McCalla Enterprises
   Museum Editions
   Pemberton & Oakes
   Warwick
   Westbury
   Edward Weston Editions
Villeroy & Boch, **Ger.**
Volair (Gorham), **U.S.A.**

WMF Geislingen, **Ger.**
Warwick (Viletta), **U.S.A.**
George Washington Mint, **U.S.A.**
Wedgwood, **G.B.**
Wendell August Forge, **U.S.A.**
Westbury (Viletta), **U.S.A.**
Westminster Collectibles, **U.S.A.**
Westmoreland, **U.S.A.**
Edward Weston Editions (Viletta),
   U.S.A.
Wheaton, **U.S.A.**
Whitehall China, **U.S.A.**
Woodmere, see: Calhoun's Collectors
   Society

Zenith Delftware, **Neth.**

Over-the-Counter Issues

Over-the-counter plates may be traded but are not listed on The Bradford Exchange with "Bradex" plates, which generally trade with greater regularity and frequency. They are, nonetheless, true collector's plates issued in editions usually limited either to an announced number or to the year of issue as indicated. With the exception of the *Jubilee Christmas* plates of Bing & Grøndahl (Denmark), any editions considered repetitious of previous editions are excluded.

Over-the-counter issues are arranged alphabetically by country, then alphabetically by maker or maker/sponsor, then chronologically by series. Each entry includes the series name, the year and name of the plate, the edition limit, and the U.S. issue price whenever available.

	Edition Limit	Issue Price
Austria		
Arta		
Mother's Day		
73 Family with Puppy	1,500	$ 50.00
Christmas		
73 Nativity – In Manger	1,500	50.00
Belgium		
Val St. Lambert		
American Heritage		
69 Pilgrim Fathers	500	200.00
70 Paul Revere's Ride	500	200.00
71 Washington on Delaware	500	200.00
Annual Old Masters		
69 Rubens & Rembrandt (Pair)	5,000	50.00
69 Van Gogh & Van Dyck (Pair)	5,000	50.00
70 Da Vinci & Michelangelo (Pair)	5,000	50.00
71 El Greco & Goya (Pair)	5,000	50.00
72 Reynolds & Gainsborough (Pair)	5,000	50.00
(Single issue)		
70 Rembrandt	Year	25.00
Canada		
Christian Bell (Schumann)		
Preserving a Way of Life		
80 Making Way for Cars	5,000	60.00
80 Atop Hay Wagon	5,000	60.00

	Edition Limit	Issue Price
80 Turning Sod	5,000	$60.00
80 Winter's Morning	5,000	60.00
81 Sugarbush	10,000	70.00
81 Fishing for Redfin	10,000	70.00
81 Wheat Harvest	10,000	70.00
81 Returning from Village	10,000	70.00
Bengough		
Christmas		
72 Charles Dickens Christmas Carol	490	125.00
Northwest Mounted Police		
72 1898 Dress Uniform	1,000	140.00
72 First Uniform	1,000	140.00
Royal Canadian Police		
72 Order Dress	1,000	140.00
China (Taiwan)		
Royal Cornwall		
The Five Perceptions of Weo Cho		
79 Sense of Touch	19,500	55.00
79 Sense of Sight	19,500	55.00
79 Sense of Taste	19,500	55.00
79 Sense of Hearing	19,500	55.00
79 Sense of Smell	19,500	55.00
Czechoslovakia		
Bohemia		
Mother's Day		
74 Mother's Day	500	130.00
75 Mother's Day	500	140.00
76 Mother's Day	500	150.00

	Edition Limit	Issue Price
Koschevak Bros.		
Mary Gregory Christmas		
73 Christmas	1,000	$ 55.00
74 Christmas	1,000	60.00
75 Christmas	1,000	60.00
76 Christmas	500	65.00
Mary Gregory Mother's Day		
73 Mother's Day	500	55.00
74 Mother's Day	300	60.00
75 Mother's Day	300	60.00
76 Mother's Day	500	65.00
Moser		
Christmas (Vanoce)		
70 Hradcany Castle	400	75.00
71 Karlstein Castle	1,365	75.00
72 Old Town Hall	1,000	85.00
73 Karlovy Vary Castle	500	90.00
Mother's Day (Den Matek)		
71 Peacocks	350	75.00
72 Butterflies	750	85.00
73 Squirrels	200	90.00
Denmark		
Bing & Grøndahl		
Jubilee Christmas		
15 First Frozen Window	Year	3.00
20 Crows Enjoying Christmas	Year	4.00
25 Dog Outside Window	Year	5.00
30 Old Organist	Year	5.00
35 Little Match Girl	Year	6.00
40 Three Wise Men	Year	10.00
45 Royal Guard Amalienborg Castle	Year	10.00
50 Eskimo	Year	15.00
55 Dybbol Mill	Year	20.00
60 Kronborg Castle	Year	25.00
65 Churchgoers	Year	25.00
70 Amalienborg Castle	Year	30.00
75 Horses Enjoying Meal	Year	40.00
80 Happiness over Yule Tree	Year	60.00
Olympic Games		
72 Olympiade – Munich	Year	20.00
76 Olympic Montreal	Year	29.50
80 Moscow by Night	Year	43.00
Bicentennial		
76 E. Pluribus Unum	Year	50.00
Heritage		
76 Norseman	5,000	30.00
77 Navigators	5,000	30.00
78 Discovery	5,000	39.50
79 Exploration	5,000	39.50
80 Helmsman	N/A	45.00
81 Swordsman	N/A	49.50
Carl Larsson (Sets of four)		
77 Flowers on Windowsill		
77 Breakfast under Big Birch		
77 Yard & Warehouse		
77 Kitchen	7,500	150.00
78 First Born		
78 Room for Mother and Children		

	Edition Limit	Issue Price
78 Portrait of Inga-Maria Thiel		
78 Iduna	7,500	$ 170.00
79 Forestry		
79 Cutting Grass		
79 Potato Harvest		
79 Fishery	7,500	165.00
(Single issue)		
77 Madonna	10,000	45.00
(Single issue)		
78 Seagull	7,500	75.00
Mother's Day Jubilee		
79 Mother's Day Jubilee	Year	55.00
Year of the Viking (Single issue)		
80 Viking	10,000	65.00
see also: Ghent Collection (U.S.A.)		
Grande Copenhagen		
Bicentennial (Single issue)		
76 Great Seal	Year	35.00
Grande Danica		
Mother's Day		
77 Dog with Puppies	10,000	25.00
78 Storks	10,000	25.00
79 Badgers	10,000	25.00
Georg Jensen		
Christmas		
72 Doves	Year	15.00
73 Christmas Eve	Year	15.00
74 Christmas Story	Year	17.50
75 Winter Scene	Year	22.50
76 Christmas in Country	Year	22.50
Chagall (Single issue)		
72 Lovers	12,500	50.00
Mother's Day		
73 Mother & Child	Year	15.00
74 Sweet Dreams	Year	17.50
75 Mother's World	Year	22.50
Svend Jensen		
Anniversary		
80 Hans Christian Andersen's Home	N/A	60.00
Kera		
Christmas		
67 Kobenhavn	Year	6.00
68 Forste	Year	6.00
69 Andersen's House	Year	6.00
70 Langelinie	Year	6.00
71 Lille Peter	Year	6.00
Moon		
69 Apollo 11	Year	6.00
70 Apollo 13	Year	6.00
Mother's Day		
70 Mother's Day	Year	6.00
71 Mother's Day	Year	6.00
Lund & Clausen		
Moon		
69 Moon Landing – Apollo 11	Year	10.00
71 Apollo 13	Year	15.00
Mother's Day		
70 Rose	Year	10.00

	Edition Limit	Issue Price
71 Forget-Me-Nots	Year	$10.00
72 Bluebell	Year	15.00
73 Lily of Valley	Year	16.00
Christmas		
71 Animal Garden	Year	13.50
72 Stave Church	Year	13.50
73 Christmas Scene	Year	13.50

Palisander

	Edition Limit	Issue Price
Christmas		
71 Red Robin on Holly	1,200	50.00
72 Flying Geese	1,200	50.00
73 Christmas	1,200	50.00
Presidential		
71 George Washington	1,000	50.00
72 Thomas Jefferson	1,000	50.00
73 John Adams	1,000	50.00
(Single issue)		
73 Bicentennial	250	50.00

Royal Copenhagen

	Edition Limit	Issue Price
Historical		
75 R. C. Bicentennial	Year	30.00
76 U.S. Bicentennial	Year	35.00
77 Electro-Magnetism	Year	35.00
78 Capt. Cook	Year	37.50
79 Adam Oehlenschlager	Year	42.50
80 Amagertorv	Year	52.50
National Parks of America		
78 Yellowstone	5,000	75.00
79 Shenandoah	5,000	75.00
80 Yosemite	5,000	75.00
80 Mt. McKinley	5,000	75.00
81 Everglades	5,000	75.00
81 Grand Canyon	5,000	75.00
(Single issue)		
80 Year of Viking	5,000	55.00
Motherhood		
82 Mother Robin with Babies	Year	29.50

Finland

Arabia

	Edition Limit	Issue Price
Christmas 100 Years Ago		
78 Inland Village Scene	Year	49.00
79 Forest Village Scene	Year	72.00
80 Seaside Village Scene	Year	79.00
81 Farm Village Scene	Year	87.00
Pictures of Lapland		
81 Laplander Village	7,000	175.00
(Single issue)		
81 Rose	2,000	360.00

France

Bayel of France

	Edition Limit	Issue Price
Flowers		
72 Rose	300	50.00
73 Lilies	300	50.00
73 Orchid	300	50.00
Bicentennial		
74 Liberty Bell	500	50.00
75 Independence Hall	500	60.00
76 Spread Eagle	500	60.00
Eagles		
74 Eagle Head	300	50.00
74 Eagle in Flight	300	50.00

Betourne Studios

	Edition Limit	Issue Price
Jean-Paul Loup Christmas		
71 Noel	300	125.00
72 Noel	300	150.00
73 Noel	300	175.00
74 Noel	400	200.00
75 Noel	250	250.00
76 Noel	150	300.00
Mother's Day (Champleve)		
74 Mother & Child	500	250.00
Mother's Day (Enamel)		
75 Mother's Day	400	285.00
76 Mother & Child	250	300.00

Cartier

	Edition Limit	Issue Price
Cathedral		
72 Chartres Cathedral	12,500	50.00
74 Chartres, Millous	500	130.00

Cristal D'Albret

	Edition Limit	Issue Price
Four Seasons		
72 Summer	1,000	75.00
73 Autumn	648	75.00
73 Spring	312	75.00
74 Winter	1,000	88.00
(Single issue)		
72 Bird of Peace	3,700	64.00

Daum

	Edition Limit	Issue Price
Four Seasons		
69 Autumn (Amethyst)	2,000	150.00
70 Winter (Aquamarine)	2,000	$150.00
70 Spring (Emerald)	2,000	150.00
70 Summer (Topaz)	2,000	150.00
Famous Musicians		
70 Bach (Emerald)	2,000	60.00
70 Beethoven (Amethyst)	2,000	60.00
71 Mozart (Tourmaline)	2,000	60.00
71 Wagner (Peridot)	2,000	60.00
72 Debussy (Topaz)	2,000	60.00
72 Gershwin (Sapphire)	2,000	60.00
Dali		
71 Ceci N'est Pas Une Assiette	2,000	200.00
71 Triomphale	2,000	200.00
Nymphea		
79 Waterliies	4,000	125.00
80 Lily Pond	4,000	150.00
81 Swan	4,000	170.00

Gourinat-Dolan Co.

	Edition Limit	Issue Price
(Single issue)		
78 Doves of Peace	3,000	60.00

Haviland

	Edition Limit	Issue Price
Presidential		
68 Martha Washington	2,500	35.00
69 Lincoln	2,500	100.00
70 Grant	3,000	100.00
71 Hayes	2,500	110.00
French Collection		
73 Breakfast	10,000	29.95
74 Wash	10,000	29.95
75 In Park	10,000	30.00
76 To Market	10,000	38.00
77 A Wash Before Dinner	10,000	38.00
78 An Evening at Home	10,000	40.00
79 Happy Mother's Day	10,000	45.00
Theatre Des Saisons		
78 Spring	5,000	120.00
78 Summer	5,000	120.00
78 Autumn	5,000	120.00
78 Winter	5,000	120.00
Mother's Day		
80 Child and His Animals	Year	55.00
Visit from Saint Nicholas		
80 Twas Night Before Christmas	Year	55.00
81 Children Were Nestled	5,000	60.00
Fleurs et Rubens		
80 Orchidée	7,500	120.00
81 Hibiscus	7,500	120.00
82 Poppy	7,500	120.00

Haviland & Parlon

	Edition Limit	Issue Price
Nan Lee (Single issue)		
73 Peaceable Kingdom	5,000	30.00
Mother's Day		
75 Laura and Child	15,000	37.50
76 Pinky and Baby	15,000	42.50
77 Amy and Snoopy	10,000	45.00
King Tut (Single issue)		
77 Scarab	2,500	80.00
Zodiac (Single issue)		
77 Astrological Man	5,000	50.00

see also: Kern Collectibles (U.S.A.)

Josair

	Edition Limit	Issue Price
Bicentennial		
72 American Eagle	400	250.00
73 American Flag	400	250.00
74 Abraham Lincoln	400	250.00
75 George Washington	400	250.00
76 Declaration of Independence	400	250.00

Poillerat

	Edition Limit	Issue Price
Christmas		
72 Three Kings	500	350.00
73 Rose	250	350.00

Puiforcat

	Edition Limit	Issue Price
Cartes a Jouer		
72 (Set of five)	2,000	300.00
(Single issue)		
73 Exodus (Silver)	2,000	200.00

Raynaud-Limoges

	Edition Limit	Issue Price
Castles		
79 Bodiam Castle	5,000	48.00
79 Glamis Castle	5,000	48.00
79 Tower of London	5,000	48.00
Wildlife Collection		
78 Tiger Bouquet	Year	50.00

Royal Limoges

	Edition Limit	Issue Price
Christmas		
72 Nativity	5,000	25.00
73 Three Wise Men	5,000	27.50

Sabino

	Edition Limit	Issue Price
Annual Crystal		
70 King Henry IV & Maria De Medici	1,500	65.00
71 Milo & Beasts	1,500	65.00

Germany

Anna-Perenna

	Edition Limit	Issue Price
Birds of Fancy		
78 Firebird	5,000	$110.00
Floral Fantasies		
78 Empress Gold	5,000	110.00
Enchanted Gardens		
78 June Dream	5,000	75.00
79 Summer Day	5,000	95.00
Oriental Tranquility		
78 Chun Li at Pond	5,000	100.00
79 Ming Tao on Path of Faith	5,000	110.00
Joy of Motherhood		
79 Gesa and Children	5,000	165.00
80 Alexandra and Children	5,000	175.00
American Silhouettes Children		
81 Fiddlers Two	5,000	75.00
Bashful Bunnies		
81 Spring's Surprise	15,000	62.50
81 Summer's Sunshine	15,000	62.50
82 Fall's Frolic	15,000	62.50
82 Winter's Wonder	15,000	62.50
Masquerade Fantasy		
82 Masquerade Party	9,800	95.00
82 Clowns and Unicorns	9,800	95.00
82 Merry-Go-Round Ballet	9,800	95.00

Bareuther

	Edition Limit	Issue Price
Mother's Day		
69 Mother & Children	5,000	12.00
70 Mother & Children	5,000	12.00
71 Mother & Children	5,000	13.50
72 Mother & Children	5,000	15.00
73 Mother & Children	5,000	15.00
74 Musical Children	5,000	19.00
75 Spring Outing	5,000	21.50
76 Rocking Cradle	5,000	23.00
77 Noon Feeding	5,000	24.50
78 Blind Man's Bluff	5,000	27.50
79 Mother's Love	5,000	35.00
80 First Cherries	5,000	37.50
Thanksgiving		
71 First Thanksgiving	2,500	13.50
72 Harvest	2,500	14.50
73 Country Road in Autumn	2,500	15.00
74 Old Mill	2,500	19.00
75 Wild Deer in Forest	2,500	21.50
76 Thanksgiving on Farm	2,500	23.50
77 Horses	2,500	24.50
78 Apple Harvest	2,500	27.50
79 Noontime	2,500	35.00
80 Longhorns	2,500	37.50
81 Gathering Wheat	2,500	39.50

Barthmann

	Edition Limit	Issue Price
Christmas		
77 Mary with Child	300	236.00
78 Adoration of Child	500	326.00
79 Holy Mother of Kasanskaja	500	361.00
80 Holy Mother by Kykos	500	385.00

Berlin Design

	Edition Limit	Issue Price
Father's Day (Historical)		
71 Brooklyn Bridge on Opening Day	12,000	14.50
72 Continent Spanned	3,000	15.00
73 Landing of Columbus	2,000	18.00
74 Adorn's Balloon	Year	25.00
75 Washington Crossing Delaware	Year	30.00
76 Tom Thumb	Year	32.00
77 Zeppelin	Year	32.00
78 Carl Benz	Year	36.00
79 Johannes Gutenberg at Mainz	Year	47.50
Mother's Day		
71 Grey Poodles	20,000	14.50
72 Fledglings	10,000	15.00
73 Duck Family	6,000	16.50
74 Squirrels	6,000	22.50
75 Cats	6,000	30.00
76 Doe and Her Fawn	6,000	32.00
77 Storks	6,000	32.00
78 Mare with Foal	6,000	36.00
79 Swans and Cygnets	6,000	47.50
80 Goat Family	6,000	55.00
81 Dachshund Family	6,000	55.00
82 Pheasant Family	6,000	55.00

Dresden

	Edition Limit	Issue Price
Christmas		
71 Shepherd Scene	3,500	14.50
72 Niklas Church	6,000	18.00
73 Schwanstein Church	6,000	18.00
74 Village Scene	5,000	20.00
75 Rothenberg Scene	5,000	24.00
76 Bavarian Village Church	5,000	26.00
77 Old Mill in Hexenloch	5,000	28.00

Fürstenberg

	Edition Limit	Issue Price
Easter		
71 Sheep	3,500	15.00
72 Chicks	4,000	$15.00
73 Bunnies	4,000	16.00
74 Pussywillow	4,000	20.00
75 Village Church	4,000	24.00
76 Country Watermill	4,000	25.00
Christmas		
71 Rabbits	7,500	14.00
72 Snowy Village	6,000	15.00
73 Christmas Eve	3,000	18.00
74 Sparrows	4,000	20.00
75 Deer Family	4,000	24.00
76 Winter Birds	4,000	25.00
Deluxe Christmas		
71 Three Wise Men	1,500	45.00
72 Holy Family and Angel	2,000	45.00
73 Christmas Eve	2,000	60.00
Mother's Day		
72 Hummingbird	5,000	15.00
73 Hedgehogs	5,000	16.00
74 Doe with Fawn	4,000	20.00
75 Swan Family	4,000	24.00
76 Koala Bear	4,000	25.00
Olympic		
72 Olympics – Munich	5,000	20.00
76 Olympics – Montreal	5,000	37.50
New York City Landscape		
81 City Hall	3,500	75.00
81 Central Park	3,500	75.00

Glaskunst/Schott-Zwiesel

	Edition Limit	Issue Price
Christmas		
77 Three Wise Men	N/A	105.00
78 Holy Family	N/A	112.50
79 Shepherd of Field	N/A	115.00
80 Annunciation of Maria	N/A	118.00

Goebel

	Edition Limit	Issue Price
Charlot Byj		
73 Santa at Tree	Year	16.50
74 Santa and Girl	Year	22.00
75 Up and Away	Year	25.00
76 Boy with Teddy Bear	Year	25.00
77 Joy to World	Year	25.00
Wildlife		
74 Robin	Year	45.00
75 Blue Titmouse	Year	50.00
76 Barn Owl	Year	50.00
77 Bullfinch	Year	50.00
78 Sea Gull	Year	55.00
79 Mallard	10,000	90.00
80 Cardinal	10,000	90.00
81 Peregrine Falcon	10,000	N/A
Mothers		
75 Rabbits	Year	45.00
76 Cats	Year	45.00
77 Panda Bears	Year	45.00
78 Doe and Fawn	Year	50.00
79 Long-Eared Owl	10,000	65.00
80 Raccoon and Baby	10,000	75.00
81 Ringed Seal	10,000	80.00
82 Swan	10,000	N/A
Robson Christmas		
75 Flight to Egypt (Porcelain)	Year	50.00
75 Flight to Egypt (Pewter)	Year	45.00
Annual Crystal		
78 Praying Girl	Year	45.00
79 Praying Boy	Year	50.00
80 Praying Angel	15,000	50.00
81 Girl with Teddy Bear	10,000	50.00
American Heritage		
78 Freedom & Justice Soaring	Year	100.00
79 Wild & Free	10,000	100.00
80 Where Buffalo Roam	4,000	125.00
Old Testament Themes		
78 Twelve Tribes of Israel	10,000	125.00
79 Ten Commandments	10,000	175.00
80 Traditions	10,000	225.00
Crystal Mother's Day		
79 Butterfly	Year	50.00
80 Sparrow	15,000	50.00
81 Doves	5,000	50.00
(Single issue)		
79 Christmas	200	500.00
Bratsoff		
79 Star Steed	15,000	125.00
Bavarian Forest		
80 Owls	7,500	150.00
81 Deer	7,500	150.00
North American Wildlife		
80 Beaver	10,000	125.00
81 Harp Seal	10,000	125.00
Christmas in Kinderland		
82 A Gift of Joy	10,000	49.50
Dolly Dingle World Traveler		
82 Dolly Visits Germany	10,000	30.00
82 Dolly Visits Italy	10,000	30.00
82 Dolly Visits Holland	10,000	30.00
82 Dolly Visits Spain	10,000	30.00

	Edition Limit	Issue Price
Grafburg		
Christmas		
75 Black-Capped Chickadee	5,000	$ 20.00
76 Squirrels	5,000	22.00
Heinrich		
UNICEF Children in the World		
77 Europe	Year	30.00
78 Asia	Year	30.00
79 Africa	Year	30.00
80 America	Year	30.00
81 Malaysia	Year	30.00
(Single issue)		
79 International Year of Child	Year	35.00
Flower Fairies Collection		
79 Lavender Fairy	21 Days	35.00
80 Sweet Pea Fairy	21 Days	35.00
80 Candytuft Fairy	21 Days	35.00
80 Heliotrope Fairy	21 Days	35.00
81 Black Thorne Fairy	21 Days	35.00
81 Apple Blossom Fairy	21 Days	35.00
Hibel Studo (Kaiser)		
World I Love		
81 Leah's Family	17,500	85.00
Hibel Studio (Rosenthal)		
Famous Women and Children		
80 Pharoah's Daughter and Moses	3,000	350.00
Hutschenreuther		
Songbirds of America		
72 Easter Bluebirds Goldfinch (Pair)	5,000	100.00
73 Mockingbird/Robins (Pair)	5,000	100.00
Christmas*		
72 On Way to Egypt	5,000	N/A
73 Adoration	5,000	N/A
74 Annunciation	5,000	N/A
*Series not available in U.S.		
Canada Christmas		
73 Parliament Building	Year	15.00
74 Moose	Year	16.00
75 Basilica	Year	21.00
76 Winter on Prairies	Year	23.00
77 Bluenose	Year	23.00
78 Lost Lagoon	Year	27.00
79 Yukon Highway Bridge	Year	33.00
80 Covered Bridge	Year	38.00
Bicentennial		
76 Freedom in Flight	5,000	100.00
76 Freedom in Flight (Gold)	200	200.00
Plates of the Month (Set of 12)		
77 January – December	5,000	780.00
Mother and Child Annual		
78 Mother and Child	Year	55.00
79 Mother and Child	Year	65.00
80 Mother and Child	Year	87.50
81 Mother and Child	Year	87.50
Birthday Annual		
78 Birthday Plate	10,000	165.00
Winther Christmas		
78 Silent Night	Year	260.00
79 Saint Lucia	Year	295.00
80 Christmas Pavillion	Year	325.00
81 Christmas Sleigh	Year	400.00
Friendship Annual		
78 Friendship Plate	Year	80.00
Dolores Valenza Enchantment		
79 Princess Snowflake	5,000	50.00
79 Blossom Queen	5,000	62.50
80 Princess Marina	5,000	87.50
80 Princess Starbright	5,000	87.50
81 Princess Aura	5,000	87.50
81 Harvest Queen	5,000	87.50
Wedding Annual		
78 Wedding Plate	10,000	210.00
Zodiac Collection (Set of 12)		
78 Aries – Pisces	1,500	1500.00
Hans Achtziger Annual		
79 Heading South	4,000	150.00
80 Playful Flight	5,000	187.50
81 Tropical Skies	5,000	245.00
Arzberg Christmas		
79 Christmas	2,500	60.00
(Single issue)		
79 Celebration Plate	Year	67.50
(Single issue)		
79 Anniversary Plate	Year	120.00
(Single issue)		
77 Allegro Ensemble	7,500	120.00
Hibel Museum (Single issue)		
77 Flower Girl of Provence	12,750	175.00
Floral Heirlooms		
77 Zinnias in Sugar Bowl	5,000	65.00

	Edition Limit	Issue Price
78 Pansies in Antique Tin	5,000	$ 65.00
79 Primroses in Staffordshire Pitcher	5,000	65.00
Legendary Animals (Set of four)		
82 Unicorn		
82 Griffin		
82 Dragon		
82 Pegasus	12,500	175.00
Songbirds of North America		
82 Eastern Bluebird	12,500	60.00
82 Mockingbird	12,500	60.00
82 American Goldfinch	12,500	60.00
82 Rosebreasted Grosbeak	12,500	60.00
Kaiser		
Passion Play		
70 Oberammergau	Year	18.00
Great Yachts		
71 Cetonia	1,000	50.00
71 Westward	1,000	50.00
Feathered Friends		
78 Blue Jays	10,000	70.00
79 Cardinals	10,000	80.00
80 Cedar Waxwings	10,000	80.00
King Tut		
78 Golden Mask	15,000	65.00
Little Men		
78 Magical Moment	9,500	60.00
People of the Midnight Sun		
78 Northern Lullaby	15,000	70.00
79 Ilaga, My Friend	15,000	75.00
80 Motherhood	15,000	85.00
81 Odark and Son Samik	15,000	90.00
Yesterday's World		
78 Time for Dreaming	5,000	70.00
79 Summer is Forever	5,000	75.00
80 Sunday Afternoon	5,000	80.00
Four Seasons (Set of 4)		
81 Spring		
81 Summer		
81 Fall		
81 Winter	N/A	200.00
Happy Days		
81 Aeroplane	5,000	75.00
Little Clowns		
81 Red Mask	9,500	35.00
Nativity		
81 Old Country Christmas	Year	20.00
Romantic Portraits		
81 Lilie	5,000	200.00
see also:		
Ghent Collection (U.S.A.)		
Hibel Studio (Ger.)		
KPM – Royal Berlin		
Christmas		
69 Christmas Star	5,000	28.00
70 Three Kings	5,000	28.00
71 Christmas Tree	5,000	28.00
72 Christmas Angel	5,000	31.00
73 Christchild on Sled	5,000	33.00
74 Angel & Horn	5,000	35.00
75 Shepherds	5,000	40.00
76 Star of Bethlehem	5,000	43.00
77 Mary at Crib	5,000	46.00
78 Three Wise Men	5,000	49.00
79 At Manger	5,000	55.00
80 Shepherd	5,000	59.00
Lihs-Lindner		
Mother's Day		
72 Mother and Child	1,000	25.00
73 Mother and Child	2,000	25.00
74 Bouquet for Mother	2,000	25.00
75 We Wish You Happiness	2,000	28.00
Union Pacific Railroad		
72 Union Pacific	1,500	22.00
73 Union Pacific Big Boy	1,500	25.00
History		
73 Tribute to Flag	3,000	60.00
74 Golden Spike Centennial	1,500	40.00
Easter		
73 Happy Easter	1,500	25.00
74 Springtime	1,500	25.00
75 With Love to You at Easter	1,500	28.00
America the Beautiful		
75 Independence Hall	1,500	42.00
75 Statue of Liberty	1,500	42.00
75 Niagara Falls	1,500	42.00
75 Grand Canyon	1,500	42.00
75 Golden State	1,500	42.00
75 Capitol	1,500	42.00
Bicentennial		
76 Freedom Train	1,500	45.00
76 Spirit of America	3,500	45.00

	Edition Limit	Issue Price
Playmates		
76 Timmy and His Pal	5,000	$ 45.00
77 Heidi and Playmate	5,000	45.00
Golden Spike Centennial		
77 Central Pacific Jupiter	1,500	25.00
77 Union Pacific 119	1,500	25.00
A Child's Christmas		
78 Holy Night	5,000	40.00
Marmot		
Father's Day		
70 Stag	3,500	12.00
71 Horse	3,500	12.50
Christmas		
70 Polar Bear	5,000	13.00
71 Buffalo	5,000	14.00
72 Boy & Grandfather	5,000	20.00
73 Snowman	3,000	20.00
74 Dancing Children	2,000	24.00
75 Covey of Quail	2,000	30.00
76 Windmill	2,000	30.00
Presidents		
71 Washington	1,500	25.00
72 Jefferson	1,500	25.00
73 John Adams	1,500	25.00
Mother's Day		
72 Seal	6,000	16.00
73 Polar Bear	2,000	20.00
74 Penguins	2,000	24.00
75 Raccoons	2,000	30.00
76 Ducks	2,000	40.00
Meissen		
Annual		
73 Winter Countryside by Sleigh	5,000	71.00
74 Sleeping Beauty	5,000	75.00
75 Archway to Albrecht's Castle	5,500	92.00
76 Doge's Palace in Venice	5,000	92.00
77 Fra Holle	5,000	114.00
78 Ice Crystal with Children	7,000	123.00
79 Winter Fairy Tale	7,000	151.00
80 Booted Cat	N/A	155.00
Mueller		
Christmas		
71 Christmas in Tyrol	Year	20.00
72 Christmas Messenger	Year	15.00
73 Bringing Home Tree	Year	20.00
74 Trimming Tree	Year	25.00
75 Family on Christmas Morning	Year	27.50
76 Christmas Fire	Year	28.50
77 Ice Skating	Year	28.50
Father's Day		
73 Three Generations	N/A	17.50
74 Fishing	N/A	20.00
75 Hiking	N/A	27.50
Porcelaine Ariel		
see: Hamilton Collection (U.S.A.)		
Rosenthal		
Annual (Porcelain)		
71 Tapio Wirkkala	3,000	N/A
72 Natale Sapone	3,000	N/A
73 Otto Piene	3,000	N/A
74 Gunther Fruhtrunk	3,000	N/A
75 Srivastava Narendra	3,000	N/A
76 Salvador Dali	3,000	N/A
77 Victor Vasarely	3,000	N/A
78 E. Paolozzi	3,000	N/A
79 Arnold Leissler	3,000	N/A
80 O.H. Hajek	3,000	N/A
Artist Plates*		
73 NR 1 Gunter Grass	5,000	N/A
74 NR 2 Jean Cocteau	5,000	N/A
74 NR 3 Eugen Gomringer	5,000	N/A
74 NR 4 Otto Piene	5,000	N/A
75 NR 5 Max Bill	5,000	N/A
75 NR 6 Hans-Werner Henze	5,000	N/A
75 NR 7 Bjørn Wiinblad	5,000	N/A
75 NR 8 Kriwet	5,000	N/A
76 NR 9 Hildegard Knef	5,000	N/A
77 NR10 Yehudi Menuhin	5,000	N/A
77 NR11 Emilio Pucci	5,000	N/A
78 NR12 Salvador Dali	5,000	N/A
78 NR13 Victor Vasarely	5,000	N/A
78 NR14 Almir Mazignier	5,000	N/A
79 NR15 Ivan Rapuzin	5,000	N/A
79 NR16 Ottmar Alt	5,000	N/A
*Series not available in U.S.		
Satire Plates*		
NR1 Konrad Adenauer	5,000	N/A
NR2 Willy Brandt	5,000	N/A
NR3 Theodor Heuss	5,000	N/A
NR4 Walter Scheel	5,000	N/A
NR5 Helmut Schmidt	5,000	N/A
NR6 Franz-Josef Strauss	5,000	N/A
NR7 Helmut Kohl	5,000	N/A
NR8 Heinz Ruhmann	5,000	N/A
NR9 Herbert Von Karajan	5,000	N/A
NR10 Marlene Dietrich	5,000	N/A

	Edition Limit	Issue Price
NR11 Mao-Tse-Tung	5,000	N/A
NR12 Bruno Kreisky	5,000	N/A
*Series not available in U.S.		
Annual (Crystal)		
74 Otto Piene (Clear)	3,000	$ 200.00
74 Otto Piene (Gold Inlaid)	3,000	250.00
74 Otto Piene (Platinum Inlaid)	3,000	250.00
75 G. Uecker	3,000	200.00
76 Bjørn Wiinblad	3,000	N/A
77 Gunter F. Ris	3,000	N/A
78 Ivan Rapuzin	3,000	600.00
79 Salvador Dali	3,000	N/A
80 Ernst Fuchs	3,000	N/A
Lorraine Trester		
75 Once Upon a Summertime	5,000	60.00
76 One Lovely Yesterday	5,000	70.00
Fantasies and Fables		
76 Oriental Night Music	N/A	50.00
77 Mandolin Players	N/A	55.00
Wiinblad Studio-Linie		
76 Madonna	2,000	150.00
77 Annuciation	2,000	195.00
78 Three Kings	2,000	225.00
79 Holy Family	2,000	230.00
80 Appearance of Angels	2,000	240.00
81 Adoration of Shepherds	2,000	295.00
Aladdin		
78 Aladdin and Lamp	N/A	65.00
79 Aladdin and Street Urchins	N/A	65.00
79 Aladdin and Genie	N/A	65.00
79 Aladdin in Magic Garden	N/A	65.00
80 Aladdin and Spirits	N/A	85.00
80 Aladdin and Princess	N/A	85.00
see also:		
Hibel Studio (Ger.)		
Kern Collectibles (U.S.A.)		
Royal Bayreuth		
see: Kern Collectibles (U.S.A.)		
Royal Tettau		
Papal Plates		
71 Pope Paul VI	5,000	100.00
72 Pope John XXIII	5,000	100.00
73 Pope Pius XII	5,000	100.00
Christmas (Single issue)		
72 Carriage in Village	N/A	12.50
Royale		
Christmas		
69 Christmas Fair in Ebeltoft	6,000	12.00
70 Kalundborg Church	10,000	13.00
71 Christmas Night	8,000	16.00
72 Elks	8,000	16.00
73 Christmas	6,000	20.00
74 Village at Christmas	5,000	22.00
75 Feeding Time	5,000	26.00
76 Christmas at Seaport	5,000	27.50
77 Sledding	5,000	30.00
Mother's Day		
70 Swan and Brood	6,000	12.00
71 Doe and Fawn	9,000	13.00
72 Rabbit Family	9,000	16.00
73 Owl Family	6,000	18.00
74 Duck Family	5,000	22.00
75 Lynx Family	5,000	26.00
76 Woodcock and Young	5,000	27.50
77 Koala Bear	5,000	30.00
Father's Day		
70 U.S. Frigate Constitution	5,000	13.00
71 Man Fishing	5,000	13.00
72 Mountain Climber	6,000	16.00
73 Camping	4,000	18.00
74 Eagle	2,500	22.00
75 Regatta	2,500	26.00
76 Hunting Scene	2,500	27.50
77 Fishing	5,000	30.00
Game		
72 Setters Pointing Quail	500	180.00
73 Fox	500	200.00
74 Osprey	250	250.00
75 California Quail	250	265.00
Royale Germania		
Annual		
70 Orchid (Blue)	600	200.00
71 Cyclamen (Red)	1,000	200.00
72 Silver Thistle (Green)	1,000	250.00
73 Tulips (Lilac)	600	275.00
74 Sunflowers (Topaz)	500	300.00
75 Snowdrops (Amber)	350	450.00
76 Flaming Heart (Red)	350	450.00
Mother's Day		
71 Roses (Red)	250	135.00
72 Elephant (Green)	750	180.00
73 Koala Bear (Lilac)	600	200.00
74 Squirrels (Topaz)	500	240.00
75 Swan Family (Amber)	350	250.00

	Edition Limit	Issue Price
Schmid		
Bavarian Christmas		
71 Family Portrait	5,000	$ 25.50
72 On Horseback	5,000	26.50
73 Bringing Home Tree	5,000	26.50
74 Decorating Tree	5,000	26.50
75 Opening Presents	5,000	26.50
76 By Fireside	5,000	26.50
77 Skating	5,000	28.50
78 Family Picking Tree	5,000	36.00
79 Breakfast by Tree	5,000	45.00
80 Feeding Animals	5,000	55.00
Ferrandiz Christmas		
72 Christ in Manger	Year	30.00
73 Christmas	Year	30.00
Golden Moments		
78 Tranquility	15,000	250.00
Christmas (Pewter)		
77 Santa	5,000	30.00
78 Beautiful Snow	5,000	45.00
79 I Hear America Singing	6,000	50.00
Beatrix Potter (Pewter)		
78 Peter Rabbit	5,000	50.00
79 Jemima-Puddle Duck	5,000	50.00
A Year with Paddington Bear		
79 Pyramid Presents	25,000	12.50
80 Springtime	25,000	12.50
81 Sandcastles	25,000	12.50
81 School Days	25,000	12.50
Reflections of Life		
80 Quiet Reflections	10,000	85.00
81 Tree of Life	10,000	85.00
Country Pride		
81 Surprise in Cellar	7,500	35.00
81 Plum Tuckered Out	7,500	35.00
81 Duke's Mixture	7,500	35.00
82 Bustin with Pride	7,500	35.00
Music Makers		
81 Flutist	10,000	25.00
82 Entertainer	10,000	25.00
82 Magical Medley	10,000	25.00
82 Sweet Serenade	10,000	25.00
My Name Is Star		
81 Star's Spring	10,000	30.00
82 Star's Summer	10,000	30.00

see also: Addams Family (U.S.A.)

	Edition Limit	Issue Price
Schumann		
Composers		
70 Beethoven	N/A	8.00
72 Mozart	N/A	13.00
Christmas		
71 Snow Scene	10,000	12.00
72 Deer in Snow	15,000	12.00
73 Weihnachten	5,000	12.00
74 Church in Snow	5,000	12.00
75 Fountain	5,000	12.00

see also:
Christian Bell (Can.)
Calhoun's Collector's Society (U.S.A.)

	Edition Limit	Issue Price
Stumar		
Christmas		
70 Angel	10,000	8.00
71 Old Canal	10,000	8.00
72 Countryside	10,000	8.00
73 Friendship	10,000	10.00
74 Making Fancy	10,000	10.00
75 Preparation	10,000	10.00
76 Drummer Boy	10,000	10.00
77 Joyful Expectations	10,000	15.00
78 Christmas	10,000	19.50
Mother's Day		
71 Amish Mother & Daughter	10,000	8.00
72 Children	10,000	8.00
73 Mother Sewing	10,000	10.00
74 Mother Cradle	10,000	10.00
75 Baking	10,000	10.00
76 Reading to Children	10,000	15.00
77 Comforting Child	10,000	15.00
78 Tranquility	10,000	19.50
Egyptian		
77 Ancient Egyptian Trilogy	5,000	45.00
78 Charioteer	5,000	54.00
Tirschenreuth		
Christmas		
69 Homestead	3,500	12.00
70 Church	3,500	12.00
71 Star of Bethlehem	3,500	12.00
72 Elk Silhouette	2,000	13.00
73 Christmas	Year	14.00
Villeroy & Boch		
Christmas		
77 Holy Family	10,000	175.00
78 Three Holy Kings	20,000	175.00
79 Mary with Child	10,000	198.00
80 Madonna in Glory	10,000	200.00

	Edition Limit	Issue Price
81 Mary Glorious	10,000	$210.00
World Wildlife		
82 Panda Bear	Year	38.00
WMF Geislingen		
Annual		
78 Rose-Motif I	2,500	117.50
79 Rose-Motif II	2,500	120.00
80 Rose-Motif III	2,500	120.00
Christmas		
78 Birth of Christ	2,500	117.50
79 Praising King	2,500	120.00
80 Praising Shepherd	2,500	120.00

Great Britain

	Edition Limit	Issue Price
Aynsley		
A Christmas Carol		
79 Mr. Fezziwig's Ball	Year	30.00
80 Marley's Ghost	Year	36.00
81 Cratchit Family	Year	41.00
Boehm Studios		
European Bird Plates		
73 Swallow	5,000	48.75
73 Chaffinch	5,000	48.75
73 Coal Tit	5,000	48.75
73 Tree Sparrow	5,000	48.75
73 King Fisher	5,000	48.75
73 Gold Crest	5,000	48.75
73 Blue Tit	5,000	48.75
73 Linnet	5,000	48.75
Honor America		
74 American Bald Eagle	12,000	85.00
Butterfly		
75 Blue Mountain Swallowtails	100	450.00
75 Jezabels	100	450.00
76 Comma with Loops	100	450.00
76 African Butterflies	100	450.00
76 Solandras Maxima	100	450.00
Hard Fruit		
75 Plums	100	450.00
75 Pears	100	450.00
76 Peaches	100	450.00
76 Apples	100	450.00
Oriental Birds		
75 Bluebacked Fairy Bluebirds	100	400.00
75 Azure-Winged Magpies	100	400.00
76 Golden-Fronted Leafbird	100	400.00
76 Golden-Throated Barbet	100	400.00
Seashell		
75 Violet Spider Conch	100	450.00
75 Rooster Tail Conch	100	450.00
76 Orange Spider Conch	100	450.00
76 Cheragra Spider Conch	100	450.00
Soft Fruit		
75 Loganberries	100	450.00
75 Cherries	100	450.00
76 Strawberries	100	450.00
76 Grapes	100	450.00
Butterflies of the World		
78 Monarch and Daisy	5,000	62.00
78 Red Admiral and Thistle	5,000	62.00
Flower		
75 Lilies	100	450.00
75 Passion Flowers	100	450.00
76 Double Clematis	100	450.00
Favorite Floral		
78 Clematis	2,500	58.00
78 Rhododendron	2,500	58.00
79 Boehm Orchid	2,500	58.00
79 Yellow Rose	2,500	58.00
80 Spider Orchid	2,500	58.00
80 Dahlia	2,500	58.00

see also: Hamilton Collection (U.S.A.)

	Edition Limit	Issue Price
Caithness Glass		
America's Favorite Birds		
79 Crystal Wren	5,000	79.50
Coalport *		
Christmas		
76 Christmas Eve	Year	12.00
77 Dangerous Skating	Year	16.00
78 Alas! Poor Bruin	Year	18.00
79 Christmas Morning	Year	22.00
80 Blind Man's Bluff	Year	27.00

*Series not available in U.S.

	Edition Limit	Issue Price
Mother's Day		
78 Clematis	Year	16.00
79 Orchid	Year	21.00
80 Peony	Year	27.00
(Single issue)		
72 Indy 500	2,000	49.95
Hornsea		
Christmas		
79 "C"—Nativity	10,000	21.00
80 "H"—Mary and Child	10,000	25.00
81 "R"—Three Wise Men	10,000	49.50

	Edition Limit	Issue Price
Mason		
Christmas		
75 Windsor Castle	Year	$75.00
76 Holyrood House	Year	75.00
77 Buckingham Palace	Year	75.00
78 Balmoral Castle	Year	75.00
79 Hampton Court	Year	75.00
80 Sandringham House	Year	75.00
Poole Pottery		
Medieval Calendar		
72 Drinking Wine by Fire (January)	1,000	100.00
72 Chopping Wood (February)	1,000	100.00
73 Digging in Fields and Setting Seeds (March)	1,000	125.00
73 Carrying Flowering Branch (April)	1,000	125.00
74 Hawking (May)	1,000	125.00
74 Mowing Hay (June)	1,000	125.00
75 Cutting Corn with Sickle (July)	1,000	125.00
75 Threshing with Flail (August)	1,000	125.00
76 Picking Grapes (September)	1,000	125.00
76 Sowing Winter Corn (October)	1,000	125.00
77 Gathering Acorns to Feed Pigs (November)	1,000	125.00
77 Pig Killing (December)	1,000	125.00
Cathedral		
73 Christ on Cross	11,000	125.00
Christmas		
73 Adoration of Magi	1,000	125.00
73 Flight into Egypt	1,000	125.00
Home at Christmas		
78 Santa's Helpers	10,000	37.50
79 Three Wisemen	10,000	37.50
Birds of North America		
79 Great Horned Owl	10,000	37.50
Mother's Day		
79 Tenderness	10,000	37.50
Royal Doulton		
Flower Garden		
75 Spring Harmony	15,000	60.00
76 Dreaming Lotus	15,000	65.00
77 Poet's Garden	15,000	70.00
78 Country Bouquet	15,000	70.00
80 From My Mother's Garden	15,000	85.00
Ports of Call		
75 San Francisco	15,000	60.00
76 New Orleans	15,000	65.00
77 Venice	15,000	70.00
78 Montmartre	15,000	70.00
Reflections on China		
76 Garden of Tranquility	15,000	70.00
77 Imperial Palace	15,000	70.00
78 Temple of Heaven	15,000	75.00
80 Lake of Mists	15,000	85.00
I Remember America		
77 Pennsylvania Pastorale	15,000	70.00
78 Lovejoy Bridge	15,000	70.00
79 Four Corners	15,000	75.00
80 Marshlands	15,000	95.00
Victorian Christmas		
77 Skater	Year	25.00
78 Victorian Girl	Year	27.50
79 Sleigh Ride	Year	29.95
80 St. Nick's Arrival	Year	42.50
81 Carolers	Year	37.50
All God's Children		
78 Brighter Day	10,000	60.00
79 Village Children	10,000	65.00
80 Noble Heritage	10,000	85.00
American Tapestries		
78 Sleigh Bells	10,000	70.00
79 Pumpkin Patch	10,000	70.00
80 General Store	10,000	95.00
Jungle Fantasy		
79 Ark	10,000	75.00
80 Compassion	10,000	95.00
Royal Grafton		
Twelve Days of Christmas		
76 Partridge in Pear Tree	3,000	17.50
77 Two Turtle doves	3,000	17.50
78 Three French Hens	3,000	21.50
79 Four colly Birds	3,000	26.50
80 Five Gold Rings	3,000	35.00
Royal Worcester		
Bicentennial		
76 Independence	10,000	150.00
Fabulous Birds		
76 Peacocks I	10,000	65.00
77 Peacocks II	10,000	65.00
Audubon Birds		
77 Warbler & Jay	5,000	150.00
78 Kingbird & Sparrow	10,000	150.00

	Edition Limit	Issue Price
Chinoiserie		
77 Bishop Summer	Year	$65.00
English Christmas		
79 Christmas Eve	Year	60,00
80 Christmas Morning	Year	65.00
81 Christmas Day	Year	70.00
Spode		
Ray Harm Birds (Set of 12)		
70 Rufus-Sided Towhee		
70 Winter Wren		
71 Eastern Bluebird		
71 Stellar's Jay		
71 Eastern Mockingbird		
71 Barn Swallow		
71 Rose-Breasted Grosbeak		
71 Cardinal		
72 Western Tanager		
72 Woodpecker		
72 Chickadee		
72 American Goldfinch	5,000	300.00
Maritime Plates (Set of six)		
80 USS United States and HMS Macedonian		
80 USS President and HMS Little Belt		
80 HMS Shannon and USS Chesapeake		
80 USS Constitution and HMS Guerriere		
80 USS Constitution and HMN Java		
80 HMS Pelican and USS Argus	2,000	300.00
Wedgwood		
Calendar		
71 Zodiac Sign	Year	12.00
72 Carousel	Year	12.95
73 Bountiful Butterfly	Year	12.95
74 Knights of Camelot	Year	14.00
75 Children's Game	Year	15.00
76 Robin	Year	25.00
77 Tonateuk—Aztec Sun	Year	30.00
78 Samurai	Year	30.00
79 Sacred Scarab	Year	35.00
80 Safari	Year	35.00
81 Horses	Year	37.50
Children's Story		
71 Sandman	Year	30.00
72 Tinder Box	Year	30.00
73 Emperor's New Clothes	Year	30.00
74 Ugly Duckling	Year	10.00
75 Little Mermaid	Year	14.00
76 Hansel & Gretel	Year	17.00
77 Rumpelstiltskin	Year	17.00
78 Frog Prince	Year	15.00
79 Golden Goose	Year	15.00
80 Rapunzel	Year	16.00
81 Tom Thumb	Year	18.00
82 Lady and Lion	Year	20.00
(Single issue)		
78 Tri-Color Decade Christmas	10,000	325.00
(Single issue)		
78 Anniversary Christmas	Year	130.00
Trophy		
78 Tutankhamun	500	1000.00
78 Ankhesenamum	500	1000.00
Child's Christmas		
79 Snowman	Year	35.00
80 Bringing Home Tree	Year	37.50
Queen's Ware Christmas		
80 Windsor Castle	Year	24.95
Remarkable World of Charles Dickens		
80 Oliver Twist and Fagin	Year	60.00
80 Scrooge and Marley's Ghost	Year	60.00

India

	Edition Limit	Issue Price
Sarna		
Christmas		
75 Holy Family	4,000	17.50

Italy

	Edition Limit	Issue Price
Anri		
Mother's Day		
72 Alpine Mother & Children	5,000	35.00
73 Alpine Mother & Children	5,000	40.00
74 Alpine Mother & Children	5,000	50.00
75 Alpine Stroll	5,000	60.00
76 Knitting	5,000	60.00
Father's Day		
72 Alpine Father & Children	5,000	35.00
73 Alpine Father & Children	5,000	40.00
74 Cliff Gazing	5,000	50.00
75 Sailing	5,000	60.00
Ferrandiz Birthday		
72 Birthday Girl	Year	15.00
72 Birthday Boy	Year	15.00

	Edition Limit	Issue Price
73 Birthday	Year	$ 20.00
74 Birthday Girl	Year	22.00
74 Birthday Boy	Year	22.00
75 Birthday Girl	Year	35.00
Ferrandiz Mother's Day		
72 Mother Sewing	2,500	35.00
73 Mother & Child	1,500	40.00
74 Mother & Child	1,500	50.00
75 Mother Holding Dove	1,500	60.00
76 Mother and Child	1,500	60.00
77 Girl with Flowers	1,500	65.00
78 Beginning	3,000	77.50
79 All Hearts	3,000	120.00
80 Spring Arrivals	3,000	150.00
81 Harmony	3,000	150.00
Ferrandiz Christmas		
72 Finishing Cradle	2,500	35.00
73 Boy with Lamb	Year	40.00
74 Nativity	Year	40.00
75 Flight into Egypt	Year	40.00
76 Mary & Joseph Pray	Year	40.00
77 Girl with Tree	4,000	65.00
78 Leading Way	4,000	77.50
79 Drummer Boy	4,000	120.00
80 Rejoice	4,000	150.00
Ferrandiz Wedding Day		
72 Wedding	Year	40.00
73 Wedding	Year	40.00
74 Wedding	Year	48.00
75 Wedding	Year	60.00
76 Wedding	Year	60.00
Jubilee (Single issue)		
78 Spring Dance	2,500	500.00
Capo Di Monte		
Christmas		
72 Cherubs	500	55.00
73 Bells & Holly	500	55.00
74 Christmas	1,000	60.00
75 Christmas	1,000	60.00
76 Christmas	250	65.00
Mother's Day		
73 Mother's Day	500	55.00
74 Mother's Day	500	60.00
75 Mother's Day	500	60.00
76 Mother's Day	500	65.00
Carlo Monti		
Mother's Day		
73 Madonna & Child	2,000	35.00
Count Agazzi		
Famous Personalities		
68 Famous Personalities	600	8.00
70 Famous Personalities	1,000	12.50
73 Famous Personalities	600	15.00
(Single issue)		
69 Apollo II	1,000	17.00
Children's Hour		
70 Owl	2,000	12.50
71 Cat	2,000	12.50
72 Pony	2,000	12.50
73 Panda	2,000	12.50
Easter		
71 Playing Violin	600	12.50
72 At Prayer	600	12.50
73 Winged Cherub	600	12.50
Mother's Day		
72 Mother's Day	144	35.00
73 Mother's Day	720	19.50
Father's Day		
72 Father's Day	144	35.00
73 Father's Day	288	19.50
Christmas		
73 Christmas	1,000	19.50
(Single issue)		
73 Peace	720	12.50
Kings		
Mother's Day		
73 Dancing Girl	1,500	100.00
74 Dancing Boy	1,500	115.00
75 Motherly Love	1,500	140.00
76 Maiden	1,500	180.00
Christmas		
73 Adoration	1,500	150.00
74 Madonna	1,500	150.00
75 Heavenly Choir	1,500	160.00
76 Girl and Brother	1,500	200.00
Veneto Flair		
Christmas		
71 Three Kings	1,500	45.00
72 Shepherds	2,000	45.00
73 Christ Child	2,000	55.00
74 Angel	2,000	55.00
Wildlife		
71 Deer	500	37.50
72 Elephant	1,000	37.50
73 Puma	2,000	37.50
74 Tiger	2,000	40.00

	Edition Limit	Issue Price
Birds		
72 Owl	2,000	$ 37.50
73 Falcon	2,000	37.50
74 Mallard Duck	2,000	45.00
Mother's Day		
72 Madonna and Child	2,000	55.00
73 Madonna and Child	2,000	55.00
74 Mother and Son	2,000	55.00
75 Daughter and Doll	2,000	45.00
76 Son and Daughter	2,000	55.00
77 Mother and Child	2,000	50.00
Easter		
73 Rabbits	2,000	50.00
74 Chicks	2,000	50.00
75 Lamb	2,000	50.00
76 Composite	2,000	55.00
Goddess		
73 Pomona	1,500	75.00
74 Diana	1,500	75.00
Mosaic		
73 Justinian	500	50.00
74 Pelican	1,000	50.00
77 Theodora	500	50.00
Cats		
74 Persian	2,000	40.00
75 Siamese	2,000	45.00
76 Tabby	2,000	45.00
Christmas Card		
75 Christmas Eve	5,000	45.00
76 Old North Church	5,000	50.00
77 Log Cabin Christmas	5,000	50.00
78 Dutch Christmas	5,000	50.00
Valentine's Day		
77 Valentine Boy	3,000	45.00
78 Valentine Girl	3,000	45.00
Flower Children		
78 Rose	3,000	45.00
79 Orchid	3,000	60.00
80 Camillia	3,000	65.00
La Belle Femme		
78 Lily	9,500	70.00
78 Gigi	9,500	76.50
80 Dominique	9,500	76.50
80 Gabrielle	9,500	76.50
American Landscape		
79 Hudson Valley	7,500	75.00
80 Northwest Cascade	7,500	75.00
Children's Christmas		
79 Carolers	7,500	60.00
80 Heading Home	7,500	70.00
81 Night Before	7,500	95.00
Mother and Child		
81 Buffalos	5,000	95.00
81 Elephants	5,000	95.00
81 Koalas	5,000	95.00
81 Lions	5,000	95.00
81 Loons	5,000	95.00
81 Polar Bears	5,000	95.00
Young Love		
81 Young Love	5,000	95.00

Japan

	Edition Limit	Issue Price
Manjundo		
Chinese Lunar Calendar		
72 Year of Rat	5,000	15.00
73 Year of Ox	5,000	15.00
Noritake		
Christmas		
75 Madonna with Child	3,000	42.00
76 Gratia Hoso Kawa	3,000	54.00
77 Julia Otaa	3,000	83.00
78 Amakusa Shiro	3,000	109.00
79 Munzio Ito	3,000	124.00
80 Furst Takayama	3,000	125.00
Annual		
77 Paradise Birds	3,000	380.00
78 Chrysanthemums	3,000	494.00
79 Cranes	3,000	556.00
80 Water Lilies and Butterflies	3,000	575.00
Sango		
Christmas		
76 Undesired Slumber	7,500	25.00
77 Togetherness	7,500	25.00
Mother's Day		
76 Spring Delight	7,500	20.00
77 Broken Wing	5,000	22.50
see also: Kern Collectibles (U.S.A.)		
Schmid		
Raggedy Ann Christmas		
75 Gifts of Love	Year	12.50
76 Raggedy Ann Skates	Year	13.00
77 Decorating Tree	Year	13.00
78 Checking List	Year	15.00
79 Little Helper	15,000	17.50
Raggedy Ann Mother's Day		
76 Motherhood	Year	13.00
77 Bouquet of Love	Year	13.00
78 Hello Mom	Year	15.00
79 High Spirits	10,000	$ 17.50
Raggedy Ann Valentine's Day		
78 As Time Goes By	Year	13.00
79 Daisies Do Tell	Year	17.50
Disney Valentine's Day		
79 Hands and Hearts	Year	17.50
80 Mickey's I Love You	Year	17.50
81 Be Mine	Year	17.50
Peanuts 30th Anniversary (Single issue)		
80 Happy Anniversary	15,000	27.50
Alice in Wonderland Anniversary (Single issue)		
81 Alice in Wonderland	7,500	17.50
Disney Anniversary (Single issue)		
81 Pluto's 50th Birthday	7,500	17.50
see also: Addams Family (U.S.A.)		

Mexico

	Edition Limit	Issue Price
Bonita Silver		
Mother's Day		
72 Mother and Baby	4,000	125.00
Roman Ceramica Excelsis		
Masterpiece Collection		
79 Adoration	5,000	65.00
80 Madonna with Grapes	5,000	87.50
81 Holy Family	5,000	95.00
Ceramica Excelsis Collection		
80 Little Children, Come to Me	15,000	45.00

Netherlands

	Edition Limit	Issue Price
Blue Delft (Schoonhaven)		
Christmas		
70 Drawbridge Near Binnehof	Year	12.00
71 St. Lauren's Church	Year	12.00
72 Church at Bierkade	Year	12.00
73 St. Jan's Church	Year	12.00
74 Dongeradeel	Year	13.00
75 Maassluis	Year	15.00
76 Montelbaanstower	Year	15.00
77 Harbour Tower of Hoorn	Year	19.50
78 Binnenpoort Gate	Year	21.00
Mother's Day		
71 Mother & Daughter of 1600s	Year	12.00
72 Mother & Daughter of Isle of Urk	Year	12.00
73 Rembrandt's Mother	Year	12.00
Father's Day		
71 Francisco Lana's Airship	Year	12.00
72 Dr. Jonathon's Balloon	Year	12.00
Crown Delft		
Christmas		
69 Man by Tree	Year	10.00
70 Two Sleigh Riders	Year	10.00
71 Christmas Tree on Market Square	Year	10.00
72 Baking for Christmas	Year	10.00
Mother's Day		
70 Sheep	Year	10.00
71 Stork	Year	10.00
72 Ducks	Year	10.00
73 Mother's Day	1,000	10.00
Father's Day		
70 Father's Day	Year	10.00
71 Father's Day	Year	10.00
72 Father's Day	1,000	10.00
73 Father's Day	1,000	10.00
Kurz (Shuler International)		
Christmas		
72 Christmas	500	60.00
73 Christmas	500	70.00
74 Christmas	500	65.00
Mother's Day		
73 Mother's Day	500	65.00
Metawa		
Christmas		
72 Skaters	3,000	30.00
73 One-Horse Sleigh	1,500	30.00
74 Sailboat	Year	35.00
Royal Delft		
Christmas		
15 Glory to God, Christmas Bells (10")	Year	N/A
15 Christmas Star (7")	Year	N/A
16 Star—Floral Design (10")	Year	N/A
16 Cradle of Child (10")	Year	N/A
17 Shepherd with Sheep in Stable (10")	Year	N/A
17 Christmas Star (10")	Year	N/A
18 Shepherd with Sheep in Stable (10")	Year	N/A
18 Christmas Star—Peace on Earth (10")	Year	N/A
19 Church (10")	Year	N/A
19 Christmas Star (10")	Year	N/A
20 Holly Wreath (10")	Year	N/A
20 Church Tower (10")	Year	N/A
21 Canal Boatman (10")	Year	N/A
21 Christmas Star (10")	Year	N/A
22 Landscape (10")	Year	N/A
22 Christmas Wreath (10")	Year	N/A
23 Shepherd (10")	Year	N/A
23 Christmas Star (10")	Year	N/A
24 Christmas Star (10")	Year	N/A
24 Town Gate with Sheperd (10")	Year	N/A
25 Towngate in Delft (10")	Year	N/A
25 Christmas Star (10")	Year	N/A
26 Christmas Star (10")	Year	N/A
26 Bell Tower (7")	Year	N/A
26 Windmill Landscape (10")	Year	N/A
27 Christmas Star (10")	Year	N/A
27 Sailing Boat (10")	Year	N/A
27 Church Tower (7")	Year	N/A
28 Christmas Poinsettia (10")	Year	N/A
28 Mill Christmas (7")	Year	N/A
28 Lighthouse Christmas (10")	Year	N/A
29 Christmas Bell (10")	Year	N/A
29 Church Spire (7")	Year	N/A
29 Small Dutch Town (10")	Year	N/A
30 Church Entrance, Delft (10")	Year	N/A
30 Christmas Rose (10")	Year	N/A
30 Sailing Boat (7")	Year	N/A
31 Christmas Star (10")	Year	N/A
31 Snow Landscape (10")	Year	N/A
31 Church Tower (7")	Year	N/A
32 Bell Tower (7")	Year	N/A
32 Fireplace (10")	Year	N/A
32 Christmas Star (10")	Year	N/A
33 Interior Scene with Exterior View (10")	Year	N/A
34 Interior Scene (10")	Year	N/A
34 Snowy Stable (10")	Year	N/A
35 Interior Scene with Exterior View (10")	Year	N/A
36 Interior Scene with Exterior View (10")	Year	N/A
37 Interior Scene with Exterior View (10")	Year	N/A
38 Interior Scene with Exterior View (10")	Year	N/A
39 Interior Scene with Well-Staircase (10")	Year	N/A
40 Interior with Christmas Tree (10")	Year	N/A
41 Interior Scene Fireplace & Tree (10")	Year	N/A
55 Christmas Star (9")	Year	N/A
55 Church Tower (10")	200	$ 20.00
56 Two Christmas Bells in Floral (9")	Year	N/A
56 Landscape (10")	200	20.00
56 Flower Design (9")	Year	N/A
57 Christmas Star (9")	Year	N/A
57 Landscape (10")	225	22.00
58 Christmas Star (9")	Year	N/A
58 View of Village at Riverside (10")	225	25.00
59 View of Village at Riverside (10")	250	25.00
59 Landscape with Mill (7")	400	10.00
60 Landscape (7")	400	10.00
60 Street in Delft (10")	250	25.00
61 Snow Landscape (7")	500	10.00
61 Village Scene with Church Town (10")	260	30.00
62 Town View (7")	500	10.00
62 Tower in Leeuwarden (10")	275	30.00
63 Mill in Zeddam (7")	500	15.00
63 Tower in Enkhuisen (10")	275	35.00
64 Tower in Hoorn (10")	300	35.00
64 Mill in Poelenburg (7")	600	15.00
65 Towngate in Kampen (7")	600	15.00
65 Corn-Mill in Rhoon (10")	300	35.00
66 Towngate in Medemblik (7")	600	20.00
66 Snuff Mill in Rotterdam (10")	325	40.00
67 Mill in Hazerswoude (7")	700	20.00
67 Tower in Amsterdam (10")	350	45.00
68 Mill in Schiedam (7")	700	25.00
68 Tower in Amsterdam "Schreierstoren" (10")	350	60.00
69 Mill Near Gorkum (7")	800	35.00
69 Church in Utrecht (10")	400	60.00
70 Mill Near Haarlem (7")	1,500	25.00
70 Cathedral in Veere (10")	500	60.00
71 Towngate at Zierikzee (7")	3,500	25.00
71 "Dom" Tower in Utrecht (10")	550	60.00

	Edition Limit	Issue Price
72 Towngate at Elburg (7")	3,500	$40.00
72 Church in Edam (10")	1,500	70.00
73 Towngate at Amersfoort (7")	4,500	50.00
73 DeWaag in Alkmaar (10")	1,500	75.00
74 Watergate at Sneek (7")	4,500	80.00
74 Kitchen in Hindeloopen (10")	1,500	160.00
75 Towngate at Amsterdam (7")	1,000	140.00
75 Farmer in Laren (10")	1,500	250.00
76 Towngate in Gorinehem (7")	4,500	115.00
76 Farmer's Wife in Staphorst (10")	1,500	220.00
77 Dromedaris Tower (7")	4,500	140.00
77 Farm Family in Spakenburg (10")	1,500	277.00
78 Winter Skating Scene (10")	1,000	277.00
78 Christmas Fisherman (7")	1,500	140.00
78 Christmas Angels (7")	1,500	140.00
Mother's Day		
71 Mother & Daughter (Volendam)	2,500	50.00
72 Mother & Daughter (Hindeloopen)	2,500	40.00
73 Mother & Daughter (Marken)	3,000	50.00
74 Mother & Daughter (Zuid-Beveland)	Year	80.00
75 Mother & Daughter (Spakenburg)	Year	100.00
76 Mother & Daughter (Scheveningen)	Year	115.00
Father's Day		
72 Father & Son (Volendam)	1,500	40.00
73 Father & Son (Hindeloopen)	2,000	40.00
74 Father & Son (Marken)	1,000	80.00
75 Father & Son (Zuid-Beveland)	Year	80.00
76 Father & Son (Spakenburg)	Year	140.00
Easter		
73 Dutch Easter Palm (7")	3,500	75.00
73 Dutch Easter Palm (10")	3,500	N/A
74 Dutch Easter Palm	1,000	110.00
75 Dutch Easter Palm	1,000	125.00
76 Dutch Easter Palm	1,000	175.00
Valentine		
73 Enduring Beauty	1,500	75.00
74 Valentine	1,000	125.00
75 Valentine	1,000	125.00
76 Valentine	1,000	175.00
Special Bicentenary		
76 George Washington	2,500	350.00
76 Eagle Plate	5,000	150.00
Schoonhaven		
see: Blue Delft (Neth.)		
Shuler International		
see: Kurz (Neth.)		
Zenith Delftware		
Hans Brinker		
72 Skating	500	60.00
73 Gretel Tending Geese	750	60.00
Anniversary		
73 Autumn	500	45.00
73 Spring	500	45.00
73 Summer	500	45.00
73 Winter	500	45.00
Birthday Boy		
73 Monday's Child	3,000	15.00
73 Tuesday's Child	3,000	15.00
73 Wednesday's Child	3,000	15.00
73 Thursday's Child	3,000	15.00
73 Friday's Child	3,000	15.00
73 Saturday's Child	3,000	15.00
73 Sunday's Child	3,000	15.00
Birthday Girl		
73 Monday's Child	3,000	15.00
73 Tuesday's Child	3,000	15.00
73 Wednesday's Child	3,000	15.00
73 Thursday's Child	3,000	15.00
73 Friday's Child	3,000	15.00
73 Saturday's Child	3,000	15.00
73 Sunday's Child	3,000	15.00

Norway

	Edition Limit	Issue Price
Porsgrund		
(Single issue)		
09 Christmas Flowers	Year	N/A
Jubilee		
70 Femboringer	Year	25.00
Father's Day		
71 Fishing	Year	10.00
72 Cookout	Year	10.00
73 Sledding	Year	10.00
74 Father and Son	Year	$10.00
75 Skating	Year	12.50
76 Skiing	Year	15.00
77 Soccer	Year	16.50
78 Canoeing	Year	17.50
79 Father and Daughter	Year	19.50
80 Sailing	Year	21.50
Easter		
72 Ducks	Year	7.00
73 Birds	Year	10.00
74 Rabbits	Year	11.00
75 Chicks	Year	16.00
76 Sheep in Field	Year	18.00
77 Butterflies	Year	23.00

Spain

	Edition Limit	Issue Price
Santa Clara		
Christmas		
70 Christmas Message	10,000	18.00
71 Three Wise Men	10,000	18.00
72 Children in Woods	10,000	20.00
73 Archangel	5,000	25.00
74 Spirit of Christmas	10,000	25.00
75 Christmas Eve in Country	10,000	27.50
76 Madonna and Child	10,000	25.00
77 Mother and Child	10,000	27.50
78 Angel with Flowers	10,000	32.00
79 Madonna and Angels	10,000	34.50
Mother's Day		
71 Mother and Child	10,000	15.00
72 Mother and Children	12,000	15.00

Sweden

	Edition Limit	Issue Price
Kosta		
Annual		
71 Madonna & Child	Year	30.00
72 St. George & Dragon	Year	30.00
73 Viking Ship	Year	40.00
74 Annual	Year	40.00
Orrefors		
Mother's Day		
71 Flowers for Mother	2,500	45.00
72 Mother and Children	2,500	45.00
73 Mother and Child	2,500	50.00
74 Mother and Child	5,000	50.00
75 Mother and Child	2,500	60.00
76 Children and Puppy	2,500	75.00
77 Child and Dove	1,500	85.00
78 Mother and Child	1,500	90.00
Rörstrand		
Christmas		
04 Christmas Night in Stockholm	Year	.27
05 Porridge Dish for Tomten	Year	.27
06 Star Boys Singing to Lucia	Year	.27
07 Christmas Eve in Lapland	Year	.27
08 Christmas Eve with Christmas Roses	Year	.27
09 Christmas Star over Jerusalem	Year	.27
10 Christmas Tree	Year	.27
11 Christmas Bells and Angel	Year	.56
12 Christmas Service	Year	.56
13 Christmas Day Early Service Trip	Year	.56
14 Returning Home	Year	.56
15 On Way to Church	Year	.56
16 Kneeling Shepherd	Year	.56
17 Three Kings Following Star	Year	.56
18 Sleigh-ride in Dalecarlia	Year	.87
19 Christmas on Snow Mountain	Year	.87
20 Mary and Child Jesus	Year	.87
21 Knight Offering Prayers	Year	.87
22 Christmas Bells on Gotland	Year	.87
23 Christmas Sheaf	Year	.87
24 Tomtefar Bearing Gifts	Year	.87
25 Christmas Star and Angels	Year	.87
Mother's Day		
71 Mother & Child	Year	15.00
72 Shelling Peas	Year	15.00
73 Old Fashioned Picnic	Year	16.00
74 Candle Lighting	Year	18.00
75 Pontius on Floor	Year	20.00
76 Apple Picking	Year	20.00
77 Kitchen	Year	27.50
78 Azalea	Year	27.50
79 Studio Idyll	Year	31.50
80 Lisbeth	Year	31.50
81 Karin with Brita	Year	42.50
Father's Day		
71 Father & Child	Year	15.00
72 Meal at Home	Year	15.00
73 Tilling Fields	Year	16.00
74 Fishing	Year	18.00
75 Painting	Year	20.00
76 Plowing	Year	$20.00
77 Sawing	Year	27.50
78 Self Portrait	Year	27.50
79 Bridge	Year	31.50
80 My Etch-Nook	Year	31.50
81 Esbjorn with Playmate	Year	42.50
Annual		
79 Silent Night, Holy Night	N/A	173.00
80 Three Holy Kings	N/A	180.00
81 O Holy Night	N/A	280.00

United States

	Edition Limit	Issue Price
Abbey Press (Viletta)		
Mother's Day		
79 Special Mothers are God's Creation	6,000	37.50
Christmas		
79 Christmas Is a Gentle Season	6,000	37.50
Accent on Art		
Mother Goose		
78 Jack & Jill	5,000	59.50
Nobility of the Plains		
78 Commanche	12,500	80.00
79 Moving Day	3,500	80.00
Addams Family (Schmid)		
Mother's Day		
72 On Tracks	Year	10.00
Christmas		
72 Christmas Dinner	Year	10.00
American Archives (International Silver)		
(Single issue)		
72 Christmas Rose	2,500	100.00
American Arts Services (Viletta)		
Children		
79 Last of Ninth	5,000	45.00
American Commemorative (Gorham)		
Southern Landmark		
73 Monticello	9,800	35.00
73 Williamsburg	9,800	40.00
74 Beauvoir	9,800	40.00
74 Cabildo	9,800	40.00
75 Hermitage	9,800	40.00
75 Oak Hill	9,800	40.00
76 Governor Tryon's Palace	9,800	40.00
76 Montpelier	9,800	40.00
77 Elmscourt	9,800	40.00
77 Ashland	9,800	40.00
78 Mt. Vernon	9,800	40.00
78 White House	9,800	40.00
79 Custis Lee	9,800	40.00
79 Drayton Hall	9,800	40.00
80 Fort Hall	9,800	40.00
80 Liberty Hall	9,800	40.00
American Express (Gorham)		
Four Freedoms		
76 Freedom to Worship	Year	37.50
76 Freedom from Want	Year	37.50
76 Freedom from Fear	Year	37.50
76 Freedom of Speech	Year	37.50
Birds of North America		
78 Saw Whet Owls	9,800	38.00
78 Bobwhite Quail	9,800	38.00
78 October Cardinals	9,800	38.00
78 Long-Eared Owl	9,800	38.00
78 Eastern Bluebirds	9,800	38.00
78 American Woodcock	9,800	38.00
78 Ruffed Grouse	9,800	38.00
78 House Wren	9,800	38.00
American Express (Lenox)		
American Trees of Christmas		
76 Douglas Fir	Year	60.00
77 Scotch Pine	Year	60.00
American Heritage Art (Crown Parian)		
Battle Wagon		
81 General Quarters	25,000	39.50
Celebrity Clowns		
81 Emmett	12,500	50.00
81 Judy	12,500	50.00
Vanishing West		
81 Hell Bent	7,500	70.00
American Historical Plates (Castleton China)		
Aviation		
72 Amelia Earhart	3,500	40.00
72 Charles Lindberg	3,500	40.00
American Preservation Guild (Gorham)		
Catesby Collection		
77 Cardinal	9,900	39.00
American Rose Society (Gorham)		
All-America Rose		
75 Oregold	9,800	39.00
75 Arizona	9,800	39.00
75 Rose Parade	9,800	39.00
76 America	9,800	39.00
76 Cathedral	9,800	39.00
76 Seashell	9,800	39.00
77 Yankee Doodle	9,800	$39.00
77 Double Delight	9,800	39.00
77 Prominent	9,800	39.00
78 First Edition	9,800	39.00
78 Color Magic	9,800	39.00
78 Charisma	9,800	39.00
79 Paradise	9,800	39.00
79 Sundowner	9,800	39.00
79 Friendship	9,800	39.00
80 Love	9,800	39.00
80 Honor	9,800	39.00
80 Cherish	9,800	39.00
81 Bing Crosby	9,800	49.00
81 White Lightnin'	9,800	49.00
81 Marina	9,800	49.00
82 Shreveport	9,800	49.00
82 French Lace	9,800	49.00
82 Brandy	9,800	49.00
82 Mon Cheri	9,800	49.00
Antique Trader		
Currier & Ives		
69 Baseball	2,000	9.00
69 Franklin Experiment	2,000	9.00
69 Haying Time	2,000	9.00
69 Winter in Country	2,000	9.00
Easter		
71 Child and Lamb	1,500	10.95
72 Shepherd with Lamb	1,000	10.95
Mother's Day		
71 Madonna and Child	1,500	10.95
72 Mother Cat and Kittens	1,000	10.95
Father's Day		
71 Pilgrim Father	1,500	10.95
72 Deer Family	1,000	10.95
Thanksgiving		
71 Pilgrims	1,500	10.95
72 First Thanksgiving	1,000	10.95
Christmas		
71 Christ Child	1,500	10.95
72 Flight into Egypt	1,000	10.95
C. M. Russell		
71 Bad One	2,000	11.95
71 Discovery of Last Chance Gulch	2,000	11.95
71 Doubtful Visitor	2,000	11.95
71 Innocent Allies	2,000	11.95
71 Medicine Man	2,000	11.95
Bible		
73 David & Goliath	2,000	10.75
73 Moses and Golden Idol	2,000	10.75
73 Noah's Ark	2,000	10.75
73 Samson	2,000	10.75
Arizona Artisan		
Christmas		
74 Mexican Christmas	Year	20.00
75 Navajo Christmas	Year	20.00
Thanksgiving		
75 Navajo Thanksgiving Feast	Year	15.00
Arlington Mint		
Christmas		
72 Hands in Prayer	Year	125.00
Armstrong		
Bicentennial		
71 Calm Before Storm	250	250.00
72 Gaspee Incident	175	250.00
Artists of the World		
World of Game Birds		
77 Mallards	5,000	45.00
78 Gambel Quail	5,000	45.00
79 American Autumn Ring-necked Pheasant	5,000	50.00
80 November Journey-Canada Geese	5,000	50.00
Don Ruffin Self-Portrait		
79 Clown Also Cries	7,500	65.00
Prowlers of the Clouds		
81 First Light-Great Horned Owl	5,000	55.00
81 His Golden Throne-Screech Owl	5,000	55.00
Audubon Crystal		
Endangered Birds		
76 Kirtland's Warbler	5,000	195.00
76 American Eagle	5,000	195.00
77 Peregrine Falcon	5,000	200.00
Avondale		
Cameos of Childhood		
78 Melissa	28,050	65.00
79 First Born	12,000	70.00
80 Melissa's Brother	Year	70.00
81 Daddy and I	Year	75.00
Myths of the Sea		
79 Poseidon	15,000	70.00
80 Maiden of Sea	15,000	75.00
Tribute to Ageless Art		
79 Court Jesters	10,000	70.00

	Edition Limit	Issue Price
World of Dance		
79 Prima Ballerina	15,000	$70.00
Christmas		
81 And Heavens Rejoiced	6,500	90.00
see also: Judaic Heritage Society (U.S.A.)		
Brantwood Collection		
Marian Carlsen Mother's Day		
78 Jennifer and Jenny Fur	Year	45.00
79 Football Brothers	5,000	45.00
Howe Christmas		
78 Visit from Santa	Year	45.00
(Single issue)		
78 Tribute to Rockwell	Year	35.00
John Falter Christmas		
79 Christmas Morning	5,000	24.50
Rockwell Mother's Day		
79 Homecoming	20,000	39.50
Little Clown		
79 Going to Circus	5,000	29.50
Braymer Hall		
Childhood Sonatas		
81 Serenade	15,000	28.50
82 Prelude	15,000	28.50
How Do I Love Thee		
82 Alaina	19,500	39.95
Briarcrest		
Toys from the Attic		
82 This Ole Bear	10 Days	45.00
John Brindle Fine Arts		
Fantasy in Motion		
78 Little Blue Horse	3,000	75.00
79 Horse of a Different Color	3,000	75.00
80 Horse with Golden Horn	3,000	75.00
Moods of the Orient		
78 Softly, Sun Sets	4,000	75.00
80 Tranquil Morn	4,000	75.00
Expressions		
79 Quiet Eyes	3,000	60.00
(Single issue)		
80 Homage	2,500	125.00
Those Precious Years		
80 Little Curt and Friend	3,000	60.00
Brown & Bigelow (Gorham)		
Clown		
77 Runaway	7,500	45.00
78 It's Your Move	7,500	45.00
79 Understudy	7,500	45.00
80 Idol	7,500	45.00
Traveling Salesman		
77 Traveling Salesman	7,500	35.00
78 Country Pedlar	7,500	40.00
79 Horse Trader	7,500	40.00
80 Expert Salesman	7,500	45.00
Wilderness Wings		
78 Gliding In	5,000	35.00
79 Taking Off	5,000	40.00
80 Joining Up	5,000	45.00
81 Canvasbacks	5,000	47.50
Four Seasons		
78 Gay Blades	Year	55.00
79 Boy Meets Dog	Year	55.00
80 Chilly Reception	Year	65.00
Rockwell Four Seasons (Bronze)		
79 Adventurers Between Adventures	9,500	55.00
Cowboy		
77 Sharing an Apple	5,000	35.00
78 Split Decision	5,000	35.00
79 Hiding Out	5,000	35.00
80 In Trouble	5,000	35.00
Mother's Day		
80 Family Circus	5,000	25.00
Rare Rockwells		
80 Mrs. O'Leary's Cow	7,500	30.00
81 Come and Get It	7,500	30.00
Hilda		
81 Toasting Marshmallows	5,000	25.00
Nostalgia		
81 Pepsi Cola Girl	5,000	25.00
Calhoun's Collectors Society		
Crystal Maidens		
79 Spring—Strawberry Season	2,500	49.50
79 Summer—Sunshine Season	2,500	49.50
79 Autumn—Scenic Season	2,500	49.50
79 Winter—Snowflake Season	2,500	49.50
Calhoun's Collectors Society (Schumann)		
Imperial Christmas		
79 Liebling	10,000	65.00
80 Hallelujah	10,000	65.00
81 Stille Nacht	10,000	65.00

	Edition Limit	Issue Price
Little People		
80 Off to Picnic	19,500	$ 34.50
80 Decorating Tree	19,500	34.50
80 Cruising Down River	19,500	34.50
80 Sweetest Harvest	19,500	34.50
80 Happy Chorus	19,500	34.50
80 Painting Leaves	19,500	34.50
California Porcelain and Bronze		
Best of Sascha		
79 Flower Bouquet	7,500	65.00
Vanishing Animals		
79 Asian Monarchs	7,500	40.00
79 Snow Leopards	7,500	45.00
80 Pandas	7,500	45.00
81 Polar Bears	7,500	50.00
Carson Mint (Vlietta)		
Yesterday's Children		
78 Lisa and Jumeau Doll	5,000	60.00
79 Adrianne and Bye-Lo Baby	5,000	60.00
80 Lydia and Shirley Temple Doll	5,000	60.00
81 Melanie and Scarlett O'Hara Doll	5,000	60.00
Hollywood Squares		
79 Peter Marshall	100 Days	28.50
80 George Gobel	100 Days	28.50
Moment in Time		
79 Freedom Flight	5,000	55.00
Old Fashioned Mother's Day		
79 Daisies from Mary-Beth	20 Days	37.50
80 Daisies from Jimmy	20 Days	37.50
81 Daisies from Meg	20 Days	37.50
81 Daisies for Mommie	20 Days	37.50
America Has Heart		
80 My Heart's Desire	Year	24.50
81 Hearts and Flowers	Year	24.50
82 Hearty Sailer	Year	28.50
Magic Afternoon		
80 Enchanted Garden	5,000	39.50
81 Delightful Tea Party	5,000	39.50
Big Top		
81 White Face	60 Days	28.50
82 Tramp	60 Days	28.50
Castleton China		
Natural History		
73 Painted Lady	1,500	40.00
73 Roseate Spoonbill	1,500	40.00
(Single issue)		
76 Gen. Douglas MacArthur	1,000	30.00
Castleton China (Shenango)		
Bicentennial		
72 New Dawn	7,600	60.00
72 Turning Point	7,600	60.00
73 Valley Forge	7,600	60.00
73 Declaration	7,600	60.00
73 Star Spangled Banner	7,600	60.00
73 U.S.S. Constitution	7,600	60.00
74 One Nation	7,600	60.00
74 Westward Ho	7,600	60.00
see also: American Historical Plates (U.S.A.)		
Caverswall		
see: Ghent Collection (U.S.A.)		
Certified Rarities		
Indian Dancer		
78 Eagle Dancer	2,500	300.00
79 Hoop Dancer	2,500	300.00
Postal Artists		
78 Colias Eurydice	15,000	60.00
79 Euphydryas Phaeton	7,500	60.00
Renaissance Masters		
78 Alba Madonna	15,000	55.00
79 Pieta	5,000	55.00
Chilmark		
Family Christmas		
78 Trimming Tree	10,000	65.00
In Appreciation		
79 Flowers of Field	10,000	65.00
Holy Night		
79 Wisemen	10,000	65.00
Twelve Days of Christmas		
79 Partridge in Pear Tree	10,000	89.50
Cleveland Mint		
Da Vinci		
72 Last Supper	5,000	125.00
Collector Creations (Reed & Barton)		
Thomas Nast Christmas		
73 Christmas	750	100.00
(Single issue)		
73 Alice in Wonderland	750	100.00
Collector's Heirlooms (Fairmont)		
Children at Play		
79 Maple Leaf Noses	7,500	60.00
Passing of Plains Indians		
79 Cheyenne Chieftain	7,500	65.00

	Edition Limit	Issue Price
Collector's Heirlooms (Vlietta)		
Childhood Memories		
78 Jennifer by Candlelight	5,000	$ 60.00
Joys of Motherhood		
78 Crystal's Joy	7,500	60.00
Collectors Weekly		
American		
71 Miss Liberty	500	12.50
72 Miss Liberty	900	12.50
73 Eagle	900	9.75
Continental Mint		
Tom Sawyer		
76 Taking His Medicine	5,000	60.00
77 Painting Fence	5,000	60.00
78 Lost in Cave	5,000	60.00
79 Smoking Pipe	5,000	60.00
(Single issue)		
79 Butter Girl	7,000	60.00
Creative World		
Pearl Buck (Single issue)		
72 Good Earth	10,000	N/A
Four Seasons		
72 Fall (Silverplate)	2,000	75.00
72 Fall (Sterling)	2,000	125.00
73 Winter (Silverplate)	2,000	75.00
73 Winter (Sterling)	250	125.00
73 Spring (Silverplate)	300	75.00
73 Spring (Sterling)	750	125.00
74 Summer (Silverplate)	300	75.00
74 Summer (Sterling)	750	125.00
Brown's Rockwells		
77 Looking Out to Sea	15,000	50.00
78 Yankee Doodle	15,000	50.00
79 Girl at Mirror	15,000	55.00
Immortals of Early American Literature		
78 Village Smithy	15,000	50.00
79 Rip Van Winkle	15,000	50.00
Aesop's Fables		
79 Fox & Grapes	9,750	85.00
Wags to Riches		
82 Benji Movie Star	100 Days	29.50
Crown Parian		
Rosemary Calder		
78 Affection	7,500	60.00
James Daly		
78 Sweet Dreams	7,500	55.00
Beautiful Cats of the World		
79 Sheena	5,000	60.00
79 Sheena and Sheena's Cubs	5,000	60.00
80 Elisheba	5,000	60.00
80 Elisheba's Cubs	5,000	60.00
81 Atarah	5,000	60.00
81 Atarah's Cubs	5,000	60.00
Penni Anne Cross		
79 Crow Baby	7,500	55.00
Julian Ritter		
79 Reve de Ballet	7,500	55.00
Western		
79 Under Surveillance	10,000	65.00
79 Promised Land	10,000	65.00
79 Winter Song	10,000	65.00
79 Boomtown and Wildcatters	10,000	65.00
Sporting Dogs		
80 Decoy	5,000	55.00
81 Dusty	5,000	55.00
Happy Art		
81 Woody's Triple Self Portrait	10,000	39.50
Nature's Beauty		
81 Winter's Peace	7,500	70
Portraits of Childhood		
81 Miss Murray	7,500	65.00
see also: American Heritage Art (U.S.A.)		
Curator Collection		
Masterpieces of Impressionism		
80 Woman with a Parasol	17,500	35.00
81 Young Mother Sewing	17,500	35.00
82 Sara in Green Bonnet	17,500	35.00
Masterpieces of the West		
80 Texas Night Herder	17,500	35.00
81 Indian Trapper	17,500	35.00
Masterpieces of Rockwell		
80 After Prom	17,500	42.50
81 Challenger	17,500	42.50
Jesse's World		
81 This Simple Faith	17,500	39.95
Magical Moments		
81 Happy Dreams	N/A	29.95
81 Harmony	N/A	29.95
82 His Majesty	N/A	29.95
Rockwell Americana		
81 Shuffleton's Barbershop	17,500	75.00
82 Breaking Home Ties	17,500	75.00

	Edition Limit	Issue Price
Special Occasions		
81 Bubbles	N/A	$ 29.95
Stockbridge Trilogy		
81 Stockbridge in Winter	N/A	45.00
Danbury Mint		
Currier & Ives (Silver)		
72 Road Winter	7,500	125.00
73 Central Park Winter	7,500	125.00
74 Winter in Country	7,500	125.00
75 American Homestead	7,500	125.00
76 American Winter-Evening	7,500	135.00
77 Winter Morning	7,500	135.00
Christmas		
75 Silent Night	N/A	24.50
76 Joy to World	N/A	27.50
77 Away in Manger	N/A	27.50
78 First Noel	N/A	29.50
Stuart Devlin Silver		
Americana Series		
72 Gaspee Incident	1,000	130.00
Ebeling & Reuss		
Christmas		
81 Waiting for Christmas	7,000	15.00
R.J. Ernst Enterprises (Vlietta)		
Performance		
79 Act I	5,000	65.00
Women of the West		
79 Expectation	10,000	39.50
79 Silver Dollar Sal	10,000	39.50
80 First Day	10,000	39.50
80 Dolly	10,000	39.50
Love Is		
80 Rufus and Roxanne	19,000	14.95
A Beautiful World		
80 Tahitian Dreamer	27,500	27.50
81 Flirtation	27,500	27.50
Hollywood Greats		
80 John Wayne	27,500	29.95
81 Gary Cooper	27,500	29.95
82 Clark Gable	27,500	29.95
Classy Cars		
81 '26 T	20 Days	24.50
Commemoratives		
81 John Lennon	30 Days	39.50
81 Elvis Presley	30 Days	39.50
82 Marilyn Monroe	30 Days	39.50
A Love Story		
81 Chapter One	20 Days	24.50
Pinups		
81 Stars and Stripes Forever	20 Days	24.50
Seems Like Yesterday		
81 Stop and Smell Roses	10 Days	24.50
82 Home by Lunch	10 Days	24.50
82 Lisa's Creek	10 Days	24.50
So Young So Sweet		
81 Girl with Straw Hat	10 Days	39.50
Turn of the Century		
81 Riverboat Honeymoon	10 Days	35.00
82 Children's Carousel	10 Days	35.00
82 Flower Market	10 Days	35.00
Fairmont		
Ruffin Annual		
76 Navajo Lullaby	10,000	40.00
77 Through Years	5,000	45.00
78 Child of Pueblo	5,000	50.00
79 Colima Madonna	5,000	50.00
80 Sun Kachina	5,000	50.00
81 Inner Peace	5,000	55.00
Carousel Horses		
77 (Set of two)	3,000	80.00
Spencer Annual		
77 Patient Ones	10,000	42.50
78 Yesterday, Today and Tomorrow	10,000	47.50
Fiddler's People		
78 Fiddler on Roof	7,500	60.00
79 Tevya	7,500	60.00
80 Miracle of Love	7,500	60.00
81 Wedding	7,500	60.00
Timeless Moments		
78 Tenderness	5,000	45.00
79 Renaissance	5,000	50.00
80 Coming in Glory	5,000	39.95
Olaf Wieghorst		
78 Sioux Warrior	5,000	65.00
79 Indian Scout	5,000	65.00
Rural America		
78 Fence	5,000	45.00
Children of America		
79 Eskimo Girl	3,000	48.00
Gnomes Christmas		
79 Christmas Bliss	10,000	24.95
Lords of the Plains		
79 Sitting Bull	5,000	60.00
Rockwell Early Works		
79 Old Man Winter	15,000	19.95

	Edition Limit	Issue Price
80 Inventor	15,000	$19.95
80 Ready for School	15,000	19.95
80 Music Master	15,000	19.95
80 Tinkerer	15,000	19.95
Children of Don Ruffin		
80 Flowers for Mother	7,500	50.00
81 Little Eagle	7,500	55.00
Gnomes Four Seasons		
80 Little Swinger (Spring)	15,000	29.50
80 Gnome de Bloom (Summer)	15,000	29.50
80 Lookouts (Fall)	15,000	29.50
80 First Skater (Winter)	15,000	29.50
81 Spring Sharing (Spring)	15,000	29.95
81 Fun and Games (Summer)	15,000	29.95
81 Up Up and Away (Fall)	15,000	29.95
81 First Skier (Winter)	15,000	29.95
82 Gnome Knowledge (Spring)	15,000	29.95
82 Summer Harvest (Summer)	15,000	29.95
82 Gnome Family Tailers (Fall)	15,000	29.95
82 Keep Gnome Fires Burning (Winter)	15,000	29.95
American's Most Beloved (Single Issue)		
80 John Wayne	5,000	13.95
Gnomes for All Seasons		
81 A Gift of Love	15,000	29.95
Long Road West		
81 Trailblazers	15,000	40.00
81 Prairie Schooner	15,000	40.00
When I Grow Up		
81 I'll Be Loved	7,500	29.95

see also:
Collector's Heirlooms (U.S.A.)
Ghent Collection (U.S.A.)
Mistwood Designs (U.S.A.)

Fenton Glass

	Edition Limit	Issue Price
American Craftsman		
70 Glassmaker	Year	10.00
71 Printer	Year	10.00
72 Blacksmith	Year	10.00
73 Shoemaker	Year	10.00
74 Cooper	Year	11.00
75 Silversmith	Year	13.50
76 Gunsmith	Year	13.50
77 Potter	Year	15.00
78 Wheelwright	Year	15.00
79 Cabinetmaker	Year	15.00
80 Tanner	Year	16.50
81 Housewright	Year	17.50
Christmas in America		
70 Little Brown Church (Blue Satin)	Year	12.50
70 Little Brown Church (Carnival)	Year	12.50
70 Little Brown Church (Brown)	Year	17.50
71 Old Brick Church (Blue Satin)	Year	12.50
71 Old Brick Church (Brown)	Year	17.50
71 Old Brick Church (Carnival)	Year	12.50
71 Old Brick Church (White Satin)	Year	12.50
72 Two Horned Church (Blue Satin)	Year	12.50
72 Two Horned Church (Brown)	Year	17.50
72 Two Horned Church (Carnival)	Year	12.50
72 Two Horned Church (White Satin)	Year	12.50
73 St. Mary's (Blue Satin)	Year	12.50
73 St. Mary's (Carnival)	Year	12.50
73 St. Mary's (White Satin)	Year	12.50
73 St. Mary's (Brown)	Year	17.50
74 Nation's Church (Blue Satin)	Year	13.50
74 Nation's Church (Carnival)	Year	13.50
74 Nation's Church (White Satin)	Year	13.50
74 Nation's Church (Brown)	Year	18.50
75 Birthplace of Liberty (Blue Satin)	Year	13.50
75 Birthplace of Liberty (Carnival)	Year	13.50
75 Birthplace of Liberty (White Satin)	Year	13.50
75 Birthplace of Liberty (Brown)	Year	20.00
76 Old North Church (Blue Satin)	Year	15.00
76 Old North Church (Carnival)	Year	15.00
76 Old North Church (White Satin)	Year	15.00

	Edition Limit	Issue Price
76 Old North Church (Brown)	Year	$ 25.00
77 San Carlos (Blue Satin)	Year	15.00
77 San Carlos (Carnival)	Year	15.00
77 San Carlos (White Satin)	Year	15.00
78 Church of Holy Trinity (Blue Satin)	Year	15.00
78 Church of Holy Trinity (Carnival)	Year	15.00
78 Church of Holy Trinity (White Satin)	Year	15.00
79 San Jose y Miguel de Aguayo (Blue Satin)	Year	15.00
79 San Jose y Miguel de Aguayo (Carnival)	Year	15.00
79 San Jose y Miguel de Aguayo (White Satin)	Year	15.00
80 Christ Church (Blue Satin)	Year	16.50
80 Christ Church (Carnival)	Year	16.50
80 Christ Church (White Satin)	Year	16.50
81 Mission of San Xavier del Bac (Blue Satin)	Year	18.50
81 Mission of San Xavier del Bac (Carnival)	Year	18.50
81 Mission of San Xavier del Bac (White Satin)	Year	18.50
Mother's Day		
71 Madonna, Sleeping Child (Blue Satin)	Year	12.50
71 Madonna, Sleeping Child (Carnival)	Year	12.50
72 Madonna of Goldfinch (Blue Satin)	Year	12.50
72 Madonna of Goldfinch (Carnival)	Year	12.50
72 Madonna of Goldfinch (White Satin)	Year	12.50
73 Cowper Madonna (Blue Satin)	Year	12.50
73 Cowper Madonna (Carnival)	Year	12.50
73 Cowper Madonna (White Satin)	Year	12.50
74 Madonna of Grotto (Blue Satin)	Year	12.50
74 Madonna of Grotto (Carnival)	Year	12.50
74 Madonna of Grotto (White Satin)	Year	12.50
75 Taddei Madonna (Blue Satin)	Year	13.50
75 Taddei Madonna (Carnival)	Year	13.50
75 Taddei Madonna (White Satin)	Year	13.50
76 Holy Night (Blue Satin)	Year	13.50
76 Holy Night (Carnival)	Year	13.50
76 Holy Night (White Satin)	Year	13.50
77 Madonna & Child (Blue Satin)	Year	15.00
77 Madonna & Child (Carnival)	Year	15.00
77 Madonna & Child (White Satin)	Year	15.00
78 Madonnina (Blue Satin)	Year	15.00
78 Madonnina (Carnival)	Year	15.00
78 Madonnina (White Satin)	Year	15.00
79 Madonna of Rose Hedge (Blue Satin)	Year	15.00
79 Madonna of Rose Hedge (Carnival)	Year	15.00
79 Madonna of Rose Hedge (White Satin)	Year	15.00
Valentine's Day		
72 Romeo and Juliet (Blue Satin)	Year	15.00
72 Romeo and Juliet (Carnival)	Year	15.00
Bicentennial		
74 Eagle (Blue Satin)	Year	15.00
75 Eagle (Red Satin)	Year	15.00
76 Eagle (Chocolate)	Year	17.50
76 Eagle (White Satin)	Year	15.00
Alliance		
75 Lafayette and Washington (Blue Satin)	Year	15.00
75 Lafayette and Washington (Red Satin)	Year	17.50
75 Lafayette and Washington (White Satin)	Year	15.00
76 Lafayette and Washington (Blue Satin)	Year	15.00
76 Lafayette and Washington (Chocolate)	Year	17.50
76 Lafayette and Washington (White Satin)	Year	15.00
Christmas Classics		
78 Christmas Morn	Year	25.00
79 Nature's Christmas	Year	30.00
80 Going Home	Year	38.50
81 All Is Calm	Year	42.50

	Edition Limit	Issue Price
Currier & Ives		
80 Old Grist Mill	N/A	$ 25.00
81 Harvest	N/A	25.00
Mother's Day Classics		
80 New Born	Year	28.50
81 Gentle Fawn	Year	32.50
82 Nature's Awakening	Year	35.00

Fleetwood Collection (Gorham)

	Edition Limit	Issue Price
Birds & Flowers of the Meadow and Garden		
80 Robin and Crab Apple Blossom	*	39.00
80 Goldfinch and Bull Thistle	*	39.00
80 Cardinal and Wild Lupine	*	39.00
80 Chickadee and New England Aster	*	39.00
80 Baltimore Oriole and Morning Glory	*	39.00
80 Blue Bird and Black-Eyed Susan	*	39.00

*Subscription period

Fostoria

	Edition Limit	Issue Price
American Milestones		
71 Betsy Ross Flag	5,000	12.50
72 National Anthem	8,000	12.50
73 Washington Crossing Delaware	Year	12.50
74 Spirit of '76	Year	13.00
75 Mount Rushmore	Year	16.00
State Plates		
71 California	6,000	12.50
71 New York	12,000	12.50
71 Ohio	3,000	12.50
72 Florida	Year	12.50
72 Hawaii	Year	12.50
72 Pennsylvania	Year	12.50
72 Massachusetts	Year	13.00
72 Texas	Year	13.00
73 Michigan	Year	13.50

Franklin Crystal

	Edition Limit	Issue Price
Historical		
76 Liberty Tree	10,927	120.00
Seven Seas		
76 Atlantic Ocean	2,799	120.00
76 Caribbean	2,799	120.00
76 Indian Ocean	2,799	120.00
76 Mediterranean	2,799	120.00
76 Pacific	2,799	120.00
76 South China Sea	2,799	120.00
76 Arctic	2,799	120.00
Annual		
77 Snowflake	3,428	185.00
78 Snowbird	798	185.00
Rockwell's American Sweethearts		
77 Youngsters at Play	1,004	120.00
77 Teenagers Together	1,004	120.00
78 Bride and Groom	1,004	120.00
78 Proud Parents	1,004	120.00
78 Graduation Day	1,004	120.00
78 Retirement Kiss	1,004	120.00

Franklin Mint

	Edition Limit	Issue Price
American West		
72 Horizon's West (Silver)	5,860	150.00
72 Horizon's West (Gold)	67	2200.00
73 Mountain Man (Silver)	5,860	150.00
73 Mountain Man (Gold)	67	2200.00
73 Prospector (Silver)	5,860	150.00
73 Prospector (Gold)	67	2200.00
73 Plains Hunter (Silver)	5,860	150.00
73 Plains Hunter (Gold)	67	2200.00
Audubon Society		
72 Goldfinch	10,193	125.00
72 Wood Duck	10,193	125.00
73 Cardinal	10,193	125.00
73 Ruffed Grouse	10,193	125.00
Mother's Day		
72 Mother and Child	21,987	125.00
73 Mother and Child	6,154	125.00
74 Mother and Child	5,116	150.00
75 Mother and Child	2,704	175.00
76 Mother and Child	1,858	180.00
Presidential		
72 George Washington	10,304	150.00
72 John Adams	4,859	150.00
72 Thomas Jefferson	4,933	150.00
72 James Madison	3,058	150.00
72 James Monroe	2,722	150.00
72 John Quincy Adams	2,501	150.00
72 Andrew Jackson	2,408	150.00
73 Martin Van Buren	2,291	150.00
73 William H. Harrison	2,182	150.00
73 John Tyler	2,144	150.00
73 James Polk	2,083	150.00
73 Zachary Taylor	2,023	150.00
73 Millard Fillmore	1,967	150.00
74 Franklin Pierce	1,907	150.00
74 James Buchanan	1,841	150.00
74 Abraham Lincoln	2,955	150.00
74 Andrew Johnson	1,777	150.00

	Edition Limit	Issue Price
74 Ulysses S. Grant	1,754	$150.00
75 Rutherford B. Hayes	1,705	150.00
75 James A. Garfield	1,675	150.00
75 Chester A. Arthur	1,604	150.00
75 Grover Cleveland	1,644	150.00
76 Benjamin Harrison	1,619	150.00
76 William McKinley	1,571	150.00
76 Theodore Roosevelt	1,555	150.00
76 William H. Taft	1,592	150.00
76 Woodrow Wilson	1,563	150.00
77 Warren G. Harding	1,544	150.00
77 Calvin Coolidge	1,527	150.00
77 Herbert Hoover	1,520	150.00
77 Franklin D. Roosevelt	1,770	150.00
77 Harry S. Truman	1,493	150.00
78 Dwight D. Eisenhower	1,494	150.00
78 John F. Kennedy	1,494	150.00
78 Lyndon B. Johnson	1,483	150.00
78 Richard M. Nixon	1,475	150.00
78 Gerald R. Ford	N/A	150.00
78 Jimmy Carter	N/A	150.00
James Wyeth		
72 Along Brandywine	19,670	125.00
73 Winter Fox	10,394	125.00
74 Riding to Hunt	10,751	150.00
75 Skating on Brandywine	8,058	175.00
76 Brandywine Battlefield	6,968	180.00
Younger's Bird		
72 Cardinal	13,939	125.00
72 Bobwhite	13,939	125.00
72 Mallards	13,939	125.00
72 American Bald Eagle	13,939	125.00
John James Audubon		
73 Wood Thrush	5,273	150.00
73 Bald Eagle	3,005	150.00
74 Night Heron	3,040	150.00
74 Audubon's Warbler	3,034	150.00
Bernard Buffet		
73 Gazelle	570	150.00
74 Panda	570	150.00
75 Giraffe	570	150.00
76 Lion	570	150.00
77 Rhinoceros	570	150.00
Bicentennial		
73 Jefferson Drafting Declaration of Independence	8,556	175.00
74 John Adams Champions Cause of Independence	8,442	175.00
75 Caesar Rodney Decides Vote on Independence	8,319	175.00
76 John Hancock Signs Declaration of Independence	10,166	175.00
Easter		
73 Resurrection	7,116	175.00
74 He Is Risen	3,719	185.00
75 Last Supper	2,004	200.00
76 Crucifixion	3,904	250.00
77 Resurrection	1,206	250.00
Presidential Inaugural		
73 Nixon/Agnew	10,483	150.00
74 Ford (Silver)	1,141	200.00
74 Ford (Gold)	11	3500.00
77 Carter	928	225.00
Thanksgiving—by Dohanos		
72 First Thanksgiving	10,142	125.00
73 American Wild Turkey	3,547	125.00
74 Thanksgiving Prayer	5,150	150.00
75 Family Thanksgiving	3,025	175.00
76 Home from Hunt	3,474	175.00
Four Seasons		
75 Spring Blossoms	2,648	240.00
75 Summer Bouquet	2,648	240.00
76 Autumn Garland	2,648	240.00
76 Winter Spray	2,648	240.00
American Revolution Bicentennial		
76 Boston Tea Party	3,596	75.00
76 Patrick Henry Urges Armed Resistance	3,596	75.00
76 Paul Revere's Ride	3,596	75.00
76 Battle of Concord Bridge	3,596	75.00
76 Capture of Fort Ticonderoga	3,596	75.00
76 Battle of Bunker Hill	3,596	75.00
77 Signing of Declaration	3,596	75.00
77 Washington Crosses Delaware	3,596	75.00
77 Burgoyne Defeated at Saratoga	3,596	75.00
77 Winter at Valley Forge	3,596	75.00
77 Alliance with France	3,596	75.00
77 Bonhomme Richard Defeats Serapis	3,596	75.00
77 Victory at Yorktown	3,596	75.00
Annual		
77 Tribute to Arts	1,901	280.00
78 Tribute to Nature	435	280.00
Belskie		
77 Mother's Day	290	210.00
Freedom		
77 Lafayette Joins Washington	546	275.00

	Edition Limit	Issue Price
Rockwell Thanksgiving		
77 Old Fashioned Thanksgiving	2,361	$85.00
Christmas		
77 Skating Party	908	55.00
Franklin Porcelain		
Hans Christian Andersen		
76 Princess and Pea	16,875	38.00
76 Ugly Duckling	16,875	38.00
76 Little Mermaid	16,875	38.00
76 Emperor's New Clothes	16,875	38.00
76 Steadfast Tin Soldier	16,875	38.00
76 Little Match Girl	16,875	38.00
77 Snow Queen	16,875	38.00
77 Red Shoes	16,875	38.00
77 Tinder Box	16,875	38.00
77 Nightingale	16,875	38.00
77 Thumbelina	16,875	38.00
77 Shepherdess & Chimney Sweep	16,875	38.00
Christmas Annual		
76 Silent Night	19,286	65.00
77 Deck Halls	9,185	65.00
Flowers of the Year		
76 January	27,394	50.00
76 February	27,394	50.00
77 March	27,394	50.00
77 April	27,394	50.00
77 May	27,394	50.00
78 June	27,394	50.00
78 July	27,394	50.00
78 August	27,394	50.00
78 September	27,394	50.00
79 October	27,394	50.00
79 November	27,394	50.00
79 December	27,394	50.00
Grimm's Fairy Tales		
78 Sleeping Beauty	27,006	42.00
78 Twelve Dancing Princesses	27,006	42.00
78 Brementown Musicians	27,006	42.00
79 Golden Goose	27,006	42.00
79 Hansel and Gretel	27,006	42.00
79 Rapunzel	27,006	42.00
Songbirds of the World		
77 Baltimore Oriole	20,225	55.00
78 Bohemian Waxwing	20,225	55.00
Mark Twain		
77 Whitewashing Fence	2,645	38.00
77 Stealing a Kiss	2,645	38.00
77 Traveling River	2,645	38.00
77 Trading Lives	2,645	38.00
77 Rafting Down River	2,645	38.00
78 Riding Bronc	2,645	38.00
78 Jumping Frog Race	2,645	38.00
78 Facing Charging Knight	2,645	38.00
78 Disguising Huck	2,645	38.00
78 Living Along River	2,645	38.00
78 Learning to Smoke	2,645	38.00
78 Finger Printing Pays Off	2,645	38.00
Hometown Memories		
79 Country Fair	Year	29.00
80 Little Red School House	Year	29.00
Country Year Collection		
80 Woodlands in April	*	55.00
80 Country Path in May	*	55.00
80 June in Country Garden	*	55.00
80 July Beside River	*	55.00
80 Wheatfields in August	*	55.00
80 September on Moors	*	55.00
80 Colors of Autumn in October	*	55.00
80 Country Lane in December	*	55.00
*Subscription period		
Calendar		
81 Calendar	Year	55.00
82 Calendar	Year	58.00
Frankoma		
Christmas		
65 Goodwill Toward Man	Year	5.00
66 Bethlehem Shepherds	Year	5.00
67 Gifts for Christ Child	Year	5.00
68 Flight into Egypt	Year	5.00
69 Laid in a Manger	Year	5.00
70 King of Kings	Year	5.00
71 No Room in Inn	Year	5.00
72 Seeking Christ Child	Year	5.00
73 Annunciation	Year	5.00
74 She Loved & Cared	Year	5.00
75 Peace on Earth	Year	5.00
76 Gift of Love	Year	6.00
77 Birth of Eternal Life	Year	6.00
78 All Nature Rejoiced	Year	6.00
79 Stay of Hope	Year	6.00
80 Unto Us a Child Is Born	Year	10.00
81 O Come Let Us Adore Him	Year	12.00
82 Wise Men Rejoice	Year	12.00
Bicentennial		
72 Provocations	Year	6.00
73 Patriots & Leaders	Year	6.00

	Edition Limit	Issue Price
74 Battles, Independence	Year	$ 5.00
75 Victories for Independence	Year	6.00
76 Symbols of Freedom	Year	6.00
Teenagers of The Bible		
73 Jesus and Carpenter	Year	5.00
74 David the Musician	Year	5.00
75 Jonathan the Archer	Year	5.00
76 Dorcas the Seamstress	Year	5.00
77 Peter the Fisherman	Year	5.00
78 Martha the Homemaker	Year	7.50
79 Daniel the Courageous	Year	7.50
Madonnas		
77 Grace Madonna	Year	12.50
78 Madonna of Love	Year	12.50
Ghent Collection		
Christmas Wildlife		
74 Cardinals in Snow	10,135	20.00
75 We Three Kings	12,750	29.00
76 Partridge and Pear Tree	12,750	32.00
77 Foxes and Evergreen	12,750	32.00
78 Snowy Owls	12,750	32.00
Mother's Day		
75 Cotton Tail	12,750	20.00
76 Mallard Family	12,750	29.00
77 Chipmunks & Trillium	12,750	32.00
78 Raccoon Family	12,750	32.00
79 Maytime	12,750	32.00
American Bicentennial Wildlife		
76 American Bald Eagle	2,500	95.00
76 American White-Tailed Deer	2,500	95.00
76 American Bison	2,500	95.00
76 American Wild Turkey	2,500	95.00
Fausett Mural (Single issue)		
76 From Sea to Shining Sea	1,976	76.00
(Single issue)		
78 Pilgrim of Peace	15 Days	29.50
Lands of Fable		
81 Xanadu	17,500	55.00
Man's Dream of Flight		
81 Flight of Icarus	19,500	37.50
Dutch Delft		
82 Hero of Haarlem	N/A	34.95
Ghent Collection (Bing & Grøndahl)		
Hans Christian Andersen		
79 Thumbelina	7,500	42.50
79 Princess and Pea	7,500	42.50
79 Wild Swans	7,500	42.50
79 Emperor's New Clothes	7,500	42.50
80 Little Mermaid	7,500	42.50
80 Nightingale	7,500	42.50
Ghent Collection (Caverswall)		
Christmas Annual		
79 Good King Wenceslaus	2,500	350.00
Country Diary of an Edwardian Lady		
79 April	10,000	80.00
79 June	10,000	80.00
Ghent Collection (Fairmont)		
Legends of Christmas		
79 Bringing in Tree	5,000	65.00
Memory Annual		
78 1977 Memory Plate	1,977	77.00
79 1978 Memory Plate	1,978	78.00
80 1979 Memory Plate	1,979	78.00
Israeli Commemorative (Single issue)		
78 Promised Land	5,738	79.00
Spirit of America		
78 Making of a Nation	1,978	78.00
79 Growing Years	1,978	78.00
Ghent Collection (Gorham)		
April Fool Annual		
78 April Fool's Day	10,000	35.00
79 April Fool's Day	10,000	35.00
80 April Fool's Day	10,000	37.50
Ghent Collection (Kaiser)		
Treasures of Tutankhamun		
78 Golden Mask	3,247	90.00
78 Golden Throne	3,247	90.00
78 Horus Falcon	3,247	90.00
78 Ivory Chest	3,247	90.00
Ghent Collection (Viletta)		
(Single issue)		
79 Official 1980 Olympic Winter Games	13 Days	24.50
Gnomes United		
Gnomes		
79 Gnome on Range	10,000	23.00
Gnome Patrol		
79 Dr. Kwik	5,000	45.00
Golf Digest		
Second Hole (Single issue)		
73 Dorado Beach Club	2,000	45.00
Twelfth Hole (Single issue)		
73 Spyglass Hill	2,000	45.00

	Edition Limit	Issue Price
Freedom		
77 Lafayette Joins Washington	546	$275.00
Gorham		
(Single issue)		
70 American Family Tree	5,000	17.00
Lionel Barrymore		
71 Quiet Waters	15,000	25.00
72 San Pedro Harbor	15,000	25.00
72 Little Boatyard (Silver)	1,000	100.00
72 Nantucket (Silver)	1,000	100.00
Bicentennial		
71 Burning of Gaspee (Pewter)	5,000	35.00
72 Burning of Gaspee (Silver)	750	550.00
72 1776 (China)	18,500	17.50
72 1776 (Vermeil)	500	500.00
72 1776 (Silver)	750	250.00
72 Boston Tea Party (Pewter)	5,000	35.00
73 Boston Tea Party (Silver)	750	550.00
Gallery of Masters		
71 Man in Gilt Helmet	10,000	50.00
72 Self-Portrait Rembrandt, with Saskia	10,000	50.00
73 Honorable Mrs. Graham	7,500	50.00
Moppets Mother's Day		
73 Flowers for Mother	20,000	10.00
74 Mother's Hat	20,000	12.00
75 In Mother's Clothes	20,000	13.00
76 Flowers	20,000	13.00
77 Gift for Mother	18,500	13.00
78 Moppet's Mother's Day	18,500	10.00
Moppets Christmas		
73 Christmas March	20,000	10.00
74 Trimming Tree	20,000	12.00
75 Carrying Tree	20,000	13.00
76 Asleep under Tree	18,500	13.00
77 Star for Treetop	18,500	13.00
78 Presents	18,500	10.00
79 Moppet's Christmas	18,500	12.00
80 Happy Merry Christmas Tree	Year	12.00
81 Happy Merry Christmas Tree	Year	12.00
82 Happy Merry Christmas Tree	Year	12.00
Remington Western		
73 Aiding a Comrade	Year	25.00
73 New Year on Cimarron	Year	25.00
73 Fight for Waterhole	Year	25.00
73 Flight	Year	25.00
(Issued as a set)		
74 Old Ramond	Year	20.00
74 Breed	Year	20.00
75 Cavalry Officer	5,000	37.50
75 Trapper	5,000	37.50
(Single issue)		
74 Streakers	Year	19.50
(Single issue)		
74 Golden Rule	Year	19.50
(Single issue)		
74 Big Three	10,000	17.50
(Single issue)		
74 Weigh-In	10,000	17.50
(Single issue)		
75 Benjamin Franklin	18,500	19.50
Boy Scouts of America		
75 Our Heritage	18,500	19.50
76 Scout Is Loyal	18,500	19.50
77 Scoutmaster	18,500	19.50
77 Good Sign	18,500	19.50
78 Pointing Way	18,500	19.50
78 Campfire Story	18,500	19.50
American Artists		
76 Apache Mother & Child	9,800	25.00
76 Black Regiment	7,500	25.00
America's Cup Plates (Set of five)		
76 America, 1861		
76 Puritan		
76 Reliance		
76 Ranger		
76 Courageous	1,000	200.00
Omnibus Muralis		
76 200 Years with Old Glory	5,000	60.00
77 Life of Christ	5,000	65.00
First Lady		
77 Amy and Rosalynn	Year	24.95
Presidential		
77 John F. Kennedy	9,800	30.00
77 Eisenhower	9,800	30.00
Julian Ritter Annual		
77 Christmas Visit	9,800	24.50
78 Fluttering Heart	9,800	24.50
Ritter's Four Seasons Clowns		
77 Falling in Love (Set of four)	5,000	100.00

	Edition Limit	Issue Price
78 To Love a Clown (Set of four)	5,000	$120.00
Santa Fe Railway Collection		
77 Navajo Silversmith	7,500	37.50
78 Turquoise Bead Maker	7,500	37.50
79 Basketweaver	7,500	42.50
80 Arrow Maker	7,500	45.00
Borsato Masterpiece Collection		
77 Serenity	5,000	75.00
78 Titan Madonna	5,000	75.00
79 Ballerina	5,000	75.00
Little Men		
77 Come Ride with Me	9,500	50.00
Moppets Anniversary		
79 Moppet Couple	20,000	13.00
(Single issue)		
78 Triple Self-Portrait	Year	37.50
Wild West		
80 Bronc to Breakfast	9,800	38.00
81 In Without Knocking	9,800	38.00
Four Seasons Landscape		
80 Summer Respite	15,000	45.00
80 Autumn Reflections	15,000	45.00
81 Winter Delights	15,000	45.00
81 Spring Recess	15,000	45.00
Rockwell Four Seasons		
81 Old Timers (Set of four)	Year	100.00
82 Life with Father (Set of four)	Year	100.00
(Single issue—Set of two)		
81 Day in Life of Boy		
81 Day in Life of Girl	Year	50.00
Four Ages of Love		
81 Sweet Song So Young	10,000	100.00
82 Flowers in Tender Bloom	10,000	100.00
Masterpieces of Rockwell		
81 Girl at Mirror	17,500	50.00
Young Love		
81 Beguiling Buttercup	17,500	62.50
82 Flying High	17,500	62.50
Encounters, Survivals & Celebrations		
82 A Fine Welcome	7,500	50.00

see also:
American Commemorative (U.S.A.)
American Express (U.S.A.)
American Preservation Guild (U.S.A.)
American Rose Society (U.S.A.)
Brown & Bigelow (U.S.A.)
Fleetwood Collection (U.S.A.)
Ghent Collection (U.S.A.)
Lincoln Mint (U.S.A.)

	Edition Limit	Issue Price
Greentree Potteries		
Grant Wood		
71 Studio	2,000	10.00
72 Antioch School	2,000	10.00
73 At Stone City	2,000	10.00
74 Adolescence	2,000	10.00
75 Birthplace	2,000	10.00
76 American Gothic	2,000	10.00
Kennedy		
72 Center for Performing Arts	2,000	20.00
73 Birthplace, Brookline, Mass.	2,000	12.00
Motorcar		
72 1929 Packard Dietrich Convertible	2,000	20.00
73 Model "A" Ford	2,000	20.00
Mississippi River		
73 Delta Queen	2,000	10.00
73 Tri-Centennial	2,000	10.00
Dave Grossman Designs		
Margaret Keane		
76 Balloon Girl	5,000	25.00
77 My Kitty	5,000	25.00
78 Bedtime	5,000	25.00
Tom Sawyer		
75 Whitewashing Fence	10,000	24.00
76 First Smoke	10,000	24.00
77 Take Your Medicine	10,000	24.00
78 Lost in Cave	10,000	25.00
Looney Tunes Mother's Day		
76 Bugs Bunny	10,000	13.00
Looney Tunes Christmas		
77 Christmas	10,000	13.00
78 Christmas	5,000	14.00
Children of the Week		
78 Monday's Child	5,000	30.00
79 Tuesday's Child	5,000	30.00
79 Wednesday's Child	5,000	30.00
80 Thursday's Child	5,000	30.00
80 Friday's Child	5,000	30.00
Annual Fall		
78 Peace	5,000	55.00
79 Santa	5,000	55.00
Rockwell		
79 Butter Boy	5,000	40.00

	Edition Limit	Issue Price
Huckleberry Finn		
79 Secret	10,000	$ 40.00
80 Listening	10,000	40.00
81 No Kings Nor Dukes	10,000	40.00
82 Snake Escapes	10,000	40.00
(Single issue)		
80 Norman Rockwell Back to School	10,000	24.00
Rockwell Christmas		
80 Christmas Trio	Year	75.00
81 Santa's Good Boys	Year	75.00
Rockwell Boy Scout Annual		
81 Can't Wait	10,000	30.00
82 A Guiding Hand	10,000	30.00
Magic People		
82 Music for a Queen	9,500	65.00
Hackett American Collectors		
Corita Kent Annual		
79 I Love You Very	30,000	19.95
80 You Bring Spring	10,000	21.95
81 Love	10,000	30.00
Endangered Species		
80 California Sea Otters	7,500	35.00
81 Asian Pandas	7,500	37.50
82 Australian Koala Bears	7,500	39.50
Ocean Moods		
80 Sunset Tide	5,000	50.00
81 Moonlight Flight	4,000	50.00
82 Morning Surf	5,000	50.00
Save the Whales		
80 Trust and Love	10,000	30.00
Snow Babies		
80 Canadian Harp Seals	7,500	39.50
81 Polar Bear Cubs	7,500	39.50
82 Snow Leopards	7,500	42.50
Friends of the Forest		
81 Forest Alert	7,500	50.00
82 Brookside Protection	7,500	50.00
Horses in Action		
81 Challenge	7,500	39.50
82 Country Days	7,500	50.00
Parkhurst Annual Christmas		
81 Christmas Tear	7,500	39.50
Wonderful World of Clowns		
81 Kiss for a Clown	7,500	39.50
81 Rainbow's End	7,500	39.50
82 Happy Days	7,500	42.50
Wonderous Years		
81 After Rains	5,000	39.50
82 I Got One	5,000	42.50
(Single issue)		
81 World Tribute	90 Days	25.00
Crazy Cats		
82 Primping Time	10,000	42.50
Daisy Cats		
82 Daisy Kitten	10,000	42.50
Everyone's Friends		
82 Springtime	10,000	42.50
Father's Day		
82 Daddy's Rose	10,000	42.50
Impressions by Joanne Mix		
82 Windy Day	10,000	42.50
Mother and Child		
82 Mothers Love	10,000	42.50
Mother's Day		
82 Daisies for Mother	10,000	42.50
Ocean Stars		
82 Sea Horses	10,000	42.50
Special Moments		
82 April	10,000	42.50
Sunday Best		
82 Stacey	10,000	42.50
Waterbird Families		
82 Marsh Venture	10,000	42.50
World of Ozz Franca		
82 Images	10,000	42.50
(Single issue)		
82 Hog Heaven	15,000	42.50
Hamilton Collection		
Story of Heidi		
81 Heidi	14,750	45.00
Story of Noah's Ark		
81 Two by Two . . . Every Living Creature	12,500	45.00
Tribute to the Ballet		
81 Nutcracker	15,000	62.50
Fairies of the Fields and Flowers		
82 Willow Fairy	N/A	45.00
Hamilton Collection (Boehm Studios)		
Rose Collection		
79 Peace Rose	15,000	45.00
79 Queen Elizabeth Rose	15,000	45.00
79 White Masterpiece Rose	15,000	45.00
79 Angel Face Rose	15,000	45.00

	Edition Limit	Issue Price
79 Tropicana Rose	15,000	$ 45.00
79 Elegance Rose	15,000	45.00
79 Royal Highness Rose	15,000	45.00
79 Mister Lincoln Rose	15,000	45.00
Boehm Owl Collection		
80 Snowy Owl	15,000	45.00
80 Boreal Owl	15,000	45.00
80 Barn Owl	15,000	45.00
80 Saw Whet Owl	15,000	45.00
80 Great Horned Owl	15,000	45.00
80 Screech Owl	15,000	45.00
80 Short Eared Owl	15,000	45.00
80 Barred Owl	15,000	45.00
Hummingbird Collection		
80 Calliope Hummingbird	15,000	55.00
80 Broadtail Hummingbird	15,000	55.00
80 Rufous Flame Bearer Hummingbird	15,000	55.00
80 Broad-Billed Hummingbird	15,000	55.00
80 Streamer-Tail Hummingbird	15,000	55.00
80 Blue-Throated Hummingbird	15,000	55.00
80 Crimson-Topaz Hummingbirds	15,000	55.00
80 Brazilian Ruby	15,000	55.00
Roses of Excellance Collection		
81 Love Rose	Year	60.00
Water Bird Collection		
81 Canadian Geese	15,000	55.00
81 Wood Ducks	15,000	55.00
81 Common Mallards	15,000	55.00
81 Green-Winged Teals	15,000	55.00
81 Ross's Geese	15,000	55.00
81 Canvas-Backs	15,000	55.00
81 Hooded Mergansers	15,000	55.00
81 American Pintails	15,000	55.00
Life's Best Wishes		
82 Longevity	15,000	75.00
Hamilton Collection (Porcelaine Ariel)		
A Tribute to Love		
80 Shaft of Light	17,500	45.00
Greatest Show on Earth		
81 Clowns-Heart of Circus	10 Days	30.00
Hamilton Collection (Royal Devon)		
Rockwell Home of the Brave		
81 Reminiscing	18,000	35.00
Hamilton Collection (Viletta)		
Coppelia Ballet		
80 Franz's Fantasy Love	28 Days	25.00
Hamilton Mint		
Picasso		
72 Le Gourmet	5,000	125.00
72 Tragedy	5,000	125.00
73 Lovers	5,000	125.00
Kennedy		
74 (Gold on Pewter)	Year	40.00
74 (Pewter)	Year	25.00
Man's Best Friend		
78 Hobo	9,500	40.00
78 Doctor	9,500	40.00
79 Making Friends	9,500	40.00
Historic Providence Mint		
(Single issue)		
79 Children's Year	3,000	95.00
Children of the Seasons		
80 Children of Spring	3,000	107.50
America the Beautiful		
81 Spacious Skies	17,500	37.50
Ralph Homan Studios (Viletta)		
Seasons of the Oak		
79 Lazy Days	5,000	55.00
80 Come Fly with Me	5,000	55.00
Home Plates (Mingolla)		
Christmas (Enamel on Copper)		
73 Christmas	1,000	95.00
74 Christmas	1,000	110.00
75 Christmas	1,000	125.00
76 Christmas	1,000	125.00
77 Scene from Childhood	2,000	200.00
Christmas (Porcelain)		
74 Christmas	5,000	35.00
75 Christmas	5,000	35.00
76 Christmas	5,000	35.00
77 Winter Wonderland	7,000	45.00
Four Seasons (Enamel on Copper)		
78 Dashing Thru Snow	2,000	150.00
79 Spring Flowers	2,000	150.00
80 Beach Fun	2,000	150.00
81 Balloon Breeze	2,000	150.00
Christmas in the Country (Enamel on Copper)		
79 Dear Santa	1,000	70.00
80 Country Cousin	1,000	90.00

	Edition Limit	Issue Price
Hudson Pewter		
Mother's Day		
79 Cherished	10,000	$ 35.00
Songbirds of the Four Seasons		
79 Hummingbird	7,500	35.00
America's Sailing Ships		
79 U.S.S. Constitution	5,000	35.00
A Child's Christmas		
79 Littlest Angels	10,000	35.00
80 Heaven's Christmas Tree	10,000	42.50
Imperial		
America the Beautiful		
69 U.S. Capitol	500	17.50
70 Mount Rushmore	500	17.50
71 Statue of Liberty	500	17.50
72 Monument Valley Arizona	500	17.50
73 Liberty Bell	500	17.50
74 Golden Gate	500	19.95
75 Mt. Vernon	500	19.95
Christmas		
70 Partridge (Carnival)	Year	12.00
70 Partridge (Crystal)	Year	15.00
71 Two Turtle Doves (Carnival)	Year	12.00
71 Two Turtle Doves (Crystal)	Year	16.50
72 Three French Hens (Carnival)	Year	12.00
72 Three French Hens (Crystal)	Year	16.50
73 Four Colly Birds (Carnival)	Year	12.00
73 Four Colly Birds (Crystal)	Year	16.50
74 Five Golden Rings (Carnival)	Year	12.00
74 Five Golden Rings (Crystal)	Year	16.50
75 Six Geese A-Laying (Carnival)	Year	14.00
75 Six Geese A-Laying (Crystal)	Year	19.00
76 Seven Swans (Carnival)	Year	16.00
76 Seven Swans (Crystal)	Year	21.00
77 Eight Maids A-Milking (Carnival)	Year	18.00
77 Eight Maids A-Milking (Crystal)	Year	23.00
78 Nine Drummers Drumming (Carnival)	Year	20.00
78 Nine Drummers Drumming (Crystal)	Year	25.00
79 Ten Pipers Piping (Carnival)	Year	22.00
79 Ten Pipers Piping (Crystal)	Year	27.00
Coin Crystal		
71 1964 Kennedy Half Dollar	Year	15.00
72 Eisenhower Dollar	Year	15.00
(Single issue)		
76 Bicentennial	Year	20.00
Incolay Studios		
Life's Interludes		
79 Uncertain Beginning	Year	95.00
80 Finally Friends	12,000	95.00
International Museum		
Masterpiece Stamp Art		
79 Gingerbread Santa	Year	29.00
80 Madonna and Child	Year	37.50
81 Botticelli's Madonna and Child	9,900	45.00
Masterpiece		
82 Portrait of Michelangelo	15,000	45.00
International Silver		
Christmas		
74 Tiny Tim	7,500	75.00
75 Caught	7,500	75.00
76 Bringing Home Tree	7,500	75.00
77 Fezziwig's Christmas Ball	7,500	75.00
78 Alleluia	7,500	75.00
79 Rejoice	7,500	100.00
80 Adoration	7,500	125.00
Presidential		
75 Washington	7,500	75.00
76 Jefferson	7,500	75.00
76 Lincoln	7,500	75.00
76 F. Roosevelt	7,500	75.00
77 Eisenhower	7,500	75.00
77 Kennedy	7,500	75.00
Seasons American Past		
76 Autumn	7,500	60.00
76 Spring	7,500	60.00
76 Summer	7,500	60.00
76 Winter	7,500	60.00
see also: American Archives (U.S.A.)		

	Edition Limit	Issue Price
Interpace		
Modigliani (Single issue)		
72 Caryatid	10,000	$ 60.00
Architects of Democracy (Set of four)		
74 George Washington		
74 John Adams		
74 Thomas Jefferson		
74 Alexander Hamilton	1,776	225.00
JM Company		
Competitive Sports		
79 Downhill Racing Slalom	10,000	25.00
Oriental Birds		
79 Window at Tiger Spring Temple	10,000	39.00
Love		
80 Love's Serenade	5,000	50.00
Joys (Viletta)		
Precious Moments		
79 Friend in Sky	28 Days	21.50
80 Sand in Her Shoe	28 Days	21.50
80 Snow Bunny	21 Days	21.50
80 Seashells	21 Days	21.50
81 Dawn	28 Days	21.50
81 My Kitty	28 Days	21.50
Judaic Heritage Society		
Jewish Holidays		
72 Chanukah (Silver)	2,000	150.00
72 Chanukah (Gold)	25	1900.00
72 Pesach (Silver)	2,000	150.00
72 Pesach (Gold)	25	1900.00
72 Purim (Silver)	2,000	150.00
(Single issue)		
74 Purim (Silver)	1,000	150.00
Great Jewish Women		
76 Golda Meir	4,000	35.00
75 Henrietta Szold	4,000	35.00
76 Emma Lazarus	4,000	35.00
Heritage Plates		
76 Rabbi	4,000	35.00
76 Hasidim	4,000	35.00
76 Shtetl	4,000	35.00
(Single issue)		
77 Jacob and Angel	5,000	45.00
(Single issue)		
77 Hatikvah (Copper)	5,000	55.00
(Single issue)		
77 Hatikvah (Gold Plated)	1,000	75.00
(Single issue)		
77 Hatikvah (Sterling Silver)	500	180.00
Jewish Holidays		
79 Chanukah	2,500	50.00
79 Purim	2,500	50.00
79 Shavouth	2,500	50.00
79 Rosh Hashanah	2,500	50.00
79 Simchat Torah	2,500	50.00
79 Pesach	2,500	50.00
Jerusalem Wedding		
79 Bride of Jerusalem	6,000	65.00
79 Hasidic Dancers	6,000	65.00
Judaic Heritage Society (Avondale)		
(Single issue)		
80 Shalom – Peace	6,000	95.00
Judiac Heritage Society (Viletta)		
Israel's 30th Anniversary (Single issue)		
79 L'Chayim to Israel	10,000	59.50
Israel's 30th Anniversary (Single issue)		
79 Prophecy of Isaiah's	4,000	59.50
Keller & George (Reed & Barton)		
Bicentennial		
72 Monticello (Damascene)	1,000	75.00
72 Monticello (Silver Plate)	200	200.00
73 Mt. Vernon (Damascene)	Year	75.00
Kensington		
Children of the Week		
80 Wednesday's Child	27,500	28.50
Kern Collectibles		
Linda's Little Loveables		
77 Blessing	7,500	30.00
78 Appreciation	7,500	37.50
79 Adopted Burro	7,500	42.50
Christmas of Yesterday		
78 Christmas Call	5,000	45.00
79 Woodcutter's Christmas	5,000	50.00
80 Making Christmas Goodies	5,000	55.00
81 Singing Christmas Carols	5,000	55.00
Adventures of the Old West		
81 Grizzly Ambush	7,500	65.00
Horses of Harland Young		
82 Quarterhorses	10,000	55.00
My Favorite Pets		
81 Schnauzers	7,500	39.95
82 Cocker Spaniels	7,500	39.95

	Edition Limit	Issue Price
Kern Collectibles (Haviland & Parlon)		
Songbird		
80 Cardinals	5,000	$ 65.00
81 Blue Birds	5,000	70.00
82 Orioles	5,000	70.00
Kern Collectibles (Pickard)		
Cowboy Artists (Sets of two)		
76 Out There		
76 Cutting Out a Stray	3,000	130.00
77 Broken Cinch		
77 No Place to Cross	1,000	130.00
Companions		
77 Cubs	5,000	40.00
78 Mighty Sioux	5,000	40.00
79 Nature Girl	5,000	50.00
80 Buffalo Boy	5,000	50.00
81 Shepherds	5,000	55.00
Kern Collectibles (Rosenthal)		
John Falter Harvest Time		
76 Gathering Pumpkins	5,000	70.00
77 Honest Day's Work	4,000	70.00
Runci Classic		
77 Summertime	5,000	95.00
78 Springtime	5,000	95.00
Kern Collectibles (Royal Bayreuth)		
Christmas		
72 Carriage in Village	4,000	15.00
73 Snow Scene	5,000	16.50
74 Old Mill	4,000	24.00
75 Forest Chalet 'Serenity'	4,000	27.50
76 Christmas in Country	5,000	40.00
77 Peace on Earth	5,000	40.00
78 Peaceful Interlude	5,000	45.00
79 Homeward Bound	5,000	50.00
Sun Bonnet Babies (Set of seven)		
74 Monday (Washing Day)		
74 Tuesday (Ironing Day)		
74 Wednesday (Mending Day)		
74 Thursday (Scrubbing Day)		
74 Friday (Sweeping Day)		
74 Saturday (Baking Day)		
74 Sunday (Fishing Day)	15,000	120.00
Antique American Art		
76 Farmyard Tranquility	3,000	50.00
77 Half Dome	3,000	55.00
78 Down Memory Lane	3,000	65.00
(Single issue)		
76 Sun Bonnet Babies Composite	15,000	75.00
L. Henry		
76 Just Friends	5,000	50.00
77 Interruption	4,000	55.00
Anniversary		
80 Young Americans	5,000	125.00
Sun Bonnet Babies Playtime		
81 Swinging	5,000	60.00
81 Round Dance	5,000	60.00
82 Marbles	5,000	60.00
Kern Collectibles (Sango)		
Living American Artist		
76 Sweethearts (Rockwell)	10,000	30.00
77 Apache Girl (Perillo)	5,000	35.00
78 Natural Habitat	5,000	40.00
Great Achievements in Art		
80 Arabian	3,000	65.00
81 Texas Longhorns	3,000	70.00
Kilkelly		
St. Patrick's Day		
75 Pipe and Shamrock	Year	16.50
76 Third Look in Logan	Year	20.00
Kirk		
DeGrazia		
72 Heavenly Blessing	200	75.00
Mother's Day		
72 Mother and Child	3,500	75.00
73 Mother and Child	2,500	80.00
Bicentennial		
72 U.S.S. Constellation	825	75.00
72 Washington	5,000	75.00
Thanksgiving		
72 Thanksgiving Ways and Means	3,500	150.00
Christmas		
72 Flight into Egypt	3,500	150.00
Lake Shore Prints		
Rockwell		
73 Butter Girl	9,433	14.95
74 Truth about Santa	15,141	19.50
75 Home from Fields	8,500	24.50
76 A President's Wife	2,500	70.00
Lapsys		
Crystal Christmas		
77 Snowflake	5,000	47.50
78 Peace on Earth	5,000	47.50

	Edition Limit	Issue Price
Lenox		
Boehm Birds		
72 Bird of Peace (Mute Swan)	5,000	$150.00
73 Young America, 1776 (Eaglet)	6,000	175.00
Colonial Christmas Wreath		
81 Virginia, First Colony	Year	65.00
82 Massachusetts, Second Colony	Year	65.00
see also: American Express (U.S.A.)		
Lincoln Mint		
Great Artists (Dali)		
71 Unicorn Dyonisiaque (Gold)	100	1500.00
71 Unicorn Dyonisiaque (Silver)	5,000	100.00
72 Dyonisiaque et Pallas Athens (Gold)	300	2000.00
72 Dyonisiaque et Pallas Athens (Gold Plate)	2,500	150.00
72 Dyonisiaque et Pallas Athens (Silver)	7,500	125.00
Easter		
72 Christ (Silver)	20,000	150.00
72 Christ (Gold Plate)	10,000	200.00
74 Christ (Pewter)	Year	45.00
Mother's Day		
72 Collies (Silver)	3,000	125.00
Christmas		
72 Madonna Della Seggiola (Gold Plate)	125	150.00
72 Madonna Della Seggiola (Silver)	3,000	125.00
Dali Cross Plate		
77 Gold Cross	5,000	225.00
77 Silver Cross	10,000	175.00
Lincoln Mint (Gorham)		
Christmas		
78 Santa Belongs to All Children	7,500	29.50
Litt		
Christmas		
78 Madonna & Child	1,000	200.00
79 O Holy Night	1,000	200.00
Annual		
79 Apache Sunset	1,250	275.00
Lynell Studios		
Little Traveler		
78 On His Way	4,000	45.00
79 On Her Way	4,000	45.00
American Adventure		
79 Whaler	7,500	50.00
79 Trapper	7,500	50.00
80 Forty-Niner	7,500	50.00
81 Pioneer Woman	7,500	50.00
All-American Soap Box Derby		
79 Last Minute Changes	Year	24.50
80 At Gate	Year	24.50
Rockwell Legendary Art Christmas		
79 Snow Queen	60 Days	24.50
80 Surprises for All	60 Days	24.50
81 Grandpop and Me	60 Days	29.50
John Wayne		
79 Man of Golden West	Year	45.00
RCA Victor Nipper Plate		
80 His Master's Voice	N/A	24.50
Rockwell Legendary Art Annual		
80 Artist's Daughter	Year	65.00
Rockwell Legendary Art Mother's Day		
80 Cradle of Love	60 Days	29.50
81 A Mother's Blessing	60 Days	29.50
82 Memories	60 Days	29.50
Rockwell Legendary Art Rare Rockwell Paintings		
80 Poor Richard	17,500	45.00
Popeye's 50th Anniversary (Single issue)		
80 Happy Birthday Popeye	Year	22.50
Great Chiefs of Canada		
80 Chief Joseph Brant	7,500	65.00
81 Crowfoot	7,500	65.00
Betsey Bates Christmas		
79 Olde Country Inn	7,500	38.50
80 Village School House	7,500	38.50
81 Village Blacksmith	7,500	38.50
Children's World		
81 Official Babysitter	15,000	24.50
81 Cowboy Capers	15,000	29.50
82 Nurse Nancy	15,000	29.50
Hagel Christmas		
81 Shhh!	15,000	29.50
How the West Was Won		
81 Pony Express	19,500	38.50
82 Oregon Trail	19,500	38.50
82 California Gold Rush	19,500	38.50

	Edition Limit	Issue Price
North American Wildlife		
81 Snuggling Cougars	7,500	$ 65.00
Oriental Dreams		
81 Tranquility	15,000	55.00
Rockwell's Scotty		
81 Scotty Stowaway	17,500	45.00
82 Scotty Strikes Bargain	17,500	45.00
(Single issue)		
81 Reagan-Bush Inaugural	17,500	45.00
Greatest Clowns of the Circus		
82 Emmett Kelly	N/A	45.00
82 Lou Jacobs	N/A	45.00
82 Felix Adler	N/A	45.00
82 Otto Griebling	N/A	45.00
Hagel Mother's Day		
82 Once Upon a Time	60 Days	29.50
Mallek Studios		
Navajo Christmas		
71 Indian Wise Men	1,000	15.00
72 On Reservation	2,000	17.00
73 Hoke Denetsosie	2,000	17.00
74 Monument Valley	2,000	18.00
75 Coming Home for Christmas	2,000	18.00
76 Deer with Rainbow	2,000	20.00
77 Goat Herders	2,000	20.00
78 Hogan Christmas	2,000	20.00
79 Navajo Madonna	3,000	25.00
80 Children's Playmates	3,500	25.00
Chinese Lunar Calendar		
72 Year of Rat	1,000	15.00
73 Year of Ox	1,000	15.00
74 Year of Rabbit	1,000	15.00
Christmas Game Birds		
72 Gambel Quail	1,000	15.00
73 Partridge	1,000	15.00
74 Owl and Cactus	1,000	15.00
75 Chinese Wood Duck	1,000	15.00
76 Wild Turkey	1,000	15.00
77 Mallard	1,000	15.00
78 Canadian Geese	1,000	15.00
79 American Woodcock	1,000	15.00
Mexican Christmas		
72 Manger	1,000	15.00
73 Madonna	1,000	15.00
74 Corona	1,000	18.00
75 Pinata	1,000	18.00
76 Procession	1,000	20.00
77 Wisemen	1,000	20.00
Navidad (Single issue)		
72 Navidad en Mexico	500	15.00
(Single issue)		
72 Amish Harvest	1,000	17.00
A.B.C.'s		
74 A.B.C. Rabbit	1,000	15.00
75 A.B.C. Mice	1,000	15.00
(Single issue)		
76 Kewpie Doll	1,000	15.00
Master Engravers of America		
Indian Dancers		
79 Eagle Dancer	2,500	300.00
80 Hoop Dancer	2,500	300.00
McCalla Enterprises (Viletta)		
Making Friends		
78 Feeding Neighbor's Pony	5,000	45.00
79 Cowboys 'n' Indians	5,000	47.50
80 Surprise for Christy	5,000	47.50
Love Letters		
80 Mail Order Bride	5,000	60.00
Metal Arts Co.		
America's First Family (Single issue)		
77 Carters	9,500	40.00
Freedom (Single issue)		
77 Washington at Valley Forge (Sterling)	500	225.00
Freedom (Single issue)		
77 Washington at Valley Forge (Pewter)	1,000	95.00
Winslow Homer's The Sea		
77 Breezing Up	9,500	29.95
Rockwell Copper Christmas		
78 Christmas Gift	Year	48.00
79 Big Moment	Year	48.00
Metlox Potteries		
see: Vernonware (U.S.A.)		
Metropolitan Museum of Art		
Treasures of Tutankhamun		
77 King Tut	2,500	150.00
Mingolla		
see: Home Plates (U.S.A.)		
Mistwood Designs (Fairmont)		
American Wildlife		
81 Desperado at Waterhole	5,000	45.00
81 Bayou Bunnies	5,000	50.00
Woodland Game Birds		
81 After Flight	5,000	60.00

	Edition Limit	Issue Price
Modern Masters		
Family Treasures		
81 Cora's Recital	15,000	$ 39.50
Horses of Fred Stone		
81 Patience	9,500	55.00
Through the Eyes of Love		
81 Enchanted Eyes	9,500	55.00
Moussalli		
Birds of Four Seasons		
78 Cardinal (Winter)	1,000	375.00
79 Indigo Bunting (Fall)	1,000	375.00
79 Hummingbird (Summer)	1,000	375.00
80 Wren (Spring)	1,000	375.00
Museum Editions (Ridgewood)		
Colonial Heritage		
74 Tidewater, Virginia	9,900	40.00
75 Pennsbury Manor	9,900	40.00
75 Old New York	9,900	40.00
76 Hammond-Harwood House	9,900	40.00
76 Joseph Webb House	9,900	40.00
77 Old Court House	9,900	40.00
77 Mulberry Plantation	9,900	40.00
Museum Editions (Viletta)		
Christmas Annual		
78 Expression of Faith	7,400	49.95
79 Skating Lesson	7,400	49.95
Colonial Heritage		
78 Moffatt-Ladd House	9,900	40.00
78 Trent House	9,900	40.00
79 Cupola House	9,900	40.00
79 Nicholas House	9,900	40.00
80 Derby House	9,900	40.00
80 Davenport House	9,900	40.00
Ohio Arts		
Norman Rockwell		
79 Looking Out to Sea	20,000	19.50
Paramount Classics (Pickard)		
Jubilee		
77 Queen Elizabeth	5,000	375.00
(Single issue)		
77 Coronation Plate	5,000	95.00
(Single issue)		
77 Queen Victoria	5,000	95.00
Queen's Jubilee		
77 Queens of England	5,000	95.00
(Single issue)		
77 King George III	5,000	95.00
Pemberton & Oakes (Viletta)		
Children at Christmas		
81 A Gift for Laurie	12,000	48.00
Nutcracker II		
81 Nutcracker Grand Finale	28 Days	24.40
Pickard		
Presidential		
71 Truman	3,000	35.00
73 Lincoln	5,000	35.00
see also:		
Kern Collectibles (U.S.A)		
Paramount Classics (U.S.A.)		
Ram		
Boston 500		
73 Easter	500	30.00
73 Mother's Day	500	30.00
73 Father's Day	500	30.00
73 Christmas	500	30.00
Great Bird Heroes		
73 Cher Ami	1,000	7.95
73 Mocker	1,000	7.95
Reco International		
Americana (Single issue)		
72 Gaspee	1,000	130.00
Four Seasons (Set of four)		
73 Fall		
73 Spring		
73 Summer		
73 Winter	2,500	200.00
Western (Single issue)		
74 Mountain Man	1,000	165.00
Christmas (Single issue)		
77 Old Mill in Valley	5,000	28.00
Games Children Play		
79 Me First	10,000	45.00
80 Forever Bubbles	10,000	45.00
81 Skating Pals	10,000	45.00
82 Join Me	10,000	45.00
Grandparents		
81 Grandma's Cookie Jar	Year	37.50
81 Grandpa and Doll House	Year	37.50
Little Professionals		
82 All Is Well	10,000	39.50

	Edition Limit	Issue Price
Reed & Barton		
Audubon		
70 Pine Siskin	5,000	$60.00
71 Red-Shouldered Hawk	5,000	60.00
72 Stilt Sandpiper	5,000	60.00
73 Red Cardinal	5,000	60.00
74 Boreal Chickadee	5,000	60.00
75 Yellow-Breasted Chat	5,000	65.00
76 Bay-Breasted Warbler	5,000	65.00
77 Purple Finch	5,000	65.00
(Single issue)		
70 Zodiac	1,500	75.00
California Missions		
71 San Diego	1,500	75.00
72 Carmel	1,500	75.00
73 Santa Barbara	1,500	60.00
74 Santa Clara	1,500	60.00
76 San Gabriel	1,500	65.00
Annual		
72 Free Trapper	2,500	65.00
73 Outpost	2,500	65.00
74 Toll Collector	2,500	65.00
75 Indians Discovering Lewis & Clark	2,500	65.00
Currier & Ives		
72 Village Blacksmith	1,500	85.00
72 Western Migration	1,500	85.00
73 Oaken Bucket	1,500	85.00
73 Winter In Country	1,500	85.00
74 Preparing for Market	1,500	85.00
Kentucky Derby		
72 Nearing Finish	1,000	75.00
73 Riva Ridge	1,500	75.00
74 100th Running	1,500	75.00
(Single issue)		
72 Delta Queen	2,500	75.00
(Single issue)		
72 Road Runner	1,500	65.00
Founding Father		
73 Ben Franklin	2,500	65.00
74 George Washington	2,500	65.00
75 Thomas Jefferson	2,500	65.00
76 Patrick Henry	2,500	65.00
76 John Hancock	2,500	65.00
76 John Adams	2,500	65.00
(Single issue)		
75 Chicago Fire	Year	60.00
(Single issue)		
75 Mississippi Queen	2,500	75.00
see also: Collector Creations (U.S.A.) Keller & George (U.S.A.)		
Ridgewood		
Bicentennial		
74 First in War	12,500	40.00
Tom Sawyer (Set of four)		
74 Trying a Pipe		
74 Lost in Cave		
74 Painting Fence		
74 Taking Medicine	3,000	39.95
Wild West (Set of four)		
75 Discovery of Last Chance Gulch		
75 Doubtful Visitor		
75 Bad One		
75 Cattleman	15,000	65.00
Leyendecker Christmas		
75 Christmas Morning	10,000	24.50
76 Christmas Surprise	10,000	24.50
Leyendecker Mother's Day		
76 Grandma's Apple Pie	5,000	24.50
77 Tenderness	Year	35.00
Little Women		
76 Sweet Long Ago	5,000	45.00
76 Song of Spring	5,000	45.00
77 Joy in Morning	5,000	45.00
see also: Museum Editions (U.S.A.)		
River Shore		
Baby Animals Collection		
79 Akiku	20,000	65.00
80 Roosevelt	20,000	65.00
Della Robbia Annual		
79 Adoration	5,000	550.00
80 Virgin and Child	5,000	450.00
Remington Bronze		
77 Bronco Buster	15,000	55.00
78 Coming Thru Rye	15,000	60.00
79 Cheyenne	15,000	60.00
80 Mountain Man	15,000	60.00
(Single issue)		
79 Spring Flowers	17,000	75.00
(Single issue)		
80 Looking Out to Sea	17,000	75.00
Grant Wood		
81 American Gothic	17,000	80.00
Rockwell's Four Freedoms		
81 Freedom of Speech	17,000	65.00

	Edition Limit	Issue Price
(Single issue)		
81 Broken Window	22,500	$19.50
(Single issue)		
81 Grandpa's Guardian	17,000	80.00
Rockwell Collectors Club		
Christmas		
78 Christmas Story	15,000	24.50
Rockwell Museum		
American Family		
78 Baby's First Step	9,900	28.50
78 Happy Birthday Dear Mother	9,900	28.50
78 Sweet Sixteen	9,900	28.50
78 First Haircut	9,900	28.50
79 First Prom	9,900	28.50
79 Student	9,900	28.50
79 Wrapping Christmas Presents	9,900	28.50
79 Birthday Party	9,900	28.50
79 Little Mother	9,900	28.50
80 Washing Our Dog	9,900	28.50
80 Mother's Little Helper	9,900	28.50
80 Bride & Groom	9,900	28.50
American Family II		
80 New Arrival	22,500	35.00
80 Sweet Dreams	22,500	35.00
80 Little Shaver	22,500	35.00
80 We Missed You Daddy	22,500	35.00
80 Home Run Slugger	22,500	35.00
80 Giving Thanks	22,500	35.00
80 Space Pioneers	22,500	35.00
80 Little Salesman	22,500	35.00
80 Almost Grown Up	22,500	35.00
80 Courageous Hero	22,500	35.00
80 At Circus	22,500	35.00
80 Good Food, Good Friends	22,500	35.00
Christmas		
79 Day After Christmas	25,000	75.00
80 Checking His List	Year	75.00
81 Ringing in Good Cheer	Year	75.00
(Single issue)		
79 Norman Rockwell Remembered	Year	45.00
Classic		
81 Puppy Love	60 Days	24.50
81 While Audience Waits	60 Days	24.50
81 Off to School	60 Days	24.50
82 Country Doctor	60 Days	24.50
82 Spring Fever	60 Days	24.50
82 Dollhouse for Sis	60 Days	24.50
Royal Cornwall		
Bethlehem Christmas		
77 First Christmas Eve	10,000	29.95
78 Glad Tidings	10,000	34.50
79 Gift Bearers	10,000	34.50
80 Great Joy	10,000	39.95
Creation		
77 In Beginning	19,500	45.00
77 In His Image	19,500	45.00
77 Adam's Rib	19,500	45.00
77 Banished from Eden	19,500	45.00
77 Noah and Ark	19,500	45.00
77 Tower of Babel	19,500	45.00
78 Sodom & Gomorrah	19,500	45.00
78 Jacob's Wedding	19,500	45.00
78 Rebekah at Well	19,500	45.00
78 Jacob's Ladder	19,500	45.00
78 Joseph's Coat of Many Colors	19,500	45.00
78 Joseph Interprets Pharaoh's Dream	19,500	45.00
Classic Christmas		
78 Child of Peace	17,500	55.00
78 Silent Night	17,500	55.00
78 Most Precious Gift	17,500	55.00
78 We Three Kings	17,500	55.00
Four Seasons		
78 Warmth	17,500	60.00
78 Voices of Spring	17,500	60.00
78 Fledgling	17,500	60.00
78 We Survive	17,500	60.00
Golden Age of Cinema		
78 King & His Ladies	22,500	45.00
78 Fred & Ginger	22,500	45.00
78 Judy & Mickey	22,500	45.00
79 Philadelphia Story	22,500	45.00
79 Thin Man	22,500	45.00
79 Gigi	22,500	45.00
Mother's Day		
78 God Bless Mommy	10,000	35.00
Alice in Wonderland		
79 Alice and White Rabbit	27,500	45.00
79 Advice from a Caterpillar	27,500	45.00
79 Cheshire Cat's Grin	27,500	45.00
79 Mad Hatter's Tea Party	27,500	45.00
79 Queen's Croquet Match	27,500	45.00
79 Who Stole Tarts?	27,500	45.00

	Edition Limit	Issue Price
Kitten's World		
79 Just Curious	27,500	$45.00
79 Hello, World	27,500	45.00
79 Are You a Flower?	27,500	45.00
79 Talk to Me	27,500	45.00
79 My Favorite Toy	27,500	45.00
79 Purr-Fect Pleasure	27,500	45.00
Promised Land		
79 Pharaoh's Daughter Finds Moses	24,500	45.00
79 Burning Bush	24,500	45.00
79 Let My People Go	24,500	45.00
79 Parting of Red Sea	24,500	45.00
79 Miriam's Song of Thanksgiving	24,500	45.00
79 Manna from Heaven	24,500	45.00
79 Water from Rock	24,500	45.00
79 Battle of Amalek	24,500	45.00
79 Ten Commandments	24,500	45.00
79 Golden Calf	24,500	45.00
79 Moses Smashes Tablets	24,500	45.00
79 Glorious Tabernacle	24,500	45.00
Treasures of Childhood		
79 My Cuddlies Collection	19,500	45.00
79 My Coin Collection	19,500	45.00
79 My Shell Collection	19,500	45.00
79 My Stamp Collection	19,500	45.00
79 My Doll Collection	19,500	45.00
79 My Rock Collection	19,500	45.00
Beauty of Bouguereau		
80 Lucie	19,500	35.00
80 Madelaine	19,500	35.00
80 Frere et Soeur	19,500	35.00
80 Solange et Enfant	19,500	35.00
80 Colette	19,500	35.00
80 Jean et Jeanette	19,500	35.00
Four Faces of Love		
80 Romeo & Juliet	17,500	55.00
80 Young Galahad	17,500	55.00
80 At Locksley Hall	17,500	55.00
80 St. Agnes Eve	17,500	55.00
Dorothy's Day		
80 Brand New Day	15,000	55.00
80 All by Myself	15,000	55.00
81 Off to School	15,000	55.00
81 Best Friends	15,000	55.00
81 Helping Mommy	15,000	55.00
81 Bless Me Too	15,000	55.00
Legendary Ships of the Seas		
80 Flying Dutchman	19,500	49.50
80 Refanu	19,500	49.50
80 Palatine	19,500	49.50
80 Gaspé Bay	19,500	49.50
80 Roth Ramhach	19,500	49.50
80 Pride	19,500	49.50
80 Copenhagen	19,500	49.50
80 Frigorifique	19,500	49.50
80 Foochow Sea Junk	19,500	49.50
80 Rescue	19,500	49.50
Memories of America		
80 Bringing in Maple Sugar	5,000	120.00
80 Old Automobile	5,000	120.00
81 Halloween	5,000	120.00
81 Rainbow	5,000	120.00
Windows on the World		
80 Golden Gate of San Francisco	19,500	45.00
81 Snow Village/Madulain	19,500	45.00
81 Rainy Day in London	19,500	45.00
81 Water Festival/Venice	19,500	45.00
81 Harvesting in Ukraine	19,500	45.00
81 Serengeti Plain	19,500	45.00
Exotic Birds of Tropique		
81 Scarlet Macaws	19,500	49.50
81 Toco Toucan	19,500	49.50
81 Great Sulphur-Crested Cockatoo	19,500	49.50
Love's Precious Moments		
81 Love's Sweet Vow	17,500	55.00
81 Love's Sweet Verse	17,500	55.00
81 Love's Sweet Offering	17,500	55.00
81 Love's Sweet Embrace	17,500	55.00
81 Love's Sweet Melody	17,500	55.00
Most Precious Gifts of Shen-Lung		
81 Fire	19,500	49.50
81 Water	19,500	49.50
81 Sun	19,500	49.50
Puppy's World		
81 1st Birthday	19,500	49.50
81 Beware of Dog	19,500	49.50
81 Top Dog	19,500	49.50
81 Need A Friend?	19,500	49.50
81 Double Trouble	19,500	49.50
81 Just Clowning	19,500	49.50
81 Guest for Dinner	19,500	49.50
81 Gift Wrapped	19,500	49.50
Peacock Maiden		
81 Dance of Peacock Maiden	19,500	69.50
Royal Devon		
see: Hamilton Collection (U.S.A.)		

	Edition Limit	Issue Price
Royal Worcester		
Currier & Ives		
74 Road-Winter	10,000	$59.50
75 Old Grist Mill	10,000	59.50
76 Winter Pastime	10,000	59.50
American History		
77 Washington's Inauguration	1,250	65.00
Annual		
77 Home to Thanksgiving	500	59.50
Royalwood		
(Single issue)		
77 Doctor and Doll	Year	21.50
Leyendecker		
78 Cornflake Boy	10,000	25.00
78 Cornflake Girl	10,000	25.00
John A. Ruthven		
Moments of Nature		
77 Screech Owls	5,000	37.50
79 Chickadees	5,000	39.50
80 California Quail	5,000	39.50
Sebastian		
American's Favorite Scenes		
78 Motif #1	10,000	75.00
79 Grand Canyon	10,000	75.00
Seeley's Ceramic Services		
Antique French Dolls		
79 Bru	5,000	39.00
79 E.J.	5,000	39.00
79 A.T.	5,000	39.00
80 Alexandre	5,000	39.00
80 Schmitt	5,000	39.00
80 Marque	5,000	39.00
Old German Dolls		
81 Dear Googly	7,500	39.00
82 Whistler	7,500	39.00
Seven Seas		
Historical Event		
69 Moon Landing, No Flag	2,000	13.50
69 Moon Landing, with Flag	25,000	13.50
70 Year of Crisis	4,000	15.00
71 First Vehicular Travel	3,000	15.00
72 Last Moon Journey	2,000	15.00
73 Peace	3,000	15.00
Mother's Day		
70 Girl of All Nations	5,000	15.00
71 Sharing Confidence	1,400	15.00
72 Scandinavian Girl	1,600	15.00
73 All-American Girl	1,500	15.00
Christmas Carols		
70 I Heard Bells	4,000	15.00
71 Oh Tannenbaum	4,000	15.00
72 Deck Halls	1,500	18.00
73 O Holy Night	2,000	18.00
74 Jingle Bells	1,200	25.00
75 Winter Wonderland	1,500	25.00
76 Twelve Days of Christmas	1,200	25.00
77 Up on Housetop	1,500	25.00
78 Little Town of Bethlehem	1,500	25.00
79 Santa Claus Is Coming to Town	1,500	25.00
80 Frosty Snowman	1,500	25.00
New World		
70 Holy Family	3,500	15.00
71 Three Wise Men	1,500	15.00
72 Shepherds Watched	1,500	18.00
Passion Play (Single issue)		
70 Oberammergau	2,500	18.00
Shenango		
see: Castleton China (U.S.A.)		
Silver Creations		
Churchillian Heritage		
72 Hour of Decision	N/A	150.00
73 Yalta Conference	N/A	150.00
73 Clydesdales	N/A	150.00
Smith Glass		
Americana		
71 Morgan Silver Dollar	5,000	10.00
Christmas		
71 Family at Christmas	N/A	10.00
72 Flying Angel	N/A	10.00
73 St. Mary's in Mountains	N/A	10.00
Famous Americans		
71 Kennedy	2,500	10.00
71 Lincoln	2,500	10.00
72 Davis, Jefferson	5,000	11.00
72 Lee, Robert E.	5,000	11.00
Sterling America		
Christmas Customs		
70 England	2,500	18.00
71 Holland	2,500	18.00
72 Norway	2,500	18.00
73 Germany	2,500	20.00
74 México	2,500	24.00

Twelve Days of Christmas

	Edition Limit	Issue Price
70 Partridge	2,500	$18.00
71 Turtle Doves	2,500	18.00
72 French Hens	2,500	18.00
73 Colly Birds	2,500	18.00
74 Five Rings	2,500	24.00
75 Six Geese	2,500	24.00
76 Seven Swans	2,500	24.00
77 Eight Maids	2,500	28.00

Mother's Day

	Edition Limit	Issue Price
71 Mare & Foal	2,500	18.00
72 Horned Owl	2,500	18.00
73 Raccoons	2,500	20.00
74 Deer	2,500	24.00
75 Quail	2,500	24.00

Stieff

Bicentennial

	Edition Limit	Issue Price
72 Declaration of Independence	10,000	50.00
74 Betsy Ross	10,000	50.00
75 Crossing Delaware	10,000	50.00
76 Serapio & Bon Homme	10,000	50.00

Syracuse China

Grandma Moses (Sets of four)

	Edition Limit	Issue Price
72 Old Checkered House in Winter		
72 Mary and Little Lamb		
72 In Harvest Time		
72 Sugaring Off	N/A	80.00
72 Hoosick Valley from Window		
72 Taking in Laundry		
72 It Snows, Oh it Snows		
72 Joy Ride	N/A	80.00

Towle Silversmiths

Valentines

	Edition Limit	Issue Price
72 Single Heart	Year	10.00
73 Entwined Hearts	Year	10.00

Christmas

	Edition Limit	Issue Price
72 Three Wise Men	2,500	250.00

U.S. Historical Society

Annual Historical

	Edition Limit	Issue Price
77 Great Events	5,000	60.00
78 Great Events	10,000	75.00

Stained Glass Cathedral Christmas

	Edition Limit	Issue Price
78 Canterbury Cathedral	Year	87.00
79 Flight into Egypt (St. John Divine)	10,000	97.00
80 Madonna and Child	10,000	125.00
81 Magi	10,000	150.00

Wildflowers of the South

	Edition Limit	Issue Price
81 Wild Honeysuckle	19,500	49.50

Vague Shadows

Plainsmen

	Edition Limit	Issue Price
79 Buffalo Hunt	2,500	300.00
79 Proud One	2,500	300.00

Great American Chieftains

	Edition Limit	Issue Price
79 Chief Sitting Bull	7,500	65.00
79 Chief Joseph	7,500	65.00
80 Chief Red Cloud	7,500	65.00
80 Chief Geronimo	7,500	65.00
81 Chief Crazy Horse	7,500	65.00

Professionals

	Edition Limit	Issue Price
79 Big Leaguer	15,000	29.95
80 Ballerina's Dilemma	15,000	32.50
81 Quarterback	15,000	32.50
82 Rodeo Joe	15,000	35.00

Santa

	Edition Limit	Issue Price
80 Santa's Joy	Year	29.95
81 Santa's Bundle	Year	29.95

Storybook Collection

	Edition Limit	Issue Price
80 Little Red Riding Hood	18 Days	29.95
81 Cinderella	18 Days	29.95
81 Hansel and Gretel	18 Days	29.95
82 Goldilocks and Three Bears	18 Days	29.95

Arctic Friends (Set of two)

	Edition Limit	Issue Price
81 Siberian Love		
81 Snow Pals	7,500	100.00

Four Princesses

	Edition Limit	Issue Price
81 Lily of Mohawks	7,500	50.00
81 Pocahontas	7,500	50.00
82 Minnehaha	7,500	50.00
82 Sacajawea	7,500	50.00

(Single issue)

	Edition Limit	Issue Price
81 Apache Boy	5,000	95.00

Nature's Harmony

	Edition Limit	Issue Price
82 Peaceable Kingdom	12,500	100.00

Vernonware (Metlox Potteries)

Songs of Christmas

	Edition Limit	Issue Price
71 Twelve Days	9,000	15.00
72 Jingle Bells	9,000	17.50
73 First Noel	9,000	20.00
74 Upon a Midnight Clear	9,000	20.00
75 O Holy Night	10,000	20.00
76 Hark! Herald Angels	10,000	$20.00
77 Away in Manger	10,000	30.00
78 White Christmas	10,000	30.00
79 Little Drummer Boy	10,000	30.00

Viletta

Disneyland

	Edition Limit	Issue Price
76 Betsy Ross	3,000	15.00
76 Crossing Delaware	3,000	15.00
76 Signing Declaration	3,000	15.00
76 Spirit of '76	3,000	15.00

Bicentennial

	Edition Limit	Issue Price
77 Patriots	15,000	37.00

In Tribute to America's Great Artists

	Edition Limit	Issue Price
78 DeGrazia by Don Marco	5,000	65.00

Days of the West

	Edition Limit	Issue Price
78 Cowboy Christmas	5,000	55.00

Moments Alone

	Edition Limit	Issue Price
80 Dreamer	15 Days	28.80
81 Reverie	15 Days	28.80

Alice in Wonderland

	Edition Limit	Issue Price
80 Alice and White Rabbit	28 Days	25.00
81 Mad Hatter's Tea Party	28 Days	25.00
81 Alice and Cheshire Cat	28 Days	25.00
81 Alice and Croquet Match	28 Days	25.00

Portraits of Childhood

	Edition Limit	Issue Price
81 Butterfly Magic	N/A	24.95

Carefree Days

	Edition Limit	Issue Price
82 Autumn Wanderer	10 Days	24.50

Wonder of Childhood

	Edition Limit	Issue Price
82 Touching Sky	22 Days	24.00

see also:
Abbey Press (U.S.A.)
American Arts Services (U.S.A.)
Carson Mint (U.S.A.)
Collector's Heirlooms (U.S.A.)
R. J. Ernst Enterprises (U.S.A.)
Ghent Collection (U.S.A.)
Hamilton Collection (U.S.A.)
Ralph Homan Studios (U.S.A.)
Joys (U.S.A.)
Judaic Heritage Society (U.S.A.)
McCalla Enterprises (U.S.A.)
Museum Editions (U.S.A.)
Pemberton & Oakes (U.S.A.)
Warwick (U.S.A.)
Westbury (U.S.A.)
Edward Weston Editons (U.S.A.)

Volair (Gorham)

Audubon American Wildlife Heritage

	Edition Limit	Issue Price
77 House Mouse	2,500	90.00
77 Royal Louisiana Heron	2,500	90.00
77 Virginia Deer	2,500	90.00
77 Snowy Owl	2,500	90.00

Warwick (Viletta)

Great Comedians

	Edition Limit	Issue Price
78 Little Tramp	7,500	35.00
78 Outrageous Groucho	7,500	35.00

George Washington Mint

American Indian

	Edition Limit	Issue Price
72 Curley (Gold)	100	2000.00
72 Curley (Proof)	100	1000.00
72 Curley (Sterling)	7,300	150.00
73 Two Moons (Gold)	100	2000.00
73 Two Moons (Proof)	100	1000.00
73 Two Moons (Sterling)	7,300	150.00

Mother's Day

	Edition Limit	Issue Price
72 Whistler's Mother (Sterling)	9,800	150.00
72 Whistler's Mother (Proof)	100	1000.00
72 Whistler's Mother (Gold)	100	2000.00
74 Motherhood (Sterling)	2,300	175.00
74 Motherhood (Proof)	100	1000.00
74 Motherhood (Gold)	100	2000.00

Picasso

	Edition Limit	Issue Price
72 Don Quixote (Gold)	100	2000.00
72 Don Quixote (Proof)	100	1000.00
72 Don Quixote (Sterling)	9,800	125.00

Remington

	Edition Limit	Issue Price
72 Rattlesnake (Gold)	100	2000.00
72 Rattlesnake (Proof)	100	1000.00
72 Rattlesnake (Sterling)	800	250.00

Da Vinci

	Edition Limit	Issue Price
72 Last Supper	N/A	125.00

N. C. Wyeth

	Edition Limit	Issue Price
72 Uncle Sam's America (Gold)	100	2000.00
72 Uncle Sam's America (Proof)	100	1000.00
72 Uncle Sam's America (Sterling)	9,800	150.00
73 Massed Flags (Gold)	100	2000.00
73 Massed Flags (Proof)	100	1000.00
73 Massed Flags (Sterling)	2,300	150.00

Israel Anniversary (Single issue)

	Edition Limit	Issue Price
73 Struggle	10,000	300.00

Picasso (Single issue)

	Edition Limit	Issue Price
74 Rites of Spring (Sterling)	9,800	125.00

Remington (Single issue)

	Edition Limit	Issue Price
74 Coming Through Rye (Sterling)	2,500	$300.00

Wendell August Forge

Great Americans

	Edition Limit	Issue Price
71 J.F.K. (Pewter)	5,000	40.00
71 J.F.K. (Silver)	500	200.00
72 Lincoln (Pewter)	5,000	40.00
72 Lincoln (Silver)	500	200.00

Great Moments

	Edition Limit	Issue Price
71 Columbus (Pewter)	5,000	40.00
71 Columbus (Silver)	500	200.00
72 Landing of Pilgrims (Pewter)	5,000	40.00
72 Landing of Pilgrims (Silver)	500	200.00
73 First Thanksgiving (Pewter)	5,000	40.00
73 First Thanksgiving (Silver)	500	200.00
74 Patrick Henry (Pewter)	5,000	40.00
74 Patrick Henry (Silver)	500	200.00
75 Paul Revere (Pewter)	5,000	45.00
75 Paul Revere (Silver)	500	200.00
76 Signing of Declaration (Pewter)	5,000	50.00
76 Signing of Declaration (Silver)	500	200.00

Wings of Man

	Edition Limit	Issue Price
71 Columbus' Ships (Pewter)	5,000	40.00
71 Columbus' Ships (Silver)	500	200.00
72 Conestoga Wagon (Pewter)	5,000	40.00
72 Conestoga Wagon (Silver)	500	200.00

Peace (Single issue)

	Edition Limit	Issue Price
73 Facing Doves (Silver)	2,500	250.00

Christmas

	Edition Limit	Issue Price
74 Caroler (Bronze)	2,500	25.00
74 Caroler (Pewter)	2,500	30.00
75 Christmas in Country (Bronze)	2,500	30.00
75 Christmas in Country (Pewter)	2,500	35.00
76 Lamplighter (Bronze)	2,500	35.00
76 Lamplighter (Pewter)	2,500	40.00
77 Covered Bridge (Bronze)	2,500	40.00
77 Covered Bridge (Pewter)	2,500	45.00

Wildlife

	Edition Limit	Issue Price
77 On Guard (Aluminum)	1,900	35.00
77 On Guard (Bronze)	1,500	45.00
77 On Guard (Pewter)	1,500	55.00
77 On Guard (Silver)	100	250.00
78 Thunderbird (Aluminum)	1,900	40.00
78 Thunderbird (Bronze)	1,500	50.00
78 Thunderbird (Pewter)	1,500	60.00
78 Thunderbird (Silver)	100	250.00

Westbury (Viletta)

Tender Moments

	Edition Limit	Issue Price
78 Old Fashioned Persuasion	7,500	40.00
79 Dandelions	7,500	45.00

Westminster Collectibles

Holidays

	Edition Limit	Issue Price
76 All Hallows Eve	5,000	38.50
77 Christmas	5,000	38.50

Westmoreland

Christmas

	Edition Limit	Issue Price
72 Holy Birth	2,500	35.00
73 Manger Scene	3,500	35.00
74 Gethsemane	1,500	35.00
75 Christ Is Risen	N/A	45.00

Edward Weston Editions (Viletta)

Unicorn Fantasies

	Edition Limit	Issue Price
79 Follower of Dreams	5,000	55.00
80 Twice Upon a Time	5,000	55.00
81 Familiar Spirit	5,000	60.00
82 Noble Gathering	5,000	65.00

Weddings Around the World

	Edition Limit	Issue Price
79 Hawaiian Wedding	5,000	75.00
80 Dutch Wedding	5,000	75.00

Wheaton

Presidential

	Edition Limit	Issue Price
71 Adams	9,648	5.00
71 Eisenhower	8,856	5.00
71 Hoover	10,152	5.00
71 Kennedy	11,160	5.00
71 Lincoln	9,648	5.00
71 Madison	9,504	5.00
71 Monroe	9,792	5.00
71 F.D. Roosevelt	9,432	5.00
71 Taft	9,648	5.00
71 Van Buren	9,576	5.00
71 Washington	10,800	5.00
71 Wilson	8,712	5.00

Whitehall China

Raphael Soyer

	Edition Limit	Issue Price
79 Model on Bed	10,000	$39.95

Woodmere

see: Calhoun's Collectors Society (U.S.A.)

Index of Bradex-listed Plate Makers and Sponsors

Note: "Maker" is a general term for the name under which a plate is issued and is not necessarily the actual "manu-facturer." A Maker can be a distrib-utor, manufacturer, or occasionally a "sponsor." See Glossary of Commonly Used Terms.

Alboth, See Kaiser
Anri, **38-A54-0.0**
Anna-Perenna, **22-A3-0.0**
Arabia, **16-A69-0.0**
Artists of the World, **84-A72-0.0**
L'Association l'Esprit de Lafayette, See D'Arceau-Limoges

Bareuther, **22-B7-0.0**
    See also Danish Church
Belleek, **26-B18-0.0**
Berlin Design, **22-B20-0.0**
Beswick Potteries, John, See Royal Doulton
Bing & Grøndahl, **14-B36-0.0**

Giuseppe Cappe, See King's
Carborundum Company, See Spode
Chambre Syndicale de la Couture Parisienne, See D'Arceau-Limoges
W. T. Copeland & Sons, See Spode
Creative World, See Veneto Flair
Crown Parian, **84-C72-0.0**

Danish Church, **22-D5-0.0**
D'Arceau-Limoges, **18-D15-0.0**
Désirée, See Svend Jensen
Dresden, **22-D68-0.0**

Eslau, See Grande Copenhagen

Fairmont, **84-F4-0.0**
Franklin Mint, **84-F64-0.0**

Fukagawa, **42-F78-0.0**

Goebel, **22-G54-0.0**
Gorham, **84-G58-0.0**
    See also Royal Devon
Grande Copenhagen, **14-G65-0.0**
Dave Grossman Designs, **42-G74-0.0**

Haviland, **18-H6-0.0**
Haviland & Parlon, **18-H8-0.0**
Heinrich/Villeroy & Boch, **22-H18-0.0**
Hibel Studio, **22-H31-0.0**
Hummelwerk, See Goebel
Hutschenreuther, **22-H82-0.0**

Incolay Studios, **84-I31-0.0**
International, **84-I61-0.0**

Svend Jensen, **14-J21-0.0**

Kaiser, **22-K4-0.0**
Kern Collectibles, **84-K20-0.0**
King's, **38-K32-0.0**
Kirke Platten, See Danish Church
Knowles, Edwin M., **84-K41-0.0**
    See also Rockwell Society
Königszelt Bavaria, **22-K46-0.0**

Lafayette Society, See D'Arceau-Limoges
Lalique, **18-L3-0.0**
Lenox, **84-L18-0.0**
Lihs-Lindner, **22-L31-0.0**
Limoges-Turgot, **18-L52-0.0**
Lladró, **72-L41-0.0**
Longton Crown Pottery, **26-L46-0.0**

Morgantown Crystal, **84-M58-0.0**
Museo Teatrale alla Scala, See di Volteradici

Orrefors, **76-O74-0.0**

Pickard, **84-P29-0.0**
    See also Kern Collectibles
Porcelana Granada, **4-P61-0.0**
Porcellanas Verbana, See Porcelana Granada
Porzellanfabrik Tirschenreuth, See Dresden
Porsgrund, **54-P62-0.0**

Reco International, **84-R60-0.0**
Reed & Barton, **84-R18-0.0**
River Shore, **84-R69-0.0**
Rockwell Society of America, **84-R70-0.0**
Rogers Brothers, See International
Rörstrand, **76-R54-0.0**
Rosenthal, **22-R55-0.0**
Roskilde Church, See Danish Church
Royal Bayreuth, **22-R58-0.0**
Royal Copenhagen, **14-R59-0.0**
Royal Devon, **84-R61-0.0**
Royal Doulton, **26-R62-0.0**
Royal Tettau, See Royal Bayreuth
Royal Worcester, (G.B.) **26-R76-0.0**
    (U.S.) **84-R76-0.0**

La Scala, See di Volteradici
Schmid, (Ger.), **22-S12-0.0**
    (Jap.) **42-S12-0.0**
Silbermann Brothers, See Kaiser
Spode, **26-S63-0.0**

Veneto Flair, **38-V22-0.0**
Verbano, See Porcelana Granada
Viletta, **84-V36-0.0**
di Volteradici, Studio Dante, **38-V90-0.0**

Wedgwood, **26-W90-0.0**

Index of Plate Artists

Glossary of Commonly Used Terms

Aftermarket. See Market.

Alabaster. A dense, fine-grained form of gypsum (calcium sulfate) stone, usually white to pink and slightly translucent. Alabaster stone can be carved in fine detail for ornamental objects and hardened by intense heat. Italian alabaster is also called Florentine marble. Ivory alabaster is composed of alabaster but is non-translucent and acquires a patina with age like that of old ivory.

Allotment. A number of plates, all alike and usually at issue, allocated by a maker to a distributor or dealer. See Lot.

Alloy. Two or more metals combined while molten. Alloying is done to achieve hardness, toughness, or luster. See Pewter.

Annual. A plate issued once each year as part of a series. The term is most often used when a plate does not commemorate a specific holiday.

Annular kiln. A round oven made from brick used to fire ceramic plates.

Art Deco, Art Décoratif. A style of decoration popular in Europe and America from 1920 to 1945. The Art Deco movement sought to glorify progress and the future by using as motifs such shapes as the cylinder, circle, rectangle, and cone.

Art Nouveau. A style of decoration in Europe and America from 1890 to 1920. The Art Nouveau movement used twining floral patterns as its primary decorative motifs.

Asked Price, Ask. The price posted for a plate by a seller on the Exchange.

At Issue. A plate being offered for sale at the time of its manufacture and at the original price set by the maker.

Back Issue. See Issue.

Backstamp. The information on the back of a plate, usually including the maker's signature, name, or trademark (logo-type). It may also record serial number, title, artist's signature, explanation of the plate, sponsor, production techniques, awards, or release initials. It may be hand-applied, stamped, incised (cut or pressed), or applied as a decalcomania.

Banding. A method for hand-application of precious metals, such as gold, silver, or platinum, to the edge or other parts of a glazed plate. The decorator uses a camel's hair brush to apply a liquid metal suspended in special oils. The plate is then fired to adhere the metal to the glaze.

Baroque. An elaborate style of decoration developed in Europe in the seventeenth and eighteenth centuries and noted for exaggerated gesture and line. Example: Dresden **(22-D68-0.0)**.

Bas-relief. See Relief Sculpture.

Bavaria. A province in the southwest corner of Germany long known as a center for porcelain factories. The region contains large deposits of kaolin, the key porcelain component.

Bearish. Marked by declining prices, either actual or expected. A bear market is one of declining prices.

Bedroom Dealer. A trade term for a small dealer who usually operates from his home, buys discounted plates, and resells them for a small profit.

Bid Price, Bid. The amount a prospective buyer offers to pay for a plate on the Exchange.

Bisque, Biscuit. A plate that has been fired but not glazed, leaving it with a matte texture. So called because of the biscuit-like appearance. Example: Lladró **(72-L41-0.0)**.

Blue Chip. An established series by a well-known maker in which nearly every issue shows a steady sequence of price rises above issue price, usually over an extended period of time.

Body. 1. The formula or combination of substances that make up potter's clay, generally referring to stoneware and earthenware. **2.** The basic plate form to which ornamentation is applied.

Bone Ash. Calcium phosphate, a component of bone china, added to give whiteness and translucency. It is obtained by calcinating (reducing to powder by heat) animal bones, usually those of oxen.

Bone China (Bone Porcelain). A type of china developed by Josiah Spode in England in the 1790s. By replacing part of the kaolin in the china formula with bone ash, greater translucency and whiteness is obtained at lower firing temperatures. The finest bone china contains up to 50% bone ash. It is the most commonly made china in England. Examples: Royal Doulton **(26-R62-0.0)** and Royal Worcester (Great Britain) **(26-R76-0.0)**.

Bradex. Common term for the *Bradford Exchange Current Quotations,* a periodic listing of the current market prices of collector's plates now listed on the Exchange. See Listed Plate, Exchange.

Broker. A representative of the Bradford Exchange Trading Center who enters bids and asks of all traders and confirms all transactions. See Trading Floor, Trader, Bid Price, Ask Price.

Bullish. Marked by rising prices, either actual or expected, and optimistic atmosphere. A bull market is one of rising prices.

Buy Order. An offer by an individual or dealer to purchase one or more plates on the secondary market. See Bid Price, Exchange.

Cameo Effect. Ornamentations in relief on a background of contrasting color to resemble a cameo. Examples: Wedgwood Jasper ware **(26-W90-0.0)** and Incolay Studios **(84-I31-0.0)**.

Celsius, Centigrade. The thermometric scale in which 0° represents the freezing point of water and 100° the boiling point. Celsius temperature is denoted by "C" after the number.

Ceramic. A general term applying to all of the various plates made from clay and hardened by firing.

Certificate. An attestation of authenticity which may accompany each plate in an edition. A certificate authenticates a plate as being part of an issue and usually confirms the plate's individual number within the edition.

China, Chinaware. A hard, vitreous ceramic whose main components are kaolin and china stone fired at high temperature. Originally the term was used for those ceramics which only came from China. Later it was applied to all "hard" and "soft" porcelain. China is often used as a generic term which includes porcelain, but is properly distinguished from it by a high bisque firing temperature and a low glaze firing temperature. The main firing (bisque) of china is approximately 7% lower than the main firing (glaze) of porcelain. In china production, the glaze is applied after the main firing and fixed with a second lower-temperature firing. A typical china formula is 40% kaolin, 10% ball clay, and varying proportions of china stone, feldspar, and flint. See Porcelain.

China Clay. See Kaolin.

China Stone, Petuntse. A feldspathic material in china formulas. China stone acts as a flux which helps dissolve and fuse the other components into a vitreous mass.

Christmas Plates, Christmas Series. Annual plates issued to commemorate Christmas, usually as part of a series. Plate names for Christmas include Noël (French), Weihnachten (German), Jul (Danish), Navidad (Spanish and Portugese), and Natale (Italian). The oldest Christmas series is that of Bing & Grøndahl, produced continuously since 1895 **(14-B36-1.0)**.

Clay. Any of various plastic, viscous earths used to make plates. It is formed by the decomposition, due to weathering, of igneous rocks such as granite, feldspar, and pegmatite.

Closed-End Series. A series of plates with a predetermined number of issues. Example: Haviland *Twelve Days of Christmas* series **(18-H6-1.0)**.

Cobalt Blue. Cobalt oxide in the form of a dark black powder which, when fired, turns a deep blue. It was the first known and is still the most commonly used ceramic under-glaze color because of its ability to withstand high firing temperatures. It can produce a variety of shades. Examples: Kaiser cobalt blue **(22-K4-0.0)**, Bing & Grøndahl Copenhagen blue **(14-B36-0.0)**, Royal Copenhagen Danish blue **(14-R59-0.0)**, and Rörstrand Scandia blue **(76-R54-0.0)**.

Collector's Plate. A decorative plate produced in a limited edition for the purpose of being collected. Although the earliest plates were not produced with this objective, they have since acquired the name by virtue of being collected and are now produced for this purpose.

Commemorative Plate. A plate produced in remembrance of an event. Example: D'Arceau-Limoges *Lafayette Legacy Collection* **(18-D15-1.0)**.

Coterie Plate. A collector's plate with a limited following which is traded too infrequently to be listed on the Exchange but which may be traded over the counter.

Crystal. See Lead Crystal.

Cut Glass. Glass decorated by the cutting of grooves and facets, usually done with a copper engraver's wheel.

China Clay. See Kaolin.

Damascene. An electroplating effect, created and patented by Reed & Barton **(84-R18-0.0)**, of etching and then depositing layers of gold, copper, and silver on bronze. Originally the term referred to the art, developed in Damascus, of ornamenting iron or steel with inlaid precious metals.

Dealer. A marketer of plates who buys primarily from makers or distributors and sells primarily to the public.

Decalcomania. The printed reproduction of original artwork which is produced by individual color separations, either in offset lithography or by silk-screen printing.

Delftware. Earthenware covered with an opaque white glaze made of stannic oxide, and oxide of tin. Originally developed in Delft, Holland, in the sixteenth century, Delftware has the appearance of being covered with a thick white paint. Similar ware is the majolica of Italy and faience of France and Germany. See Faience, Majolica, Tin Glaze.

Dilute Colors. Solutions of metallic salts which are absorbed by the bisque body of a plate when it is glazed and fired, producing soft, impressionistic tones. Perfected in Copenhagen in about 1883. Examples: Royal Copenhagen **(14-R59-0.0)** and Bing & Grøndahl **(14-B36-0.0)**.

Distributor. A marketer of plates who buys from manufacturers and sells to dealers. Some distributors also act as makers and as dealers.

Dresden, Meissen. Neighboring cities now in East Germany where the first hard-paste procelain outside of China was produced by Johann Friedrich Böttger in 1708.

Dresden China. Term used in England beginning in the eighteenth century to describe true hard-paste porcelain. See Dresden, Porcelain.

Earthenware. A term for any ceramics which are not vitrified. Typical components of earthenware are 43% ball clay, 24% kaolin, 23% flint, and 10% pegmatite. Fired earthenware is normally covered with either a transparent or opaque glaze. High-fired earthenware is fired at a higher temperature to produce a harder ware. Example: Royal Doulton *Beswick Christmas* series **(26-R62-1.0)**.

Edition. The total number of plates, all with the same decoration, produced by a maker. Editions of collector's plates are normally limited to a fixed number and are not repeated.

Electroplating. A process by which metal plates are coated with another metal by electrical charges.

Embossed Design. Raised ornamentation produced by the plate mold or by stamping a design into the body of the plate. Example: Belleek **(26-B18-0.0)**.

Enamel. A glaze material colored with suspended mineral oxides for decorating plates.

Engraved Design. Decoration produced by cutting into the surface of metal, glass, or china plates with either a tool or acid, as in etching. Example: Veneto Flair **(38-V22-0.0)**. See Intaglio.

Etched Design. Decoration produced by cutting into the surface of a plate with acid. The plate is first covered with an acid-resistant paint or wax, and the design is carved through this coating. When the plate is immersed in acid, the acid "bites" into the plate surface in the shape of the design. Example: Franklin Mint silver plates **(84-F64-0.0)**. See Intaglio.

Exchange. A place where plates are traded, most commonly the Bradford Exchange, the world's largest trading center in limited-edition collector's plates. Incorporated in 1962, it was formerly known as Bradford Galleries Exchange. See Trading Floor.

Faience. Tin-enameled earthenware from France, Germany, or Spain developed in the seventeenth century and named for the Italian town of Faenza, a center for majolica, another name for this ware. See Delftware.

Feldspar. A mineral composed of aluminum silicates with either potassium, sodium, calcium, or barium. Feldspar decomposes to form kaolin, the key ingredient of china and porcelain. The addition of undecomposed feldspar to china formulas gives the ware greater hardness.

Fire. The heating process which hardens ceramic plates in a kiln. Ceramic clay begins to undergo chemical change at 500° C and vitrifies at around 1300° C.

First Edition. The first, and presumably the only, edition of a collector's plate. The term (or its abbreviation, "FE") is sometimes used for the edition which is the first issue in a series of collector's plates. However, since no edition is normally ever reopened and therefore no "second edition" is possible, all issues of collector's plates are properly termed first editions.

First Issue. Chronologically, the first plate in a series, i.e., the plates issued in the first year of an annual series.

Flint Glass. See Lead Crystal.

Flux. Finely ground material added to porcelain formulas which lowers the vitrification temperature and helps fuse the components. See Feldspar.

Glaze. Glassy, hard surface coating on plates made of silicates (glass-forming compounds) and mineral oxides. Glaze is put on ceramic ware to make it wear-resistant, waterproof, decorative, and to seal the pores. Glaze material suspended in water is applied after the first firing and is heated to the glaze's vitrification point when it fuses to the plate body. Glaze is applied by dipping, spraying, or painting. Decorating is added under, over, or with the glaze layer. See Underglaze Decoration, Overglaze Decoration.

Incised Design. Ornamentation cut into the body of the plate.

Incolay Stone. The material from which the cameo-like plates produced by Incolay Studios are made. Incolay stone may contain, among other minerals, semi-precious carnelian and crystal or topaz quartz. Example: Incolay Studios **(84-I31-0.0)**.

Inlaid. Decoration on a plate created by etching, incising, or engraving a design on the surface and filling with another material.

Intaglio. Decoration created by cutting beneath the surface of the plate. Example: Morgantown Crystal **(84-M58-0.0)**. See Engraved Design, Etched Design.

Iridescence. A rainbow effect on a plate's surface caused by the diffraction of light. True iridescent color effects are readily distinguished from a plate's inherent color because the pattern will change as the plate is moved. Example: Belleek **(26-B18-0.0)**.

Issue. 1. The release for sale of an edition of plates by a maker. **2.** A plate in an edition. **3.** An edition within a series. A *new issue* is the release of the most recent plate in a continuing series. A *back issue* is a plate other than the most recently-issued plate in a series. Back issue usually denotes a plate that has sold out at issue price and is available only on the secondary market. See Market.

Issue Price. Original or first price of plate established by the maker at the time the plate is released for sale.

Jasper Ware. Hard, fine-grained, unglazed stoneware made by adding barium sulfate to clay, developed by Josiah Wedgwood in the 1770s. The term "jasper" does not indicate the presence of jasper stone but most likely denotes the variety of colors in which Jasper ware can be produced. Though white in its original form, Jasper ware can be stained in blue, green, lilac, yellow, maroon, or black to serve as a background for embossments of white Jasper relief for a cameo effect. When stained throughout, the body of it is called solid Jasper ware. Example: Wedgwood **(26-W90-0.0)**.

Kaolin. The only clay which yields a white material when fired and the indispensable element of porcelain and china plates. Also called true clay or china clay, it is formed by the complete decomposition by weathering of feldspar. Kaolin is a refractory clay which can be fired at high temperatures without deforming. It produces a vitreous, translucent ceramic when fired with fluxes (fusible rocks) such as feldspar. The components of kaolin clay are 50% silica, 33% alumina, 2% oxides, 1% magnesia, 2% alkali, and 12% water.

KPM. The trademark on plates from Königliche Porzellan-Manufaktur, Berlin, Germany. Plates made by this manufacturer date from as early as 1763.

Lead Crystal. Extremely transparent fine quality glass, also called flint glass and lead glass, which contains a high proportion of lead oxide to give extra weight, better refractiveness and a clear ringing tone when tapped. Full lead crystal is the term used to identify glass with a 24% or greater lead content. Example: Lalique **(18-L3-0.0)**.

Lead Glass. See Lead Crystal.

Limited-Edition Plates. Plates produced in a fixed quantity, either predetermined by number or determined by a specific period of production. All true collector's plates are limited-editions.

Limoges. A town in south central France famous for its procelain production since the discovery of kaolin deposits nearby in 1768. Limoges porcelain manufacturers have joined together to enforce quality standards. Examples: D'Arceau-Limoges **(18-D15-0.0)**, Haviland **(18-H6-0.0)**, Haviland & Parlon **(18-H8-0.0)**, and Limoges-Turgot **(18-L52-0.0)**.

Listed Plate. A plate listed and regularly quoted on the *Bradford Exchange Current Quotations.* Such a plate is often referred to as being "Bradex-listed." See Bradex, Exchange, Over-The-Counter Plate.

Lot. A number of plates, all in the same edition and represented by a sell order on the Exchange, usually on the secondary market and not at issue. See Allotment.

Luster. Decoration applied to a plate surface by application of metallic oxides such as gold, silver, platinum, or copper over the glaze. When gently fired, this leaves a thin metallic film.

Majolica, Maiolica. Earthenware finished with opaque white enamel, similar to faience and Delftware, but first made in the Spanish island of Majorca. See Delftware.

Maker. The name by which a plate is known or under which it is issued, e.g., manufacturer, distributor, or sponsor. In most cases the "maker" is the actual manufacturer, e.g., Bing & Grøndahl **(14-B36-0.0)**. However, it can also be a commissioner or distributor, e.g., Schmid **(22-S12-0.0)**, using a trade name, while the physical production is in fact done by a sub-contractor.

Market. The structure within which plates are bought and sold. The primary market consists of new issues which are sold by the makers or their sales representatives to dealers and distributors. Dealers and distributors in turn normally sell the new issues to the public at issue price. Secondary market or after-market refers to the buying and selling of plates previously sold, and usually sold out, on the primary market. In many cases secondary market prices are higher than those of the primary market.

Market Bradex. A kind of "Dow Jones" index of the overall collector's plate market expressed as a percentage, based on the current price/issue price ratio of twelve key indicator series.

Market Price. The price at which a plate is currently traded, regardless of its issue price. See Issue Price.

Market Price Order. An open bid posted on the Exchange to purchase a top advancing issue at the price the market demands.

Meissen. See Dresden.

Mint Condition. A plate in new or like-new condition accompanied by any original certificates and packing materials included at issue.

Modeling. The process of making the original pattern from which the master mold is made for a sculptured plate.

Mold. A general term for the form which gives a plate its shape. Clay, metal, or glass is pressed into a mold to form a blank (without ornamentation). Intaglio decoration or raised ornamentation may also be formed in the mold. China or porcelain slip-casting is done in plaster of paris molds. Slip (diluted clay formula) is poured into the mold, and the excess water is absorbed into the plaster of paris. See Slip.

New Issue. See Issue.

Open-End Series. A continuing series of annual plates with no established termination. Example: Royal Copenhagen *Christmas* series **(14-R59-1.0)**.

Open Stock. Plates available in or produced in unlimited numbers or for an unlimited time period (and therefore not considered collector's plates).

Overglaze Decoration. A decoration consisting of precious metals such as gold, platinum, or silver and/or lithographic patterns in up to twenty-five colors, applied by hand to a porcelain piece after it has been glazed and fired a second time (glost fired). Hand-applied lithographic decoration — the most widely used form of overglaze decoration — can also be used underglaze. See Glaze, Underglaze Decoration.

Over-The-Counter Plate. A collector's plate not traded in sufficient volume to be *listed* on the Exchange. The majority of such plates, however, are *traded* on the Exchange and can be obtained, when available, at the prevailing market prices. See Listed Plate.

Parian China. A highly vitrified, translucent china characterized by an iridescent luster and rich, creamy tint much like that of parian marble, for which it is named. The process for making parian ware was invented by the Copeland and Garrett firm in England in the mid-nineteenth century. Example: Belleek **(26-B18-0.0)**.

Paste. The combination of substances that make up potter's clay, generally that for porcelain or china.

Pewter. An alloy of tin with copper and antimony as hardeners. The greater the amount of copper and antimony, the harder the ware. Fine pewter is composed of 80% tin and 20% antimony and brass or copper. Examples: International **(84-I61-0.0)** and Royal Worcester (U.S.A.), **(84-R76-0.0)**. See Alloy.

Point, Bradex Point. One percentage point of the Market Bradex.

Porcelain. The hardest vitreous ceramic fired at the highest temperatures. Although the term porcelain is often interchanged with china, true porcelain, as the term is used in the field, is distinguished from china by its very high glaze firing and low bisque firing temperature compared with the high bisque firing and low glaze firing of china. The main firing (glaze) of porcelain is approximately 7% higher than the main firing (bisque) of china. The glaze fuses with the porcelain plate body and produces an extremely hard surface. Hard-paste or true porcelain is made from a formula whose primary components are kaolin and china stone (petuntse). When fired, the china stone vitrifies, producing a hard, glassy ceramic. True porcelain is translucent when thin, white unless colored, impervious to scratching, and transmits a ringing tone when struck. A typical porcelain formula is 50% kaolin, 25% quartz and 25% feldspar. Soft-paste porcelain was developed in Renaissance Europe in an attempt to imitate the true porcelain of China. Soft-paste porcelain was a mixture of white sand, gypsum, soda, alum, salt, and niter, fired until it vitrified. It had a soft texture, great sensitivity to sudden temperature changes, was warmer to the touch than true porcelain, and could be scratched with a file. The terms "hard" and "soft" porcelain refer to the "hard" firing temperature (around 1450°C) required for true porcelain and the "soft" firing temperature (around 1150°C) used for soft-paste porcelain. See China.

Pottery. 1. A general term used for all ceramic ware, but, strictly speaking, properly applied to earthenware and non-vitrified ceramics. **2.** The place or kilns where ceramic objects are fired.

Primary Market. See Market.

Queen's Ware. An earthenware of ivory or cream color developed by Josiah Wedgwood. The name "Queen's Ware" was adopted by other potters for similar stoneware; also often referred to as "white ware."

Quote. The current market value and selling price of a collector's plate on the Exchange.

Relief Sculpture. Sculpture in which the design or figure is not free-standing but is raised from a background. There are three degrees of relief sculpture: Alto-relievo or high relief, where the design is almost detached from the background; Basso-relievo or bas-relief, where the design is raised somewhat; and Relievo-stiacciato, where the design is scarcely more than scratched. Relief designs on plates may be formed in the plate mold or formed separately and applied to the plate body.

Saggers. Boxes of fire-clay into which objects to be glost fired are put for protection against direct contact with the flames.

Second, Second Sorting. A plate judged to be a grade below first quality, usually indicated by a scratch or gouge through the glaze over the backstamp on the back.

Secondary Market. See Market.

Sell Order. An offer at an asked price given by an individual or dealer to sell one or more plates of the same edition on the secondary market. See Asked Price, Exchange.

Slip. Ceramic paste or body diluted with water to a smooth, creamy consistency used for slip-casting. See Mold.

Steatite, Soapstone. A natural rock whose primary component is talc. Steatite is used in porcelain formulas as a flux.

Sterling Silver. An alloy which, by United States law, must have the minimum fineness of 92.5% by weight of pure silver and a maximum of 7.5% by weight of a base metal, usually copper. Example: Franklin Mint **(84-F64-0.0)**.

Stoneware. A hard ceramic fired to vitrification but not to translucency. Typical components of stoneware are 30% ball clay, 32% kaolin, 15% flint, and 23% cornish stone. Example: Wedgwood's Jasper Ware **(26-W90-0.0)**.

Supermarket Plate. Common term for a plate edition of dubious limitations, cheaply produced and not considered a true collector's plate.

Swap 'n' Sell Event. An open auction for the trading of plates from one collector to another. Swap 'n' Sell events have been organized at major plate conventions, traveling shopping mall shows, and between collector's clubs. A registration fee is normally charged for those plates displayed by sellers.

Terra Cotta. A general term for any kind of fired clay. Strictly speaking, terra cotta is an earthenware produced from a clay which fires to a dull ochre or red color. The ware, left unglazed, is coarse and porous. Example: Veneto Flair **(38-V22-0.0)**.

Tin Glaze. A glaze, colored white by oxide of tin, which produces a heavy opaque surface when fired. See Delftware.

Toriart. The process by which wood shavings and resin are combined to form a wood material which is then molded and carved into three-dimensional forms. Example: Anri **(38-A54-0.0)**.

Trader. An individual or a dealer who buys, sells, or bids on plates through the Exchange. See Trading Floor, Exchange.

Trading Floor. The physical area of the Bradford Exchange where the trading of plates actually takes place. All secondary market trading on the Exchange originates here, and it is the daily market activity on the Trading Floor that determines the prices quoted on the Exchange. See Broker, Secondary Market, Bradex, Quote.

Transfer-Printing. Method by which an engraved design may be transferred from an engraver's plate or lithographer's block to the surface of a plate. Originally, thin papers were inked with a mixture of metallic oxide in an oily medium, or sometimes used with a greasy substance onto which metallic oxide could be dusted. Transfer-printing may be overglaze or underglaze.

Translucency. The quality of transmitting light without transparence. In a plate, translucency depends on the quality of the china or porcelain, thickness of the plate, and firing temperature. Underfired porcelain is not translucent.

Triptych. A set of three panels hinged side by side, bearing paintings or carvings, usually on a religious theme and originally used as a portable altarpiece. Example: Anna-Perenna **(22-A3-3.0)**.

True Clay. See Kaolin.

Underglaze Decoration. Decoration applied after a plate has been fired once (bisque fired) but before it is glazed and fired a second time. Underglaze painting is most commonly done in cobalt blue pigment (although other colors can be used) because this is the most stable color and can withstand high firing temperatures. True underglaze technique indicates that such painting was done by hand. See Glaze, Overglaze Decoration.

Vitrification. A fusion of potters clay at temperatures between 1250°C and 1450°C to form a glassy, non-porous substance. With continued heating, the substance will become translucent.